P9-EFH-773

Poison Detection
in
Human Organs

Publication Number 749

AMERICAN LECTURE SERIES®

A Monograph in
The BANNERSTONE DIVISION *of*
AMERICAN LECTURES IN LIVING CHEMISTRY

Edited by

I. NEWTON KUGELMASS, M.D., Ph.D., Sc.D.
Consultant to the Departments of Health and Hospitals
New York, New York

Poison Detection
in
Human Organs

Second Edition

By

ALAN CURRY
M.A., Ph.D., F.R.I.C., M.C. Path.
Director of the
Home Office Central Research Establishment
Aldermaston, Reading, U.K.
Scholar of Trinity College, Cambridge

With an Introduction by

Keith Simpson, M.D., F.R.C.P.
Professor of Forensic Medicine
University of London

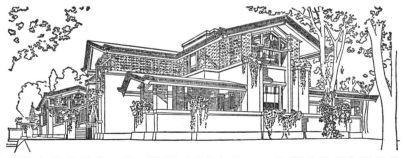

CHARLES C THOMAS · PUBLISHER
Springfield · Illinois · U.S.A.

RELEASED

Bib # 210

© 9⌒/ *p*

2 nd. ed

1969

Published and Distributed Throughout the World by
CHARLES C THOMAS • PUBLISHER
BANNERSTONE HOUSE
301-327 East Lawrence Avenue, Springfield, Illinois, U.S.A.
NATCHEZ PLANTATION HOUSE
735 North Atlantic Boulevard, Fort Lauderdale, Florida, U.S.A.

This book is protected by copyright. No
part of it may be reproduced in any manner
without written permission from the publisher.

© *1963 and 1969, by* CHARLES C THOMAS • PUBLISHER
Library of Congress Catalog Card Number: 69-14785

First Edition, 1963
Second Edition, 1969

With THOMAS BOOKS *careful attention is given to all details of
manufacturing and design. It is the Publisher's desire to present
books that are satisfactory as to their physical qualities and artistic
possibilities and appropriate for their particular use.* THOMAS
BOOKS *will be true to those laws of quality that assure a good name
and good will.*

Printed in the United States of America
N-10

W
700
C976
1969

FOREWORD

Our Living Chemistry Series was conceived by Editor and Publisher to advance the newer knowledge of chemical medicine in the cause of clinical practice. The interdependence of chemistry and medicine is so great that physicians are turning to chemistry, and chemists to medicine in order to understand the underlying basis of life processes in health and disease. Once chemical truths, proofs and convictions become sound foundations for clinical phenomena, key hybrid investigators clarify the bewildering panorama of biochemical progress for application in everyday practice, stimulation of experimental research, and extension of postgraduate instruction. Each of our monographs thus unravels the chemical mechanisms and clinical management of many diseases that have remained relatively static in the minds of medical men for three thousand years. Our new Series is charged with the *nisus élan* of chemical wisdom, supreme in choice of international authors, optimal in standards of chemical scholarship, provocative in imagination for experimental research, comprehensive in discussions of scientific medicine, and authoritative in chemical perspective of human disorders.

Dr. Curry presents a new, systematic approach to the chemical detection of unsuspected poisoning with maximum efficiency and minimum duplication of analytical procedure. Analyses of samples from the living or dead are considered within the framework of the organs on which they are performed to ensure that each poison is sought in the particular tissue in which it is most likely to concentrate. Rapid chemical detection of poisoning with accurate interpretation of results is paramount for crucial saving of life or establishing the cause of death. It can be done by simple color tests or by more modern techniques involving chromatography, ultraviolet spectrophotometry, and infrared spectroscopy, with complete satisfaction to both chemist and clinician, faced with jars of organs and the knowledge of thousands of poisons.

v

The action of poison upon the animal organism was first observed in the ancient practice of divination well expressed by Ovid (10 B.C.), who considered the arrows of Hercules charged with the venoms of the Lerneian serpent. Poisons have always played a dominant role in literature, history, romance, and crime. Each age had its own poisons, the silent and subtle weapons readily administered without violence or suspicion. Maccabees, x, 13, refers to poison as a suicidal agent. The Greeks were partial to hemlock juice, a galaxy of poisons. The Egyptians discovered the poisonous effects of animals, plants, and minerals. Hippocrates described poisoning from fungi, herbs, plants, and foods. The Medes appointed official food tasters to combat intentional food poisoning. The Romans (82 B.C.) enacted the first law against criminal poisoning. Nero's physician, Adromachus, developed the universal antidote of seventy-three components to combat poisoning. Avicenna (1010), a Persian, remained the authority on the diagnosis and treatment of poisoning until Orfila (1814), a Spaniard, founded modern toxicology, as professor of legal medicine at the Sorbonne. It liberated the occult in toxicology from the ancient thralldom, replacing its threadbare garments with a raiment suited to a rapidly expanding science.

The tremendous rise in potentially poisonous substances in the homes, factories and fields is an index of degradation, a disgrace to mankind. It is only partially reflected in the vital statistics of civilized countries involving individual, occupational, or mass poisoning in peace or war. The annual number exceeds 15,000 fatal, and 1 million nonfatal, poisons in the United States alone, and is ever on the increase. Acute poisoning cannot wait for the identification of the toxic agent or the use of specific antidote. Successful treatment depends on prompt action to prevent further exposure to the poison; to keep the airways clear; control respiratory depression, shock, convulsions, and infection; and inactivate the toxic material.

Investigation of poisoning requires ingenious clinical detective work and painstaking chemical analyses by a team of trained technicians in close cooperation with the family and police. The mental process is identical with that by which Cuvier restored the extinct animals of Montmartre from fragments of their bones. Clues may be obtained from the common components of household drugs, medicines, cosmetics, insecticides, cleaning fluids, and fuels; from exhaustive analyses of urines and stools; from systematic chemical examination of specific organs. Clinical diagnosis alone may elude the medical examiner even though the toxic actions of most drugs are characteristic. There is scarcely a poisoning syndrome which does not stimulate some disease, e.g., acute poisoning by central nervous system stimulants may be mistaken for epilepsy or tetanus; by central nervous system depressants, uremic coma or brain tumor; chronic poisoning by manganese may be mistaken for parkinsonism; by carbon tetrachloride, hepatitis; by bromides, neuropsychiatric disorders.

The analytical biochemistry of toxicology compels the determination of the poisonous substances found in the body and its excreta. Methods vary to enable the reader to choose the procedures that best fit his laboratory facilities, personal preferences, and the conditions of the moment involving a living patient or an exhumed body. Fortunately, the volume is much more than an uncritical manual of techniques since each chapter offers discussions of the principles on which the methods are based and the applications to which they may be adapted in the laboratory. The author clearly explores the innumerable and interlinked reactions that determine, in part, at least, the chemical behavior of the "thing called Man" reacting to accidental, suicidal, or criminal poisoning.

> *"The body, for a time the unwilling sport*
> *Of circumstance and passion, struggles on;*
> *Fleets through its sad duration rapidly."*

I. NEWTON KUGELMASS, M.D., PH.D., SC.D., *Editor*

PREFACE TO THE SECOND EDITION

In the five years that have passed since the first edition of this book several new techniques have been brought into use in the toxicological laboratory. These include especially gas and thin layer chromatography and, for the lucky few, atomic absorption, mass spectrometry, spectrofluorometry and neutron activation analysis. Sophisticated instrumentation is becoming essential, however, because of the need for high sensitivity coupled with the problems of identifying the ever increasing number of highly toxic chemicals available to the general public. Drug doses are now often in the milligram range and occasionally are as low as a few micrograms. To find such compounds in body fluids requires apparatus that will detect and identify nanogram (10^{-9}g) and often picogram (10^{-12}g) quantities. The aim of the book — "to detect the unknown poison" — is unchanged however, but it has been necessary to rearrange extensively the layout. It is realised that hospital laboratories do not have the time, or in many cases, the facilities to perform complex analyses in all patients who are admitted as cases of suspected poisoning. The need for rapid screening procedures has been recognised and integrated with the full toxicological analysis which is necessary if the patient dies. The first part of this book, therefore, consists of the systematic search; the second part is confined to experimental details once a positive screening test has been obtained.

It is hoped that in this way the book will be of assistance both in the treatment of the living patient and in the establishment of a true cause of death.

A.S.C.

PREFACE TO THE FIRST EDITION

T HE MAIN WORK OF A forensic toxicologist is concerned with analyses of parts of the human body for poisons and drugs and with the interpretation of his results for clinician or legal authority.

In addition the toxicologist may operate a Poison Information Centre whose functions include the identification of common toxic chemicals and the dissemination of expert advice to clinicians responsible for treating the patient. Urgent analyses concerning samples from persons suspected of having been poisoned may also be his concern and he may have to ensure that accidental poisoning resulting from enviromental conditions is not repeated.

The world demand for toxicologists is only beginning to reach a sufficiently high level for universities to consider providing degree courses in toxicology. The present system whereby practising toxicologists pass on their experience therefore sets the background for this book in which it is hoped that scientists who for the first, or even the thousandth time are faced with jars full of organs and a note saying "?Poison" may find guidance.

The book describes the analyses for each of the organs necessary in a comprehensive analysis. Although only systematic chemical analysis can hope to reveal a poison, the identity of which is not known, tests on many parts of the body may be necessary if detection is to be ensured. In addition, the sequence of tests must be designed to provide results as quickly as possible.

The logical, stepwise, chemical testing of viscera is therefore the guiding principle throughout this book.

A.S.C.

INTRODUCTION

Poisoning has become an important current problem. Over 20,000 cases are taken to hospital for treatment each year in England and Wales, and over 5,000 die — four-fifths of these being found dead, many from swallowing unknown, unlabelled or uncertain mixtures of the wide choice of modern synthetic drugs poured in ever-increasing number on the market by the commercial chemist.

The detection and assay of such poisons in the body has become a highly specialized branch of analytical chemistry. Few have any experience of the technical problems involved when the clinician or pathologist present their specimens. What the toxicological analyst needs from the body, how to extract the residues of poisons often metabolised with great rapidity, and what kind of quantitative arithmetic to do to estimate dosage form the substance of Alan Curry's new book.

The author of this important laboratory guide has acquired a fine reputation for skill, pertinacity and accuracy in this new field. His clarity of expression and a flair for getting at the heart of a problem will encourage all those who approach the "synthetic unknown" with uncertainty, for he is obviously writing with the tips of well trained and experienced fingers. There is no such writing in the English language, and Dr. Curry will earn the gratitude of hundreds of clinical toxicologists and chemists who have no such expert at their elbow by solving their bench problems as he does so ably in this guide to modern toxicological techniques.

Keith Simpson, M.D., F.R.C.P.
Professor of Forensic Medicine
University of London

ACKNOWLEDGMENTS

MY INTRODUCTION TO toxicology occurred nearly twenty years ago when I joined the Home Office Forensic Science Laboratory, Wakefield, under the direction of Dr. F. G. Tryhorn. Since then I have worked in Home Office Laboratories at Harrogate, Nottingham and Aldermaston, and I acknowledge the opportunity given me to work in this specialised field of analysis. At Wakefield and Harrogate I was closely associated with the Home Office pathologist, Dr. D. E. Price; I acknowledge the debt I owe to him for teaching me the problems of the pathologist, for over ten years of the closest professional cooperation involving many poison murder cases, and for his personal friendship. I also acknowledge in particular the guidance of Professor C. J. Polson. To my many colleagues, particularly R. H. Fox, R. G. L. Osborne, E. R. Rutter and G. S. Simpson, I give my thanks.

In 1963, the International Association of Forensic Toxicologists was formed and for three years I had the honour to serve as its secretary. The Association publishes a bulletin, edited by J. V. Jackson, and the sharing of toxicological information by this means has been of great value to all practising toxicologists. As this bulletin is not published in the normal sense, any information from this source quoted in this book has been noted with the author's consent, as a "personal communication." I acknowledge the debt I owe to these authors.

Any toxicologist must receive the help and cooperation of the police forces, pathologists and coroners in the area he serves. I have never had other than the greatest assistance from all those with whom I have been in contact. To all of them I express my thanks.

In the past year, the Home Office Central Research Establishment and the Royal Air Force Institute of Pathology and Tropical Medicine, Halton (Air Vice Marshal W. P. Stamm, C.B.E., Q.H.S., F.R.C.P., F.C.Path.) have cooperated in investigations on aircraft accident toxicology. My experience has been greatly enriched by this cooperative effort and I express my thanks to the Royal Air Force and the Home Office for the opportunity; I acknowledge my debt to Flight Lieutenant D. J. Blackmore, in particular. My knowledge of alkaloids has been greatly enlarged by my friendship with Dr. E. G. C. Clarke, and I wish to thank him for all the help he has given me. I have for many years had a regular tape recorded correspondence with Dr. Irving Sunshine (Coroners Office, Cleveland, Ohio), R. J. Abernathy (until recently Chief Toxicologist, Los Angeles) and E. B. Hensel, (Forensic Science Adviser, USAID, United States Government). I acknowledge the stimulus given me by these sessions with three of the world's most experienced toxicologists.

I thank C. Brown, R. Jenkins, A. T. Jones and Mrs. I. L. White for technical and secretarial assistance.

I acknowledge the permission of the Fisher Scientific Company to publish their method for arsenic.

I give thanks to the Elsevier Publishing Company (*Journal of Chromatography*) to reproduce Table XXI and John Wiley and Sons, Ltd. (Interscience) to quote extensively from Dr. Clarke's Chapter on Alkaloids in *Methods of Forensic Science*, Volume 1, in Table XII.

A.S.C.

CONTENTS

PART II
Alphabetical List of Poisons

LIST OF TABLES

Poison Detection
in
Human Organs

PART I

Chapter 1

TOXICOLOGY: GENERAL CONSIDERATIONS

In CASES OF POISONING when the patient is still alive two different sets of conditions can apply; firstly, those in which the poison agent is known or suspected, and secondly, those in which there is no reliable background information and poisoning is suspected because of the clinical condition of the patient. In both circumstances the aim must be to provide information which will assist the clinician in his handling of the patient. It is axiomatic that the analyses must be finished in time to be of assistance and that that the results must be capable of intelligent interpretation.

When the patient is dead there is also a need for rapid screening procedures even when the circumstances of the death are apparently straightforward. The criminal poisoner is cunning — to quote Mr. Justice Diplock in the "insulin" case — "poisoning is a cool, calculated, premeditated crime." Only systematic analysis can reveal such murders. A forensic toxicologist cannot hope to perform analyses for all known poisons in all cases that come to his attention, but he can perform a large number of very simple screening tests in addition to looking for the poison apparently involved in the case from circumstantial evidence.

It is the aim of this book to present the analyses in such a form that a sequence of tests is performed so that not only is there the greatest probability of detecting any poison, but also that the complications arising from different routes of administration (oral, injection, inhaled, through the skin, into orifices) as well as differing times between the onset of the illness and the taking of the samples, are taken into account.

One complication in modern medical practice is that laboratories do not all have the same available instrumentation. Many can only perform chemical testing coupled with paper and thin layer chromatography; others have an ultra-violet spectrophotometer, while the larger units have gas chromatographic apparatus, an infra-red spectrophotometer and, possibly a mass spectrometer. In order to fulfill the interests of all these workers, the following procedure has been adopted. The tests are described in a rational operating sequence; simple spot tests and extraction routes are used wherever possible; paper and TLC chromatography with ultra-violet spectrophotometry are considered to be "simple procedures." Where an improved, more sophisticated, test may be used, then this is noted and the detailed description is given with a quantitative method in the alphabetical list in Part II of the book. This has the advantage that both clinical biochemist and forensic toxicologist can utilise the same *modus operandi*. In cases where a specific analysis for a known poison is required, both the simple and more sophisticated methods may be found by reference to the index. It should be noted that inspired guesses are a waste of time and available material.

The toxicologist should perform first those analyses which will be of primary value to the clinician; for example, the level of urea in the blood may be of more immediate interest than the exact concentration of lead in the urine in a case in which the diagnosis of lead poisoning has been made from other considerations. Conversely, the identification of the poison responsible for the patient's condition may on other occasions be paramount so that the correct antidote may be administered promptly.

Analyses are often complicated and highly technical procedures and it is prudent in all cases to ask the following question before undertaking a particular analysis which has been requested by clinician, policeman or lawyer, What will the result of this analysis tell you? In some cases the answer is so unsatisfactory that alternative procedures can be suggested by the poison expert which will save his own time and also provide the answer which the questioner really needs.

Analyses in cases when the patient is dead have two main aims: firstly, to assist in establishing the cause of death, and secondly, the collection of information which will further scientific knowledge.

Three questions will be asked of the toxicologist when he has completed his analyses of specimens in a case in which either poisoning has been suspected or where a post-mortem examination by an experienced pathologist has failed to reveal an adequate cause of death. These are:

1. Did you find any poison — if so, what was it?
2. When and how was the poison taken into the system?
3. How much did you find and hence how much did the victim take?

It will be noted here that one question that should *not* be asked of the toxicologist at this stage is, Did the deceased die from poisoning?

In each section of this book will be found details of the blood, urine or tissue levels that have been found as a result of therapeutic, chronic high level or acute overdose administration of the drug or poison. The analyst must be careful to survey these critically before coming to his conclusion. To take a simple example, it is common to find blood levels in cases of acute poisoning that fall within the quoted therapeutic range, either because death has occurred rapidly, (when some tissue levels may be very high), or because death has occurred a considerable time after ingestion and metabolism has destroyed the bulk of the drug. Similarly, urine concentrations must take into account clearance rates over long and short term periods. There is sometimes a tendency to ask the toxicologist, Is this a fatal level? Often an unequivocal answer can be given; on other occasions only exposure to the drug or poison can be categorically assured. To deduce nonpoisoning from a low level is equally as bad as diagnosing acute suicidal poisoning from a high level when chronic high intake may be indicated. When there is a danger of this situation occurring the toxicologist must be capable of suggesting alternative samples or procedures that will lead to a solution of the problem and so provide the answer the clinician or pathologist requires.

The establishment of the cause of death cannot be made solely by the toxicologist although it is true that the presence of certain poisons in a large dose, cyanide for example, would immediately and probably rightly lead him to conclude that life was brought to an end by the poison: in all cases the diagnosis should only be made after a consideration of all the facts of the death by the team of medical and scientific experts who have been concerned in its investigation. The toxicologist must be most careful not to try to extend his own function beyond its proper boundaries but should be capable of providing reliable analyses and deducing useful information from them.

A. INFORMATION REQUIRED BY THE TOXICOLOGIST: THE COLLECTION OF SAMPLES, THEIR PACKING AND PRESERVATION

In order to answer the three questions posed above, adequate properly preserved samples must be submitted to the laboratory. Although additional information may be not really essential, important results will be available more quickly if the details surrounding the circumstances of the incident are supplied. This could be vital in cases when the patient is still alive. A close liaison must be maintained therefore with the clinicians, pathologists and investigating authorities in the area.

i. Information Required by the Toxicologist

In analyses on samples from both the living patient and the dead, questions shown in Table 1 should be asked of the authority submitting the samples. It will be seen that the weight of the patient or deceased is asked as well as the obvious questions concerning name, age and sex. This is because calculations as to ingested dose from tissue or blood concentrations depend on both weight and sex variables. Apart from the example of the differences between calculations concerning a twelve-month-old child and a 220-pound man, the minor variations in Widmark factors between men and women in reports on body contents of alcohol can be important. Defence attorney could pass comment if the toxicologist has ascribed male status to "J. Smith" who, it subsequently transpires is a female.

The remaining questions have two aims; firstly, to set a time framework, and secondly, to elicit clinical information.

The time framework is most desirable so that the analysis can be designed to search for poison in the sample in which it is likely to be in the highest concentration. The beginning of the incident is dealt with in question 1, the end at questions 2 and 3. The clinical picture is asked in question 9 in which the investigating authority is asked to put a mark against salient features. Other questions enable the presence of drugs in therapeutic doses administered by way of treatment to be identified and quickly eliminated from the enquiry. The possibility of therapeutic accidents must also not be overlooked. There should be full cooperation between clinician and toxicologist as a matter of routine, but in some cases, the samples may be delivered to the laboratory by a messenger who knows little or nothing of the case. In that position it is helpful to have duplicated copies of the form so that it can be returned to the responsible officer for subsequent retransmission to the laboratory.

TABLE I

REQUEST FOR CHEMICAL TOXICOLOGICAL EXAMINATION IN CASES OF SUDDEN DEATH

Police Force:	*Name of Deceased*	*Date*
Sex:	*Age of Deceased:*	*Approx. Weight of Deceased:*

1. On what date and at approximately what time was the deceased last seen to have been in his usual state of health?
2. Time and date of death, if known.
3. If the time of death is not accurately known, when was the deceased found to be dead?
4. If deceased died suddenly give details and time of last known meal.
5. Was the deceased admitted to hospital while still alive? If so, on what day and at what time?
6. Give details of the type and quantity of the substance thought to have been the cause of death.
7. Did the deceased take any medicine, pills, etc., in the three days prior to death? If so, give details?
8. Name of any medicine, pills, antibiotics, etc., given to deceased in hospital or elsewhere. If possible give quantities and times administered.
9. Please put a tick against any of the following symptoms that apply:

Diarrhoea	Constipation	Loss of weight	Eye pupils contracted
Vomiting	Blue tinge to the skin (Cyanosis)	Shivering	Delirium
		Hallucinations	Drunkenness
Thirst	Jaundice	Convulsions	Sweating
Blindness		Eye pupils dilated	Unconsciousness

10. When giving dates and times please be as exact as possible.
11. It would be appreciated if the pathologist could inform the laboratory of the findings of his post-mortem.
12. Name and address of Coroner.

ii. The Samples

(a) *The Living Patient*

In cases where the patient is still alive the samples should consist of stomach aspirate, stomach wash, 15 ml of blood and as much urine as possible. Occasionally, when the time interval between exposure to the poison and the taking of the samples is measured in days instead of hours then faeces may be valuable. This collection is easy to ask for, in practice it may be extremely difficult to collect, and the toxicologist must be aware of his colleagues' problems. The necessity for the addition of anticoagulant or preservative to the ante-mortem blood sample depends on the type of poison that may be present. As a general rule it is probably best to divide the sample into two parts, one being submitted with no additive whatsoever while to the other solid sodium fluoride is added to make a final concentration of about 1 per cent. The fluoride acts as both a preservative and as an anticoagulant. In temperate climates it is not necessary or desirable to add anything to the other samples. Clinicians must be encouraged to submit all the stomach aspirate and stomach wash. It is not unusual to have only a one ounce sample sent from a bucketful of stomach wash; this is useless. It is difficult enough to analyse for poisons under the best conditions — to be sent only one hundredth part of the available samples is to make the task impossible.

(b) *The Post-Mortem Examination*

The following samples should be sent in *all* cases. The emphasis is placed here on the submission of a full set of samples even in cases where the circumstances are apparently straightforward. Although it is common in an obvious case of carbon monoxide poisoning for only a blood sample to be submitted for analysis, the circumstances surrounding the death often do not become clear for several days. The investigating authority then may become suddenly very interested in a suggestion that the victim may have been drugged before being exposed to the gas. This is not an uncommon occurrence and, in my opinion, it is far better for all the organs to be taken at the time of the original post-mortem examination than for the body to be exhumed or for the toxicologist to have to work on embalmed fluids. Samples should not be mixed but should be packed in separate jars. A kit of at least two large and three medium sized jars (of 1 litre capacity) with four one-ounce bottles is required. The liver and intestines are put in the large jars; the stomach and contents, brain and kidneys are put in the medium sized jars; the smaller bottles are for blood, bile, and urine samples. (It has been found recently that bile is a most useful source of many drugs and its routine inclusion is to be encouraged.)

1. Stomach Wall and Stomach Contents. Even if the stomach is empty to the naked eye the wall should still be sent. Pathologists will no doubt wish to inspect the mucosa. Abernethy (personal communication) suggests that the stomach be tied off at both ends, removed gently to a pan, slit lengthwise and carefully opened with examination for areas of colour, tablets, etc., which can be removed with a spoon and preserved separately. The wall can then be unfolded to inspect the mucosa. This technique avoids disintegration of capsules and tablets due to disturbance and continued soaking. After inspection and the taking of samples for histology the wall can be put in the same jar as the gross contents. The only exception to this is in cases in which a fatty liver has been found and poisoning by yellow phosphorus is suspected. On theoretical grounds it is then probably advisable to open the stomach under nitrogen immediately before analysis so that the chance of oxidation is minimised. It should be part of normal autopsy technique for the stomach and contents to be preserved until the cause of death has been established.

2. The Intestines and Contents. The toxicologist will wish to work on the contents of the intestines and the pathologist can greatly help by either separating them at the time of his examination or submitting the intestines in a continuous separated length so that the contents can be easily squeezed out at the time of the analysis. Not only is it much easier for the pathologist to cut off adherent fat but the task can be unpleasant when done under laboratory conditions instead of in the mortuary. The analysis of the intestine contents is often necessary when death occurs many hours after the ingestion of poison or when it is desired to establish how long before death ingestion occurred.

It should be normal practice for the intestines to be tied at about two feet lengths to minimise mixing of the contents during submission of the samples to the laboratory. In one of my cases the coincidence of drug with the lunch-time meal in the stomach contents was of vital importance — the separate submission of stomach, duodenum and tied-off small intestines amply repaid the pathologist the small extra amount of trouble at the autopsy. In another case the differential distribution of two barbiturates in the alimentary tract was of great assistance in deciding the formulation of the ingested drug. The *routine* submission of intestines is recommended; there are several tablets which have an enteric coating and when these dissolve they cause sudden and unexpected collapse of the patient. The inspection of the intestine contents often reveals whole undigested tablets.

The technique for removing the contents from the alimentary tract varies slightly with individual preference. When the intestines have been separated into a continuous easily handleable length by dissection, the analyst can either squeeze from one end forcing the content out at the other end into a previously weighed beaker, or he can cut open the wall longitudinally and, by means of a spoon, transfer the content to the beaker. In either case the wall is subsequently inspected for damage to the mucosa and then well washed with water and the weighed washings added to the contents. My own preference is for the squeezing technique if the wall is intact.

3. The Blood Samples. Two separate samples should be submitted, each of 1 ounce in volume. Both should be from different peripheral parts of the body and approximately 250 mg of sodium fluoride should be added to one sample. Sub-axilla, neck veins and femoral artery are the usual sites for collection. Blood from the portal vein should be avoided because very high drug concentrations can be found in this blood immediately following ingestion and this could give a misleading impression of the total amount of drug or poison in circulation. There is insufficient data to enable one to be dogmatic on the correlation between concentrations of drugs in peripheral blood and in heart blood but, because the heart usually contains a relatively large amount of blood and concentrations often parallel peripheral levels, it is acceptable. Because glucose diffuses from the liver into the right side of the heart after death, a similar phenomenon may occur with some drugs, and it is therefore wiser for the pathologist to put left and right heart blood samples in separate bottles if for any reason sufficient peripheral blood cannot be obtained — in the case of young children for example. The reason for taking two blood samples is to provide by analysis a check on the uniform distribution of the drug throughout the blood in the body. This is especially important in cases involving alcohol determinations when no urine is available. Pathologists should be actively discouraged from sending large volumes of blood from body cavities taken at the end of the post-mortem examination by means of a sponge. The "quality" of this blood, i.e., its authenticity as a circulating sample uncontaminated by other body fluids is more important nowadays than the volume.

4. The Liver. After removal of samples for histology all the liver should be sent for analysis. There are two reasons for requesting this large quantity. The first is seen from a consideration of the toxic dose of many poisons — often less than a few milligrams per kilo of body weight. At death the concentration left in the body can be much less than this figure and it is therefore necessary to analyse several hundred grams of tissue in order to obtain the micrograms of poison required for detection and identification. The second reason depends on the fact that the liver as the major detoxication organ has the power of concentrating many poisons. This means that there may be a hundred-fold higher concentration in the liver than in the blood and this makes the liver one of the most important specimens. Arsenic, barbiturates and imipramine are three widely different examples which can illustrate this power of concentration.

5. The Kidneys. In all cases both kidneys should be sent to the laboratory. Analysis of the kidney is usually confined to cases in which metal poisoning is suspected or in investigations in a general search for poison and in cases in which histology has shown crystals of calcium oxalate or of a sulphonamide.

6. The Brain. The lipoid tissue of the brain has the property of retaining many poisons. Chloroform is said to be retained even when the tissue is grossly putrified. Although it would be logical to suggest that drugs that have an action on the brain are concentrated there, this premise unfortunately does not always hold. Nevertheless brain tissue and its extracts are technically more easy to handle than liver tissue and, because a kilogram is normally available, all the brain should be taken. In deaths of young children the relatively large bulk is especially valuable. Cholinesterase determinations on portions of the brain can also be important in cases of suspected exposure to organo-phosphorus insecticides.

7. Urine. This is a most valuable fluid in toxicological analysis. As well as being an excretory route which in many cases concentrates the drug or poison, urine provides a fluid which is suitable for simple direct spot tests, enabling the toxic agent to be rapidly identified. This is important not only in clinical work but also in systematic toxicological analysis in providing a rapid lead in the enquiry. As in the case of blood, urine provides an easy means of studying the metabolism of the body and the tests normally employed by the clinical chemist must not be forgotten. In cases in which death occurs after a period of illness, prolonged perhaps for several days, traces of the toxic agent may be found in the urine when none is detectable in the viscera. Close inspection of the bladder by the pathologist is to be encouraged because as little as a single drop of urine may prove invaluable to the chemist. Urine is especially useful in screening for narcotics and stimulants.

8. Bile. The gallbladder should not be opened and the contents allowed to spill over the liver. Emulsions during the extraction may be traced to this particular autopsy technique which is to be avoided. Bile itself concentrates some poisons, for example, glutethimide, oubain and morphine and research into this aspect of toxicology is being actively pursued. Its separate collection should be encouraged.

These eight samples — stomach, intestines, blood, liver, kidneys, brain, urine and bile, will provide all the information that is necessary in the vast majority of cases where acute poisoning has occurred as a result of oral ingestion. Some toxicologists ask for other organs — spleen, heart, CSF, etc., and it is not intended here to discourage this procedure or to suggest that it is not desirable; anything that helps to answer the questions posed earlier in this chapter is to be encouraged. It may be that muscle will be more popular in the future as it constitutes a major proportion of the body; fat, too, on occasions may be considered necessary for example in deaths involving anaesthetics and insecticides, but the samples discussed above are the ones for which the bulk of the literature relating concentration to dose intake will be found to apply.

Four other sets of circumstances must be considered. These are death following inhalation, injection or absorption of poison through the skin, and death from chronic poisoning. In deaths apparently occurring from inhalation of a gaseous poison the lungs must be put in an air-tight container. The use of modern chemical techniques now enables mixtures of gases to be separated from the tissue and the air space above the lungs. In deaths where hypodermic injection marks or areas where absorption of poison through the skin may have occurred, surrounding tissue should be excised and sent for analysis. An area of about four inches radius about the site should be taken with as much underlying fat and muscle as possible. If chronic poisoning is suspected, hair and bone are necessary further samples. Hair should be pulled, not cut, from the head and it is desirable to send as large a sample as possible. It should be tied in locks with cotton at the time of taking so that the toxicologist knows which ends are roots without recourse to microscopy of individual hairs. The femur is the most common bone utilised for analysis. In cases where death follows inhalation berylliosis, lung lymph can give positive results ten years after exposure to the dust. Another special case is that of LSD where, in animals, lung blood is said to give higher concentrations than circulating plasma.

(c) Preservation of Samples

In temperate climates only one of the blood samples should be preserved and that with fluoride. In cases of driving a motor vehicle under the influence of drink, the urine sample taken from the accused may be preserved by the addition of phenyl mercuric nitrate or sodium benzoate. This is not a procedure to be adopted without much consideration: it often happens that, as an afterthought, the possibility of drugs being involved is mentioned and preservative may interfere in the determination. It is more acceptable to the toxicologist if he adds preservative to an aliquot of urine after the first analyses rather than the whole sample be contaminated before he has seen it. To the other samples nothing should be added: it is even desirable that the first stomach wash should be made with water and that submitted for analysis; subsequent washes with bicarbonate, permanganate or other antidotes are best kept separate as their object is to destroy the poison and hence make it immune to detection.

In hot climates where some form of preservation is essential it is usual to use alcohol as a preservative. This is a procedure which has one disadvantage — it makes analysis for volatile poisons extremely difficult and analysis for alcohol obviously impossible. There is, therefore, a strong case for a portion of the stomach contents and at least 100 g of blood, brain or liver tissue being preserved separately with a nonvolatile preservative. Sodium fluoride solution may be suitable but those with experience of this problem will find their own preferred solution. Undoubtedly refrigeration is the ideal. This will normally be employed for all samples when they arrive at the laboratory. Injection sites which are to be analysed for insulin can be stored at 0°C for several weeks without gross loss of hormone. Once deep frozen, the tissue must not be allowed to thaw before analysis.

(d) Containers

Any containers for the samples are suitable provided they are large enough, resist breakage and have air-tight caps to stop not only the loss of volatile gases but also to prevent blood and faeces from spilling over the carrier. They must be clean and dry before use. In general, glass jars should be used. Plastic jars are convenient but, unfortunately, volatile poisons diffuse through them and, in addition, contaminants from plastic pipes have been involved in cases of suspected poisoning. To date, no substitute for well-washed glass jars has been found. Rubber inserts should not be used under caps because this material can extract from the contents certain poisons such as chloroform and phenols.

As part of the normal working notes made by the toxicologist a description of the containers and their contents is essential. Table II illustrates a *pro forma* which covers the main features. A mark is placed against the relevant description for each sample. Four copies of this form fit well on to one foolscap page.

A convenient system whereby suitable containers for the organs are readily available in the mortuary is also essential. One is for the toxicologist to replace jars when a case is received into the laboratory. In this way there is no possibility of accidental contamination with such substances as lysol, formaldehyde or alcohol because the jars will have come from the toxicologist's own laboratory.

(e) Sealing of Containers

Adhesive tape makes a suitable seal under normal conditions with a signature across the join. An apparently straightforward suicide may eventually turn out to be a murder and it is essential that this elementary medico-legal principle should be followed routinely where the pathologist is not able to hand the specimens into the toxicologist's possession.

B. ANALYSIS OF EXHUMED AND DECOMPOSED BODIES

It is often thought that exhumations should be performed at midnight by the light of a policeman's torch so that secrecy can be maintained. This, however, is a fallacy — nothing is more likely to excite the population than a crowd of uniformed police officers watching digging in a graveyard in the dead of night. Daylight exhumation behind screens causes no abnormal suspicion and, as well as providing much needed additional light, is to be recommended. Police officers should wear plain clothes. A twenty-four-hour delay, if the weather is inclement, is often of no consequence to the enquiry, but a great technical advantage to the professionals. The earth lifted from above the coffin should be placed well clear of the sides of the grave so that there is easy access to the coffin.

TABLE II
DESCRIPTION OF CONTAINERS

Case No.		Date:	
Name:		Exhibit No.	
Sample:			
Quantity:			
Volume:			
Appearance:	Normal		
	Abnormal		
Preservative:	Fluoride, Oxalate, Phenyl Mercuric Nitrate, others.		
Container:	1 oz.	Screw cap	
	4 oz.	Metal	
	8 oz.	Bakelite	
	medicine bottle	Cork	
	Buttock jar		
	½ size		
	Large		
	Squat		
Label:	Laboratory	Sealing:	Any
	Hospital		Nil
	Police		
	Written		
	Nil		

Soil should be lifted from *below* the coffin so that the adhesion between the base of the coffin and the ground does not cause the bottom to fall out when lifting is attempted. Planks should be manoeuvered under the coffin and ropes placed around the coffin and under the planks. In this way a firm support is achieved before lifting begins.

Photographs should be taken at all stages and legal identification of the coffin and body is essential. The mortuary to which the coffin is to be taken should be prepared in advance and an ample supply of labelled glass jars ensured. Warmth and refreshments will be appreciated by all concerned. Some authorities refer to the dangers of infection from coffin dust — presumably, a rich source of bacteria. Forewarned is forearmed.

Sometimes the coffin will be full of water and pumping may even be necessary to keep the grave free from water. A generous supply of buckets should be available so that when a hole is drilled in the base of the coffin adequate collection facilities are ensured.

The basic problems associated with analyses on exhumed bodies are no different to those associated with analyses on reasonably fresh bodies. These cases can, however, be considered more interesting because of the production of artefacts during putrefaction and because the interpretation of analytical results, on the badly rotted body, may sometimes be difficult. Because of the former it is necessary to collect at the time of the exhumation samples of soil from above, below and from each side of the coffin. Any fluid and debris in the coffin should be collected and portions of the shroud should also be taken. The samples obtained at the post-mortem examination should be even more comprehensive than those indicated in section Aii (b) because it may become necessary to make calculations on the ingested dose from tissue concentrations by simple arithmetic instead of making use of published data.

Exhumations are usually performed because a suspicion has arisen from circumstantial evidence that the cause of death was poisoning. In such cases it is also usual for the nature of the poison to be suspected and analysis is immediately directed to that poison. In my experience it is equally important that tests for other common poisons should be performed as well. Poisoners display great cunning and the toxicologist should be prepared for all eventualities. If, because of lack of time, manpower, equipment or for any other reason, a full analysis has not been performed, arrangements should be made for the preservation of suitable samples for other analyses that may become necessary as the course of any subsequent trial unfolds the whole story. This applies in all cases of murder by poison; a negative result for one poison may eventually be as important as a positive for another (*R v Barlow*, 1957, when it was suggested that ergometrine and not insulin was injected; *R v Wilson*, 1958, when aphrodisiac pills containing yellow phosphorus and strychnine were produced by the defence: there was yellow phosphorus but no strychnine in the bodies).

The number of artefacts in exhumed bodies naturally depends on the decomposition reactions that have occurred; but in recent years a considerable amount of work has been done on the normal constituents of decomposing tissue. There is no doubt that cyanide is produced in toxicologically significant amounts — levels of up to 10 mg/100 ml of blood have been found in three-month-old blood, and most bacteria can produce ethanol. Only the belated realisation that anaerobic bacteria, in relatively good-looking muscle, can do this, has saved the author from erroneous conclusions in this field. However, blood ethanol levels are normally below 100 mg/100 ml when decomposition is involved and values above this would arouse suspicion of alcohol intake.

The production of other higher alcohols can be expected during decomposition and the gas chromatographic examination of the concentrated ether extract of a distillate of decomposing tissue always reveals a multitude of volatile components.

The apparent production of small amounts of carbon monoxide (less than 10%) in blood has been noted, using spectroscopic methods and by gasometric analysis after the addition of ascorbic acid and hydrogen peroxide. There is little experimental evidence on which to be dogmatic about the significance of elevated carbon monoxide in exhumed bodies. Undoubtedly, gas chromatography is the method of choice for analysis (see Part II).

An assessment of the distribution of these simpler molecules in the tissue, coupled with sufficient control experiments with incubated biological material, will often enable the toxicologist to reach firm conclusions but, as with all scientific conclusions, they must be based on adequate experimental evidence.

The presence of several substituted phenols in decomposing tissue has been noted, particularly those related to p-hydroxyphenyl derivatives, and these can cause a lot of interference in the analysis of the weak acid fractions (*vide infra*) ; phenylethylamine, isopentylamine, piperidon, harman, norharman, hydroxyharman, 1-hydroxymethyl-β-carboline, nicotinamide, uracil and thymine, have all been described as "artefacts" in "normal" tissue. It behoves toxicologists to have control samples of these compounds for exclusion purposes. Where tissues have been fixed in formalin, it is still possible to extract several drugs and poisons from the tissue and the preserving fluid, and Tiess reports success for barbiturates, methaqualone, glutethimide, chloroquine and nicotine, even after more than a year's storage. In cases where embalming has occurred and an autopsy has been ordered, the pathologist can still usually get plenty of unpreserved tissue, such as leg muscle, suitable for analyses of poisons affected by preserving fluid.

An important paper by McGeer and his co-workers gives paper chromatographic data of some 220 aromatic compounds of biological interest, some of which are of importance in this field.

Metallic poisons present their own difficulties; the incorporation and concentration of arsenic into hair from dilute solutions of the metal salts is the classic example of this type of artefact and it is for this reason that adequate soil samples must be taken from about the coffin. The soil may, however, also be useful in providing cultures for microbiological experiments.

REFERENCES

KAEMPE, B.: Interfering substances in the determination of poisons at autopsy. *Acta Pharmacol Toxicol, 21:*326, 333, 1964; *22:*82, 126, 1965; *23:*15, 360, 1965; *25:*155, 249, 1967.

MARKIEWICZ, J.: Investigations on endogenous carboxyhaemoglobin. *J For Med, 14:*16, 1967.

McGEER, E.G.; ROBERTSON, M.C., and McGEER, P.L.: Chromatographic characteristics of some aromatic compounds of biological interest. *Canad J Biochem Physiol, 39:*605, 1961.

SJÖSTRAND, T.: The *in vitro* formation of carbon monoxide in blood. *Acta Physiol Scand, 24:*314, 1952.

TIESS, D.: Moglichkeitin toxikologisch - chemischer Analytik an gelargerten formaldehydefixierten Organasservation. *Z Anal Chem, 43:*43, 1967.

C. THE WRITING OF REPORTS AND THE INTERPRETATION OF RESULTS

A positive report issued by a toxicologist usually consists of two parts; First, a statement of the poison that has been found and its concentration in the samples that have been analysed; the second part deals with the interpretation of the figures for the benefit of other persons who are not toxicologists.

In the first part it is most desirable that the amount found in the tissues should be expressed as a concentration and the form used in most parts of the world nowadays is milligrams (or micrograms) per 100 grams (or millilitres) of sample. The only valid exception to this is in the examination of the contents of the alimentary tract when the total amount of poison in the contents should also be stated. Reports which state the total weight of poison per whole organ without giving the weight of the organ are to a large extent valueless for the purposes of comparative toxicology.

In the part dealing with the conclusions to be drawn from the analyses, efforts must be made to answer the questions posed earlier in this chapter. A simple statement on the toxicity of the poison in question can also justifiably be included so that the non-expert can easily deduce whether a therapeutic dose or a small or large overdose has been involved in the particular case.

The problems associated with calculations of the probable ingested dose from the results of the analyses can only be fully resolved by comparing the concentrations in the blood and tissues with those in other cases in which the ingested dose was known. The toxicologist must therefore make extensive use of the published literature and of his own experience. Sometimes, when a new drug is involved, it may be necessary to take blood and urine samples from hospital patients receiving it in therapeutic quantities; if in these patients the concentration is twenty-fold lower than in the case under investigation this implies that an overdose was taken. The control series should include patients who have received many therapeutic doses so that the possibility of accumulation will become apparent.

In other cases this may not be possible and because self-dosing with, for example, a new insecticidal poison is not to be encouraged the results on animals must be studied. In such cases it is also necessary to calculate the quantity of poison isolated from the viscera actually analysed and then by inference the amount in the whole body. If the concentrations in the blood, liver and kidney do not differ within themselves by a wide margin (say factor of 3 or 4) then the arithmetic for multiplication up to the whole body weight is relatively simple and acceptable. The result will certainly enable the toxicologist to deduce whether a single therapeutic dose or twenty times such a dose had been taken.

When the poison is not evenly distributed and it is a completely new poison the problem becomes acute and occasionally the interpretation may have to be deferred until more data is available. However, in some of these cases, the mere presence of the poison is sufficient when all the other circumstantial evidence from pathologist and clinician has been taken into account to satisfy all concerned that death was from poisoning.

Chapter 2

THE ANALYSES

T WO SETS OF CIRCUMSTANCES must be considered — firstly, when the toxic agent is known or strongly suspected, and secondly, when there is no evidence as to the probable causative agent for the person's illness or death. The index at the back of the book provides the entry suitable for the first occasion; when the poison is unknown the analyses must be systematic and in a planned sequence.

The following chapters describe the tests to be performed for such a case. It cannot be too strongly emphasized that tests should not be omitted because they do not seem to be pertinent — it is only by *not* believing all he is told and relying on his skill as an analyst, that the toxicologist will uncover the poison murder. In such cases, premeditation and planning by the criminal lead to deliberate distortion of fact and systematic analysis unclouded by circumstance is essential. Even in straightforward cases where the poison is strongly suspected and revealed by subsequent analysis it is good practice to perform as many additional tests for other poisons as possible. It is not uncommon in cases of the "accidental" taking of drugs or household commodities by young children to find completely unsuspected positive results for other drugs and poisons. In my opinion, the use of a biochemical profile on all cases will become increasingly important in the future with the availability of fully automated clinical laboratories. The detection of poisoning must be sought not only in the demonstration of the poison but also by the detection of the biochemical lesion that results in the illness or death of the patient.

If the patient is still alive usually blood, urine and stomach wash are available and the only tests which can be done must be quick, simple and use the minimum of available material. In the case of analyses on post-mortem samples rapid screening tests are also a great advantage. There are several tests which fulfil these conditions in that they give a clear indication as to the presence or absence of poison or drug in as little as 1 ml of blood or one drop of urine either by direct observations on mixing sample and reagent or within an hour when a volatile poison has diffused into the reagent and changed its colour.

These "spot tests" are the obvious first step in any analysis because they require the minimum of operator manipulation. It is desirable, next in sequence, to search for the poisons that are common in the area served by the laboratory but which cannot be detected, as yet, by a simple spot test.

The detection of barbiturates by a simple colour test on blood is described on p. 28. If gas chromatography apparatus is available, then a much more comprehensive analysis on the living patient is possible. Not only can acetone and the many important alcohols be detected but also petrol or glue from sniffers, chloroform or anaesthetics from addicts, and industrial solvents from accidental exposures.

It should not be thought that gas chromatography can detect only "volatile" compounds; a preliminary extraction with organic solvent followed by examination of the concentrated extract by gas chromatography will readily reveal such compounds as the barbiturates, glutethimide, and meprobamate, using readily available columns. Drugs given in smaller dosage with corresponding low blood or urine concentrations may require special treatment and more sophisticated columns but there is no doubt that gas chromatography is one of the most potent tools of investigation in the hands of the toxicologist. Although simple spot tests are still of great value, very much more can be done if gas chromatographic equipment is available and its inclusion as a screening procedure for "volatiles" is therefore justified at the present time.

The analyst who has no gas chromatograph, will require to extract the common drugs such as sedatives, tranquillisers, hypnotics, antianxiety and antidepressive agents and detect and estimate them in 5 ml of blood. If the name of the drug involved is known, then the index is best consulted. If not, there is a limit to what can be done. There is no universal extraction scheme and a method for one class of drugs often destroys another group.

Mild, direct extraction with solvent does not isolate drugs bound to protein. The phenothiazines form such a group which require strong acid hydrolysis before extraction. When suspected drug addiction is being investigated the fluid of choice is urine and reference should be made to Chapter 4.

In the living patient every case is bound to be an analytical compromise but, provided the pathologist has submitted adequate samples, in the investigation of a sudden death, the analyses can be systematic and comprehensive. In these cases spot tests, especially on urine, have great value but they should not use more than a small proportion of the available sample. Blood drainings from the jar containing the liver can be used if the volume of the circulatory blood sample is small. The value of the spot test is that it provides a lead — and often a surprising one — early in the investigation. Simultaneously with the spot tests, a start should be made on the analyses of the liver as described in Chapter 7. A large number of drugs and poisons concentrate in this organ and by extracting one hundred-gram quantities of tissue, the toxicologist can often isolate milligram amounts of poison. The ease of identification and assay of this order of magnitude amply repays extra time and cost involved in handling the larger weights of tissue. The greater quantity of poison one isolates, the less difficult become the problems of identification.

In addition to the tungstic acid and hydrochloric acid digestions, separate tests are made for arsenic and zinc phosphide.

In the first edition of this book, a test for yellow phosphorus was also done at this stage. This rodenticide was then on free sale in the United Kingdom and had achieved some notoriety as a murder agent. Since then its sale has been banned and it can no longer be classed as a common poison. The continued inclusion in the book of the same test is now designed to detect zinc phosphide, another common rat poison. It behoves toxicologists to consider the most common rodenticide in their area (thallium compounds, for example) and to substitute tests for them at this place in the scheme.

After the relatively simple analyses on blood, urine and liver, a more prolonged and difficult stage is entered. It must include a full analysis of the contents of the alimentary tract for volatile poisons, for toxic metals, anions and organic solvent soluble poisons; treatment of at least 250 g of liver or brain by continuous extraction with alcohol; distillation of 100 g of brain for volatile poisons and screening tests for numerous metals on liver and kidney. In addition, uncommon poisons not fitting into the general scheme must be sought.

Needless to say, on many occasions this full analysis can be shortened because sufficient reliable circumstantial evidence is available but, when this is not so, short cuts are not recommended.

The purpose of each stage is basically different; although analyses for several poisons are duplicated or even triplicated their function is not only to guard against mishaps in analysis but also to detect different modes of administration of poisons — for example, in a death from the inhalation of chloroform, a positive test may be found in the blood and brain but not in the stomach or urine.

It is the primary aim throughout this book to suggest means for the detection of poison. In many cases this will not be the most difficult part of the problem but it is the most important stage and leads on to quantitative measurement. This is also considered in detail and the emphasis is put on specificity, for it is essential for the toxicologist to realise that many tests developed for use on the pure compound are relatively nonspecific and useless for extracts from decomposed bodies.

When the analyses have been completed, all with negative results, the toxicologist will be able to report "no poisons detected" with the knowledge that he has satisfactorily eliminated the vast majority of toxic compounds that at the present time *can* be detected.

Chapter 3

PRELIMINARY TESTS ON BLOOD

A. BLOOD ANALYSES — FIRST STAGE: SCREENING TESTS

T HE ORDER IN WHICH these screening tests will be done depends a great deal on the type of laboratory doing the work and the availability of instrumentation. One laboratory may use the rapid colorimetric screening method for barbiturate and a diffusion technique for ethanol, while another may prefer extraction and ultra-violet spectrophotometry for barbiturate and gas chromatography for ethanol and other volatiles. The approach may vary even from case to case and day to day, depending on the availability of a particular instrument at a particular time. Tables III and IV give lists of the poisons and tests to be considered at this very first stage of the analysis and it is convenient to have a note of Table IV, with spaces for the results of the tests, attached to each set of case records. It is also convenient to perform the spot tests on urine at the same time (see Chap. 4).

The tests for alcohols, carbon monoxide, methylpentynol, cyanide, fluoride and halogenated hydrocarbons can be performed by the use of a simple diffusion apparatus such as the Cavett flask or the Conway unit. The poison is liberated from the blood, homogenised tissue or, where applicable, urine and trapped by reagent whose colour it changes in the other compartment. The result can be seen by visual inspection. A half-hour is usually time for an obvious positive to be apparent. The other test, for salicylate, which is even simpler is also used to measure the concentration. The diffusion methods can all be adapted to give quantitative results as will be detailed below; at this stage however they are considered primarily as screening tests.

i. Barbiturates and Glutethimide

Barbiturates are the most widely prescribed drugs and the most common poison in most Western countries today. The toxicologist will, therefore, find them frequently in his analyses. In

TABLE III

RAPID SCREENING OF BLOOD

Poison	Volume of Blood Used	Details of Test	Quantitative Procedures	Interpretation of Results
Barbiturates, Glutethimide	1 ml	Extraction into chloroform, Forming mercury complex, titrate with dithizone, see p. 28	Colour test can be adapted to give rough guide — see p. 32 Extraction and ultra-violet spectrophotometry, see p. 57	See p. 65 In relation to tissue levels and time between ingestion and death, see p. 126
All volatile poisons	1 ml	GLC on head space, see p. 33 This is to be preferred to the dichromate test for volatile poisons	Gas chromatography, see p. 164 See below for colorimetric of alternatives. Normally by GLC comparison	Benzene, etc. see p. 35, 167 Halogenated hydrocarbons see p. 51
Methanol Ethanol Isopropanol Paraldehyde Acetone	1 ml	Diffusion into acid dichromate, see p. 35.	Methanol colorimetric see p. 36 Ethanol by dichromate see p. 199 Ethanol by GLC see p. 197 Acetaldehyde and paraldehyde colorimetric see p. 242	Methanol: p. 37 Ethanol: p. 39 Paraldehyde: p. 41
Carbon monoxide	1 ml	Diffusion into PdCl₂ see p. 43.	Colorimetric see p. 181	See p. 43
Insulin and oral hypoglycaemics	0.2 ml 0.05 ml	Blood sugar Acetest Tablet	GLC see p. 182 As preferred See screening test	Depends on method used; Blood glucose below 40mg/100ml suggests poisoning. See p. 188
Organo-phosphorus pesticides	0.1 ml	Test paper see p. 45	See p. 188	
Salicylate Methyl-pentynol	1.0 ml 1.0 ml	Colour with reagent see p. 46 Diffusion into ammoniacal silver nitrate: see p. 47	See p. 46 See p. 234	See p. 46 Very little information
Cyanide	1.0 ml	Liberation of HCN onto test paper see p. 53	See p. 47	See p 48
Fluoride	1.0 ml	Diffusion of HF into alizarin complexone	See p. 203	See p. 54
Halogenated hydrocarbons: Chloroform, Chloral, Chlorbutol, etc.	1.0 ml	Extraction and formation of red colours on heating with pyridine/NaOH see p. 49 Best by GLC, see p. 51	See p. 50	See p 51

TABLE IV
SPOT TESTS

1. Barbiturates and glutethimide	7. Salicylate
2. Gas chromatography (volatiles)	8. Methylpentynol
3. Alcohols and Aldehydes	9. Cyanide
4. Carbon monoxide	10. Halogenated hydrocarbons
5. Blood sugar/acetone	11. Fluoride
6. Cholinesterase	

cases of sudden death they will be best detected, estimated and identified by the analyses on 100 g of liver (Chap. 7) but many hospital laboratories have found the need for a rapid screening procedure that can be set up in a corner of the laboratory or in a side ward. In the mortuary the test described below has proved of value in detecting unsuspected barbiturate deaths and, although not highly quantitative, it is useful to clinician, biochemist and pathologist as a "do it yourself" screening procedure. Its inclusion here as the first test on blood reflects the widespread availability and misuse of these drugs.

It is essential to use this particular test for unchanged barbiturates in blood and not urine as several of the short-acting barbiturates are not excreted unchanged in the urine and false negatives could so be obtained. Stomach contents should not be used in this test because often they contain such large amounts of barbiturate that the glassware becomes overwhelmingly contaminated. The apparatus (see Fig. 1) is self-cleaning and although the test is not specific for barbiturate and glutethimide the only likely interfering substance to be met is bemegride. No significant difference exists between serum and whole blood barbiturate levels.

Method. (Curry, A.S., 1963, 1964) Reagents are as follows:

1. **Phosphate buffer:** pH 6.95, M/15. Add 0.624 g of Na_2HPO_4. $2H_2O$ and 0.363 g of KH_2PO_4 to distilled water and make up the volume to 100 ml.
2. **Mercury reagent:** 0.5 g mercuric chloride is dissolved in 50 ml of distilled water to which three drops concentrated nitric acid have been added; 1 ml of this solution is diluted to 50 ml with distilled water and 0.42 g sodium bicarbonate is added.

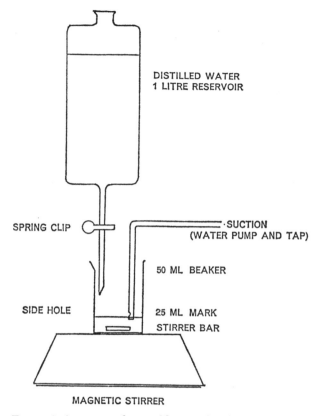

FIGURE 1. Apparatus for rapid screening for barbiturates.

3. **Dithizone (diphenylthiocarbazone) solution:** Dithizone decomposes in light and old stock should not be used. A solution of 3.75 mg/100 ml in chloroform should be suitable. When one volume is diluted with two of chloroform, an optical density at 605 mμ (1 cm cell) of approximately 1.0 should be obtained. The concentrated solution which is used for the test is stable for at least one week when stored in a dark bottle at 0°C. (It is essential that both storage bottle and stopper, when first used, be well washed and stood with a concentrated solution of dithizone in chloroform to remove all traces of metallic impurity.)

The Test. Blood (1 ml) and phosphate buffer (3 ml) are magnetically stirred with chloroform (25 ml) for four minutes. After settling, the aqueous layer is removed by suction and discarded. The chloroform layer is washed with two 15 ml portions of water which are also discarded. By manipulation of the beaker, all but a drop of the aqueous layer can be removed. It is important at this stage to try not to remove a large amount of the chloroform layer; if a trace is inadvertently lost, it is made up by dropwise addition until the level again reaches the lower end of the suction-tube. The chloroform layer is then slowly stirred for two minutes with mercury reagent (1 ml). After settling, as much as possible of the top layer is removed by suction. The chloroform layer must be free from aqueous droplets. Water (15 ml) is added and then immediately removed by the suction-tube. It is essential to remove as much as possible of the aqueous layer. Dithizone solution (2 ml) is then pipetted into the beaker under the surface of the chloroform. If barbiturate is present, an orange colour is seen; if none is present, the dithizone remains green. If the colour is intermediate between orange and green, the barbiturate concentration is below 2 mg/100 ml and before diagnosing barbiturate intoxication repeat the test removing any possible remaining traces of excess mercury reagent by washing with an additional 15 ml water before adding dithizone (1 ml). An orange colour in the final dithizone solution then indicates relatively low levels of barbiturate and the patient should be conscious in less than twenty-four hours.

It should be noted that blood samples from epileptics on phenobarbitone therapy and from other patients on long-term barbitone dosage are likely to give positive results; conversely, blood from patients with acute barbiturate poisoning, terminating in death in less than four to five hours may give a negative or doubtful positive result.

A more accurate estimate of the blood level can be made by titration, using the dithizone colour from the orange to green as the end point; each millilitre of dithizone corresponds to 1 mg/100 ml of barbiturate in blood. It assists if at the final stage 3 ml of 0.5 N ammonia are added and very gentle stirring used during the titration.

Identification of the Barbiturate. See pages 59, 62, 126, 164.
Interpretation of Results. See pages 65, 126.

REFERENCES

CLOW, W.M., and SMITH, A.C.A.: Rapid quantitative barbiturate estimation: a critical study of a bedside method. *Scot Med J, 12:*307, 1967.

CURRY, A.S.: Rapid method of screening for barbiturate, *Brit Med J, ii:*1040, 1963.

CURRY, A.S.: Rapid quantitative barbiturate estimation. *Brit Med J, i:*354, 1964.

GEE, D.J., and DALLEY, R.A.: Unsuspected poisoning. *Med, Sci Law, 7:*56, 1967.

ii. Gas Chromatography (Volatiles)

Many toxicological laboratories have gas chromatographs and the second screening test involves the use of this instrument. The make of instrument is of little consequence. The bulk of my experience has been on the Pye Model 104 series and the Perkin-Elmer Biomedical F11 machines.

A column of 5′ of 10% PEG400 on 100-120 Celite with a flame ionisation detector is used at 70°C; 1 ml of blood, tissue homogenate, or urine is injected into the apparatus shown in Figure 2 which has a total capacity of 7 ml and to which has been added previously 0.5 g of solid potassium carbonate. (Any other suitable container may be used). After warming to 70°C by immersion in hot water, a 1 ml air sample from within the container is withdrawn by means of a hypodermic syringe and injected into the gas chromatograph. Volatile poisons are revealed and the retention time gives a lead as to identity. This simple test will reveal not only the common poisons such as methanol and ethanol, but also as Table V shows, a large number of toxicologically impor-

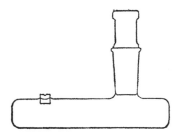

FIGURE 2. Apparatus for the GLC screening of volatiles.

tant compounds. It should be noted that if an electron capture detector is available, it is possible to selectively detect the halogenated hydrocarbons. Quantitation can be achieved either by direct comparative studies or by the use of the internal standard technique as described by Machata who has used the method to analyse automatically large numbers of samples for ethanol.

The accurate determinations of ethanol in $10\mu l$ of blood by gas chromatography is described in Part II.

TABLE V
RETENTION TIMES FOR VOLATILES USING 5' OF
10% PEG400 ON CELITE AT 70° C

Order of Elution	Approximate Time in Minutes
Ether	1
Acetaldehyde	1.5
Tetrachloroethane	
Acetone	
Diacetonealcohol	3
Carbon tetrachloride	
Ethyl acetate	4
Methyl-ethyl ketone	
Dichloromethane	5
Benzene	
Methanol	6
Trichloroethylene	7
Isopropanol	
Methyl n-propyl ketone	
Perchloroethylene	8
Ethanol	
Chloroform	
Methyl-isobutyl ketone	9
Toluene	10
Dichloroethane	11
Butyl acetate	13
Paraldehyde	15
Amyl acetate	18

This air space test can also be applied at the same time with a urine sample, but it should be noted that at high sensitivity settings, several compounds can be found in "normal" urine, for example, acetone and sometimes traces of ethanol. A profile of urines *not* containing poison should be examined before red herrings are chased. It is also worth taking an 5 ml air sample from the container holding the liver at room temperature. This will readily show the presence of petrol in fire victims if they were breathing the fumes of accelerant at the time of the incident.

Ethchlorvynol can also be detected by the head space method, but with a column at 70°C it has a long retention time. Finkle (personal communication) uses a 2% SE30 column at 150°C for the detection and assay of this compound (see also Part II). Bonnichsen *et al.*, using GLC methods as well as paper chromatography and TLC, report on thirty-five cases (26 fatal) involving benzene, toluene, xylene and nitrobenzene and found tissue levels of the order of 0.1-2 mg/100 g. They used 20% Apiezon on Chromosorb at 190°C.

REFERENCES

BONNICHSEN, R.; MAEHLY, A.C., and MOELLER, M.: Poisoning by volatile compounds; aromatic hydrocarbons. *J For Sci, 11:*186, 1966.
CURRY, A.S.; HURST, G.; KENT, N.R., and POWELL, H.: Rapid screening of blood samples for volatile poisons by gas chromatography. *Nature, 195:* 603, 1962.
MACHATA, G.: Uber die gaschromatographische Blutalkoholbestimmung. *Blutalkhol, 4:*252, 1967.

iii. Alcohols and Aldehydes

This test depends on the reaction of the volatile poisons with a potassium dichromate/sulphuric acid solution. It can be performed in a Conway unit or Cavett flask; a positive result is seen by the change in colour of the dichromate from orange to green. If positive, identification of the alcohol or aldehyde and its quantitative assay are necessary.

Method. Place 1 ml blood (or 1 ml urine, depending which is more readily available) with 1 ml saturated aqueous potassium carbonate solution in the base of a Cavett flask (assembly 2BC, Quickfit and Quartz). In the hanging cup put 0.5 ml of 0.1N potassium dichromate in 60% v/v sulphuric acid solution. Seal the flask with Ucon Lubricant.* Place in an oven at about 50°C or on a hot plate at about 60°C-70°C. A complete colour change from orange to green is observed with 50 mg ethanol/100 ml fluid.

A green colour, developing after half to one hour indicates ethanol, methanol, paraldehyde or possible acetone. If positive, repeat with 0.2 ml blood. If still positive, ethanol is most probably

*Union Carbide Co. Ltd.

present but if the patient has been ill for several hours suspect methanol. Metaldehyde may react similarly. (Extreme cleanliness of containers and purity of reagents is essential.)

After this test has been set up it is followed by the one described on p. 42.

Because ethanol is the most common volatile poison it is probable that analysis will be directed to it first. Methanol however is often a cause of obscure acidotic coma which may not develop for several hours after ingestion of the poison. Although the metabolism of ethanol is relatively rapid, the rate of disappearance of methanol from the blood is so slow that appreciable amounts may be present over forty-eight hours after ingestion. It is therefore important that this test should be applied routinely.

The differentiation of the volatile reducing poisons is best made by gas chromatography and the tests made in the previous section will have already provided answers if it has been possible to use this technique. In its absence recourse must be made to colour tests.

(a) Methanol

Methanol is detected by controlled oxidation to formaldehyde and determination of this compound with chromotropic acid or with Schiff's reagent under conditions specific for formaldehyde. Omission of the oxidation step makes the method suitable for formaldehyde. It is essential to perform exact controls with methanol added to blood.

Method. (Feldstein, M., and Klendshoj, N.C.: *Anal Chem, 26:* 932, 1954). Sulphuric acid (2.2 ml of 10%) is pipetted into the centre well of a Conway cell. In the outer compartment is placed 1 ml of saturated aqueous potassium carbonate solution. Sealing of the ground glass plate is made with Vaseline.

Half a millilitre (0.5 ml) of sample is introduced into the outer compartment, the cell sealed and tilted several times to thoroughly mix the sample and carbonate. Diffusion is allowed to proceed for two hours at room temperature. At the end of this period 1 ml of the sulphuric acid is pipetted into a 25 ml test-tube: one drop of 5% aqueous potassium permanganate is added and the tube shaken. After five minutes at room temperature, drops of a saturated aqueous solution of sodium bisulphite are added until the permanganate is decolourised. After the addition of 0.2 ml of freshly prepared 0.5% aqueous chromotropic acid, the tube is cooled in ice and 4 ml of concentrated sulphuric acid added. The tube is shaken and then immersed in a boiling water bath for fifteen minutes after which it is cooled to room temperature. After making up to exactly 10 ml readings at 580 mμ are taken for the test and controls. Suitable standards are in the range 0-80μg of methanol.

Schiff's reagent can be used to test for methanol by adding it to the permanganate oxidised distillates made up to 10% with sulphuric acid. Acetaldehyde does not then interfere and estimates of concentration can be made by comparison with standards (Bamford) . See also part II.

Interpretation of Results. Methanol is considerably more toxic than ethanol and correspondingly lower concentrations are found in cases of poisoning. Levels over 80 mg/100 ml of blood must be considered extremely dangerous to life.

References

Bamford, F.: *Poisons, their Isolation and Detection,* 3rd ed. London, Churchill, 1951, p. 40.

Polson, C. J., and Tattersall, R. N.: *Clinical Toxicology.* London, English Univ. Press, 1959, p. 383-387.

(b) Ethanol

This is the most common substance that gives a positive test with the acid dichromate test described above.

Identification and Assay. Absolute identification of ethanol rarely used to be achieved in the methods used by the toxicologist. The valid inference was made that in the concentrations necessary to produce clinical symptoms of intoxication, if the volatile substance was any other but ethanol then the person would have been dead from poisoning at much lower tissue concentrations of that other compound. Two methods are now used, however, to provide identification—the enzyme, alcohol dehydrogenase, and gas chromatography. The former is not entirely specific for ethanol, reacting to varying extents with n-propanol, n-butanol and allyl alcohol but if two columns of differing packing material are used in a gas chromatographic examination (e.g., 5' lengths of PEG400 at 85°C and Porapak Q at 180°C) then the combination of different retention times can result in the conclusion that no other known compound gives the same figures and hence identification is achieved.

The enzymatic method is most useful and is suitable for routine determinations: it requires a spectrophotometer capable of reading at 340 mμ. The method is based on the oxidation of alcohol to acetaldehyde with diphosphoropyridine nucleotide (DPN) as coenzyme. Semicarbazide is used to remove the acetaldehyde and this forces the reaction to completion. Details of the method have been described by Lundquist in a review on the determination of ethanol and reference to the original paper is recommended.

Gas chromatography is now also a routine procedure in the Home Office Forensic Science Laboratories for the analysis of capillary blood samples taken in relation to traffic offences and standard deviations of better than 1 per cent are achieved on 10μl samples of blood. The method is described in detail in Part II.

It must be stressed that dichromate methods are reliable and accurate for alcohol determinations when the ethanol concentrations are relatively high (over 100 mg/100 ml). Below this figure, and especially if post-mortem samples are being analysed, then efforts should be made to use either a gas chromatographic method or ADH. Two methods using the dichromate oxidation procedure for quantitative ethanol measurement are described in Part II.

Interpretation of Results. It should be noted that, in general, it is extremely difficult to interpret post-mortem blood alcohol concentrations when these are below 50 mg/100 ml. Many types of bacteria will produce small amounts of alcohol and the presence of traces of ethanol in the blood or tissues from a body that has not been autopsied within twenty-four hours of death, should be expected and ignored unless circumstances require special investigations such as an intensive bacteriological study. If urine has been obtained the interpretation becomes much easier. If death occurs shortly after the bulk of alcohol ingestion ceased, it is to be expected that the urine concentration will be lower than the blood alcohol concentration; if death occurs over two hours after the ingestion of alcohol then the urine concentration will be higher than the blood alcohol concentration, usually about 33 per cent higher. If these generalisations do not fit what the toxicologist is told about the circumstances, the samples should be reinvestigated critically and, if a dichromate method has been used, the alcohol results double checked by a different method.

To reach a blood alcohol concentration of 200 mg/100 ml a man of eleven stones (154 lbs.) would have to drink seven pints of 3%w/v beer (120 g of alcohol) or just over ten ounces of spirits (70% proof spirit, 93.3 g of alcohol). These figures are based on a Widmark factor of 0.90 for beer and 0.70 for spirits. Other figures can be obtained by direct proportion, increasing directly with weight and with blood alcohol concentration.

Normally, no difficulty will be experienced in interpreting blood alcohol concentrations in samples from the living patients provided the clinician has not used ethanol to swab down the patient's arm or to sterilise his hypodermic syringe!

It should be remembered that even small amounts of alcohol will be of significance if other depressants of the central nervous system are also present.

In post-mortem blood samples two precautions have to be taken. The first is to guard against the post-mortem production of alcohol in the blood by yeasts, fungi and bacteria and the second is to ensure that no diffusion of alcohol has occurred from the gastrointestinal tract into the blood in the period between death and the autopsy. As indicated above, both these precautions are covered by the pathologist taking two separate samples from peripheral parts of the body well away from any injuries and adding a little solid sodium fluoride to one of them. The concentration should be at least 1 per cent.

Relation of blood alcohol with clinical effect: (a) 50 mg/100 ml of blood — usually little apparent clinical effect.

(b) 80 mg/100 ml of blood — legal limit in the United Kingdom for driving a motor vehicle; loss of driving license for a twelve-month period is mandatory in addition to a fine or gaol sentence. It is of interest to note that it is the alcohol concentration in the blood sample that is the deciding factor and not the subsequently back calculated value for the time of the driving offence. This is at variance with the practice of many European countries. Capillary blood is normally collected into a specially designed plastic cup that contains fluoride and oxalate.

(c) 300 mg/100 ml of blood: clinically drunk; increasing tendency to asphyxiate from inhalation of vomit.

(d) 460 mg/100 ml: death from respiratory depression.

REFERENCES

Alcohol and Road Traffic, Proceedings Third International Conference. London, B.M.A. Publication, 1962.

Alcohol and Traffic Safety, Proceedings Fourth International Conference. Bloomington (Ind.), Indiana Univ., 1966.

GORMSEN, H.: Alcohol production in the dead body. *J. For Med, 1:*170, 1954. *idem, ibid, 1:*314, 1954.

HARGER, R.N.: In Stewart, C.P., and Stolman, A. (Eds.): *Toxicology, Mechanisms and Analytical Methods.* New York, Academic, 1961, vol. II, pp. 86-147.

HARGER, R.N.: In Stolman, A. (Ed.): Progress in Chemical Toxicology, vol 1. New York, Academic, 1963, p. 54.

HARGER, R.N., and FORNEY, R.B.: In Stolman, A. (Ed.): *Progress in Chemical Toxicology.* New York and London, Academic, 1967, vol. III, p. 1.

KIRK, P.L.; GIBON, A., and PARKER, K.P.: Determination of blood alcohol; improvements in chemical and enzymatic procedures. *Anal Chem, 30:* 1418, 1958.

KOZELKA, F.L., and HINE, C.H.: A method for the determination of ethyl alcohol for medico-legal purposes. *Ind Eng Chem, Anal Ed, 13:*905, 1941.

LUNDQUIST, F.: Ethyl alcohol in blood and tissues. In Glick, D. (Ed.): *Methods of Biochemical Analysis.* New York, Interscience, 1959, vol. 7, p. 217.

MUEHLBERGER, C.W.: Medico-legal aspects of alcohol intoxication. In Gradwohl, R.H.B. (Ed.): *Legal Medicine.* St. Louis, Mosby, 1954, pp. 754-796.

PLUECKHAHN, V.D.: The significance of blood alcohol levels at autopsy. *Med J Aust, 2:*118, 1967.

Report of a special Committee of the British Medical Association. *The Relation of Alcohol to Road Accidents.* London, British Medical Association, 1960.

SOUTHGATE, H.W., and CARTER, B.: Alcohol in urine as a guide to alcoholic intoxication. *Brit Med J, 1:*463, 1926.

WARD SMITH, H.: Methods for determining alcohol. In Curry, A.S. (Ed.): *Methods of Forensic Science,* London and New York, Interscience, 1965, vol. IV, p. 1.

(c) Acetaldehyde and Paraldehyde

Identification and Assay. Acetaldehyde disappears rapidly from stored blood and, in cases in which it is thought that tetra-ethyldithiuram disulphide and alcohol may have been taken together resulting in acetaldehyde poisoning, it is essential that the analyses should be done within a few hours of death.

Paraldehyde, whose ingestion is usually apparent from the smell of the patient, decomposes on storage when an antioxidant it contained has itself been decomposed. One sample examined by the author contained 40% acetic acid and, when taken by a patient with tuberculosis in a therapeutic dose, resulted in death. Untoward reactions after the use of paraldehyde should be investigated with this in mind.

Assay can be achieved by quantitative gas chromatography using the head space-air injection method against comparative controls either of paraldehyde itself or the acetaldehyde liberated on warming with an equal volume of 6N sulphuric acid. The PEG400 column at 85°C described above is suitable.

Alternatively, colorimetric methods may be used — See Part II.

Interpretation of Results. Fifty mg/100 ml of paraldehyde in blood must be considered a serious case of poisoning.

Paraldehyde is frequently used as a sedative in the management of psychotic patients and even in the treatment of alcoholics. There have been cases in which too enthusiastic therapeutic administration has resulted in profound respiratory depression and death and this can occur with blood levels slightly below 50 mg/100 ml. Often, a history of additional medication with other tranquillisers is noted in such cases. Conversely, in addicts regularly taking large doses over long periods, blood levels over 50 mg/100 ml can be found in a conscious patient. There is no published evidence for paraldehyde accumulation in the body when it is taken in therapeutic amounts; in investigations the author did on the blood of a tetanic patient who was receiving regular repeated doses for several weeks the blood level did not rise over 10 mg/100 ml. In the 1930's some confusion over dosage with neat paraldehyde and a diluted liquorice mixture was noted with subsequent therapeutic misadventures.

REFERENCES

AGRANAT, A.L., and TRUBSHAW, W.H.D.: Two cases of poisoning from deteriorated paraldehyde. *S Afr Med J, 29*:1021, 1955.

COPEMAN, P.R. v.d. R.: Review of Analytical findings in cases of poisoning by paraldehyde. *J For Med, 3*:80, 1956.

FELDSTEIN, M., and KLENDSHOJ, N.C.: The determination of volatile substances by microdiffusion analysis. *J For Sci, 2*:39, 1957.

REHLING, C.J.: Poison residues in human tissues. In Stolman, A. (Ed.): *Progress in Chemical Toxicology*, vol. 3. New York, Academic, 1967.

STOTZ, E.: The determination of acetaldehyde in blood. *J Biol Chem, 148*: 585, 1943.

iv. Carbon Monoxide

There are two basic methods for measuring the concentration of carbon monoxide in blood. The first depends on examining the visible spectrum of diluted blood to determine the relative amount of carboxyhaemoglobin to oxyhaemoglobin or total haemoglobin, while in the second, the volume of gaseous carbon monoxide liberated from a measured amount of the total haemoglobins is determined. Fully saturated normal blood contains approximately 20 ml of carbon monoxide in 14 g of haemoglobin or 100 ml of blood, but in all cases the actual saturation should be found by comparison of results for the blood under examination with the same blood which has been saturated with carbon monoxide. It should be noted that old blood does not take up carbon monoxide as readily as fresh blood; it is essential to pass pure carbon monoxide from a cylinder or generator (formic acid with concentrated sulphuric acid) through diluted blood, to which a small spatula end (50 mg) of sodium hydrosulphite has been added, for half an hour before stoichimetric conversion of the haemoglobin is complete.

Screening Test. (a) Use of the Hartridge reversion spectroscope: blood is diluted with 0.3N ammonia to a dilution which gives sharp bands when viewed through the instrument. At least five separate readings are taken for the sample and for controls of blood 0 per cent and 100 per cent saturated with carbon monoxide.

(b) Use of palladium chloride: this depends on the reaction
$$H_2O + CO + PdCl_2 = Pd + 2HCl + CO_2$$

1 ml of blood and 1 ml of 10% sulphuric acid are put separately into one compartment of a Conway unit or into the base of a Cavett flask. 0.5 ml of 0.001N palladium chloride solution is put into the other section of the diffusion vessel and the top sealed. The carbon monoxide is liberated by mixing the blood and the acid and the liberated palladium can be seen as a black film if carbon monoxide is present, within about thirty minutes. False positive results can be obtained on putrefying blood.

Either method is suitable for use in rapid screening to indicate the possible occurrence of carbon monoxide intoxication, but for accurate quantitation, especially on blood that is more than a few hours old, it is essential to cross check using two methods that fall into both basic categories described above. In my opinion, there is no doubt that the gas chromatographic method is the one of choice for really reliable results; only the fact that many laboratories do not have a machine that can be permanently set up for this one purpose has made it necessary to describe the less specific techniques.

Methods for quantitation are described in Part II.

The next screening test is described on p. 44.

Interpretation of Results. Twenty-five per cent saturation of carbon monoxide in the majority of cases marks a division between minor and the beginning of major symptoms of poisoning. In cases of exposure to high concentrations ($>1.0\%$) of carbon monoxide in the air, the blood contains a high concentration ($>60\%$ saturation); where death follows prolonged exposure to low concentrations of the gas, the blood usually only contains about 40 per cent saturation.

In anaemic old people death may occur with slightly lower concentrations.

A screening test for carbon monoxide should always be done in any general search for poisons; it is not unknown for the pink colour of the blood to escape the pathologist's attention, usually because of inadequate or bad quality lighting in the mortuary. In badly decomposed blood from exhumation cases simple spectroscopic methods such as Hartridge's method should not be trusted.

In a living patient only half the concentration of carbon monoxide can be expected to be replaced by oxygen in an hour and it is therefore worthwhile taking samples several hours after exposure if criminal investigation proceedings require confirmation of exposure.

REFERENCES

CONWAY, E.J.: *Microdiffusion Analysis and Volumetric Error,* 3rd ed. London, Crosby Lockwood, 1950, p. 257.

DALZIEL, K., and O'BRIEN, J.R.P.: Kinetics of reduction of oxyhaemoglobin by sodium dithionite. *Biochem J, 67:*122, 1957.

DOMINGUEZ, A.M.; CHRISTENSEN, H.E.; GOLDBAUM, L.R., and STEMBRIDGE, V.A.: A sensitive procedure for determining carbon monoxide in blood and tissue utilising gas-solid chromatography. *Toxic Appl Pharmacol, 1:* 135, 1959.

DOMINGUEZ, A.L.; HALSTED, J.R., and DOMANSKI, T.J.: The effect of post-mortem changes on carboxyhaemoglobin results. *J For Sci, 9:*330, 1964.

FELDSTEIN, M., and KLENDSHOJ, N.C.: The determination of carbon monoxide by micro-diffusion. *Canad J Med, Tech, 16:*81, 1954.

FELDSTEIN, M.: Methods for determination of carbon monoxide. In Stolman, A. (Ed.) : *Progress in Chemical Toxicology,* vol. 3. New York, Academic, 1967.

HESSEL, D.W., and MODGLIN, F.R.: The determination of carbon monoxide in blood by gas-solid chromatography. *J For Sci, 12:*123, 1967.

MAEHLY, A.: Quantitative determination of carbon monoxide. In Lundquist, F. (Ed.) : *Methods of Forensic Science,* vol. 1. New York, Interscience, 1962.

MANT, A.K.: A review of 100 cases of carbon monoxide poisoning. *Medicoleg J, 28:*31, 1960.

ROCHE, L.; LEJEUNE, E.; BACHELOR, M., and VERSININ, C.: Evolution de l'oxycarbonemie dans les intoxications aigues par l'oxyde de carbone. *Ann Med Leg (Paris), 40:*132, 1960.

SIMPSON, K.: Carbon monoxide poisoning. Medico-legal problems. *J For Med, 2:*5, 1955.

v. Blood Sugar

This is such a well known clinical procedure that experimental details will not be repeated here. The test is of little value on post-mortem blood samples but in the living, ill, person, its determination should be routine. Coma from suicidal, accidental or malicious administration of insulin or the oral hypoglycaemic agents is not uncommon and this simple test will provide a rapid result of great value. Acetone in blood can also be conveniently tested for at this stage by putting a drop of serum on an Acetest tablet,* scraping off the supernatant thirty seconds later and inspecting for a violet colour. It can also be detected by gas chromatography (Test ii above). Acetone is found not only in uncontrolled diabetics but in starvation and as a metabolite of isopropanol — an ingredient of many dangerous synthetic intoxicant brews.

vi. Cholinesterase

Because of the widespread availability of organo-phosphorus insecticides which have the property of depressing this enzyme, the routine inclusion of the following simple test is recommended.

Acholest test papers* can be used for the rapid roughly quantitative measurement of serum cholinesterase, or Wang's method can be used to prepare papers in the laboratory.

Method. A fresh 0.04% solution of bromothymol blue is prepared in glass distilled water. Acetylcholine bromide is added to this solution at a concentration of 100 mg/ml.

A piece of Whatman No. 1 paper is impregnated with this solution, transferred to a clean glass surface and allowed to dry at room temperature for about one hour. Cut into strips and store in tightly-closed bottles in a dessicator. Use within one month. Approximately two drops of plasma free from red cells is pipetted onto a glass slide and a piece of test paper placed over the plasma with clean forceps; another clean glass slide is gently pressed on it to exclude air bubbles. The time is noted for the aquamarine colour to change through green to match the pale yellow formed when a pH 5 buffer is put on another piece of test paper. Normal activity at $23 \pm 3°C$ takes about five minutes. Poisoning is readily recognizable as the change in colour, if any, is delayed for as long as an hour.

---

*Ames Co. Ltd., Miles Laboratories, Stoke Poges, Slough, U.K.

An accurate method for cholinesterase determination is given in Part II.

REFERENCES

CHURCHILL-DAVIDSON, H.C., and GRIFFITHS, W.J.: Simple test paper method for the clinical determination of plasma pseudocholinesterase. *Brit Med J, ii*:994, 1961.

WANG, R.I.H.: Determining cholinesterase activity in human plasma. *JAMA, 183*:792, 1963.

vii. Salicylate

Screening Test and Assay (Trinder, P.: *Biochem J, 57*:301, 1954). Blood (1 ml) is mixed with 5 ml of reagent and centrifuged. A violet colour in the supernatant indicates the presence of a salicylate. The reagent is made as follows: 40 g of mercuric chloride are dissolved in 850 ml of water with warming. After cooling, 120 ml of N hydrochloric acid and 40 g $Fe(NO_3)_3 9H_2O$ are added and the solution is made up to 1 litre with water.

For the quantitative assay, decant off the supernatant and read against standards and controls at 540 mμ.

Identification. Salicylamide, which is only rarely encountered, and salicylic acid from aspirin or methyl salicylate both give violet colours with ferric salts but no other interfering substances have been noted. The screening test is simple and gives an accurate assay of salicylate within five minutes.

Interpretation of Results. Levels greater than 30 mg/100 ml of salicylic acid in blood lead to an increasing probability of a major metabolic upset with a fatal outcome. Normally "headache cure" levels do not normally exceed 5 mg/100 ml but, in the treatment of rheumatoid arthritis with aspirin, levels of 25 mg/100 ml are common. Such patients, however, have to be kept under observation and therapeutic accidents are not unknown if routine blood levels are not performed.

Excretion varies greatly with the pH of the urine.

Ingestion of methyl salicylate gives free salicylic acid as a metabolite with corresponding interpretation of toxic levels. Salicylic acid from ointment is readily absorbed through the intact skin.

viii. Methylpentynol (methylparafynol)

Screening Test. Repeat the Cavett flask distillation using 1 ml blood with 1 ml saturated aqueous potassium carbonate in the base and 0.5 ml methylpentynol reagent in the hanging cup. Place on a hot plate at about 60°C-70°C.

To obtain a known positive, dissolve the contents of one capsule of Oblivon (250 mg methylpentynol) in 10 ml ether. Shake with 10 ml water. Use 1 ml of water layer.

A white cloud in the methylpentynol reagent after about one hour indicates the presence of methylpentynol. Perform in parallel with negative and positive controls.

Reagent for Methylpentynol (Perlman, P.L., Johnson, C.: *J Amer Pharm Ass. 41*:13, 1952) : To a 250 ml volumetric flask add 125 ml water, 2.12 g silver nitrate and after solution, 15 ml 6N-sodium hydroxide. Add just sufficient concentrated ammonia (S.G. 0.880) to dissolve the precipitate. Make up to mark with water. Store at 0°C in the dark. Do not keep for longer than one month.

For quantitative estimation see Part II.

ix. Cyanide

Because cyanide is a volatile poison it too is conveniently analysed by microdiffusion techniques. Its presence in stomach contents can be missed at autopsy but in the laboratory its distinctive smell soon reveals its presence. Two other routes of absorption can occur and the first, inhalation, can leave no trace until analyses on the blood are performed. The other route—absorption through the skin occurs only through broken or burnt skin—usually in accidents at chemical plants. In such cases the degree of absorption, and its possible continuance from particles still on the skin, may be paramount in the mind of the clinician. Routine analyses on blood are therefore essential.

Screening Test and Assay: Method (Gettler, A.O., and Goldbaum, L. R.: *Anal Chem, 19*:270, 1947 [modified]). The apparatus is similar to that used for alcohol (see p. 199) with the addition of a Gutzeit type paper holder. A convenient one which can be easily made from plastic sheet and standard B 10 joints is shown in Figure 3. Nitrogen is blown through water in the bubbling Tube A which acts as a flow meter and then through 2 ml of blood placed in the tube B with 3 ml of water, two drops of saturated lead acetate solution and 5 ml of 10% trichloroacetic acid. Tube B is then immersed in a water bath at 90°C. The liberated hydrogen cyanide is slowly blown through a ferrous hydroxide paper held by the Gutzeit holder at the exit of B, ten minutes is sufficient; the flow rate should be held constant. The paper is prepared by soaking a Whatman No. 50 paper in 10% ferrous sulphate for five minutes, drying, immersing the dried paper in 20% sodium hydroxide and quickly blotting. The cyanide reacts with the ferrous hydroxide and can be seen as a stain of Turnbull's blue by immersing in 1:4 hydrochloric acid. The stain is quantitative: 1 to 5μg are convenient standards.

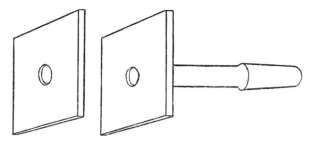

FIGURE 3. A simply made holder for paper in a Gutzeit apparatus.

An alternative method is given on p. 190.

Interpretation. Cyanide is very toxic but blood from healthy adults can contain up to 15μg/100 ml. In death from inhalation of the gas, blood levels of about 100μg/100 ml or more are found. Rapid loss of cyanide from post-mortem blood not preserved with fluoride can occur and, in any case, the analyses should be done as quickly as possible. In deaths from large overdoses by oral ingestion blood levels are often much higher — sometimes of the order of mg/100 ml.

Recovery has been noted in victims whose cyanide level in the blood reached 750μg/100 ml. Cyanide can be produced in blood that is stored, probably both by enzyme action and by bacteria;

the addition of 1% sodium fluoride prevents this. If cyanide is found in the above test then 5 g from the centre, undecomposed area, of the brain should be excised and analysed. In fatal cases of cyanide poisoning, levels in the brain are usually very much lower than blood levels — as low as $10\mu g/100$ g — but a positive finding, even of this low concentration, can be extremely useful in confirming the cause of death and excluding cyanide production. Cyanide is bound to red cells and the concentration in the spleen is usually high.

REFERENCES

BONNICHSEN, R., and MAEHLY, A.C.: Poisoning by volatile compounds: hydrocyanic acid. *J For Sci, 11(4)*:516-528, 1966.

CURRY, A.S.: Cyanide poisoning. *Acta Pharmacol Toxicol, 20*:291-294, 1963.

CURRY, A.S.; PRICE, D.E., and RUTTER, E.R.: The production of cyanide in postmortem material. *Acta Pharmacol Toxicol, 25*:339, 1967.

GETTLER, A.O., and GOLDBAUM, L.: Detection and estimation of microquantities of cyanide. *Anal Chem, 19*:270, 1947.

GETTLER, A.O., and BAINE, J.O.: The toxicology of cyanide. *Amer J Med Sci, 195*:182, 1938.

HALSTROM, F., and MOLLER, K.: The content of cyanide in human organs from cases of poisoning with cyanide taken by mouth. *Acta Pharmacol Toxicol, 1*:18-28, 1945.

PATTY, F.A.: The production of hydrocyanic acid by bacillus pyocyaneus. *J Infect Dis, 29*:73-77, 1921.

REHLING, C.J.: Poison residues in human tissues. In Stolman, A.: *Progress in Chemical Toxicology*, vol. 3. New York, Academic, 1967.

SUNSHINE, I., and FINKLE, B.: The necessity for tissue studies in fatal cyanide poisonings. *Int Arch Gewerbepath, 20*:558-561, 1964.

x. Halogenated Hydrocarbons

Identification and Assay. There are many halogenated aliphatic hydrocarbons which the toxicologist must consider. These include chloroform, carbon tetrachloride, ethylene dichloride, trichloroethylene, perchloroethylene and methylene dichloride. In addition chloral hydrate is still in widespread use and tablets containing a chloralphenazone compound may be encountered. Because of their volatility, the halogenated hydrocarbons can be separated from blood or a tissue slurry by microdiffusion and selectively absorbed into an organic solvent. Alternatively the blood can be shaken with the solvent. Toluene, hexane and heptane have been used most but with the increasing use of gas chromatography for the examination of this fraction, the purity of the solvent is becoming paramount. Propyl acetate is usually reasonably pure and traps chloroform well in microdiffusion but is a little too volatile.

On a PEG 400 column at 70°C ether can also be used and, as this has a very short retention time, relatively large volumes can be injected without causing interference to the halogenated hydrocarbon peaks which have considerably longer retention times. It is also possible to concentrate the ether extract carefully to about one tenth its volume prior to injection into the gas chromatograph without great loss of many of these compounds. If time, or lack of suitable apparatus, does not permit a full-scale search for these compounds, the following procedure is used.

Method. Shake 1 ml of blood with 2 ml of ether, pipetting off into a test-tube 1 ml of the supernatant and after adding to it 1 ml of pyridine and 1 ml of 20% w/v sodium hydroxide, immerse the tube in a boiling water bath for one minute.

Red colours in the pyridine shows a positive result provided a full "blank" determination has been done at the same time.

Some measure of differentiation of the various compounds can be achieved by varying the conditions of the reaction and noting those for maximum colour development; Table VI shows some of these together with the recommended isolations.

For the routine screening in blood, the diffusion technique described in Reference 1, Table VI, is also recommended.

For details of quantitative colorimetric analysis see Chapter 8.

The carbon tetrachloride test (Ref. 4, Table VI) requires amounts of the order 0.1 mg of the poison and the test is therefore only applicable in this form to distillates of at least 100 g quantities of tissue or stomach contents which may be expected to contain this amount.

Moss and Rylance have investigated the red complex, formed from different halogenated compounds, by spectrophotometry and TLC (using ethyl acetate saturated with water on Merck Kieselgel GF254). They give absorption maxima for the normal reaction as follows: chloroform, chloral hydrate, trichloroacetic acid and chlorbutanol, 365 and 530 mμ; trichloroethylene, 365 and 540 mμ; trichloroethanol, 365 and 430 mμ.

TABLE VI
CONDITIONS FOR THE FUJIWARA REACTION

Ref.	Volume of Blood	Method	Reagents	Time of Heating	Compound
1	1–4 ml	Diffuse into 1 ml toluene at 37°C for 2 hours.	0.5 ml toluene 2.5 ml 20% NaOH 5 ml pyridine	5 min. at 100°C	chloroform
2	5 ml	Cool, add 1 ml 30% KOH, shake for 1 minute. Add 6 ml heptane, shake 2 minutes	5 ml heptane. 2 ml 30% KOH 4 ml pyridine.	10 min. at 80°C	chloroform chloral
3	3 ml	Shake with 7 ml acetone and centrifuge	2 ml acetone 7 ml pyridine 3.5 ml 20% NaOH	2.5 min. at 100°C	carbon tetrachloride
4	—	—	10 ml pyridine 0.4 ml 0.1N NaOH	15 min. at 100°C	carbon tetrachloride

References
1 FELDSTEIN, M., and KLENDSHOJ, N. C.: *J For Sci*, 2:39, 1957.
2 KAYE, S., and GOLDBAUM, L.: *Legal Medicine*. St. Louis, Mosby, 1954, p. 620.
3 KLONDOS, A. C., and McCLYMONT, G. L.: *Analyst*, 84:67, 1959.
4 BURKE, T. E., and SOUTHERN, H. K.: *Analyst*, 83:316, 1958.

Jain and his co-workers add an equal volume of 50% aqueous ethanol solution containing 5μg/ml chlorbutanol as an internal standard to blood or tissue homogenate supernatants and inject 1μl on to 5' x $\frac{1}{8}$ inch 15% FFAP on 60-80 acid washed Chromosorb W at 105°C and 120°C using an electron capture detector to separate and assay chloral and trichloroethanol.

For the differential determination of chloral hydrate, trichloroethanol and trichloroacetic acid in tissues and urine by the use of the Fujiwara pyridine-alkali-reaction and by gas chromatography the reader is referred to the list of references.

Interpretation of Results. A major problem exists in interpreting tissue levels of halogenated hydrocarbons because there is a progressive loss of the volatile compound between death and analysis. Fortunately, in the majority of cases, the presence of the poison coupled with the pathologist's findings are sufficient to account for death. In general, it is obvious that lower concentrations of the highly toxic carbon tetrachloride are more significant than the less toxic perchloroethylene. It is sometimes necessary to distinguish between a therapeutic dose and an overdose of chloral hydrate and although this may be difficult, levels in the blood of 10-20 mg/100 ml will indicate that considerably more than a single therapeutic dose has been taken.

Jain and his co-workers report a trichloroethanol level of 0.9 mg/100 g in the blood of a fatal overdose of chloral. They confirm the very rapid *in vivo* conversion of chloral to trichloroethanol.

In the case of chloroform 7 mg/100 ml in the blood indicates a condition associated with light surgical anaesthesia and by the time 15-25 mg/100 ml has been reached the patient is in a state of fourthplane anaesthesia. Gettler and his co-workers have also shown that the concentrations of chloroform in the brain are similar to those in the blood as far as interpretation is concerned, and that the poison could be detected in this organ even after several months storage. Weinig in a review says that chloroform has been detected at exhumation 103 days after death.

Manning (personal communication) reports a death from trichloroethylene in which the blood level was only 10μg/100 ml; liver and urine concentrations were 0.2 and 0.5 mg/100 g respectively. Hall and Hine report two cases of fatal trichloroethane poisoning by inhalation with blood levels of 13.0 and 72 mg/100 g respectively. Bonnichsen and Maehly report on six chloroform, twenty-three trichloroethylene (3 survivors) and three chloral hydrate poisonings. These results clearly show that the detection method should be capable of showing the presence of 0.1 mg/100 g of blood if the involvement of these compounds is to be demonstrated.

REFERENCES

BONNICHSEN, R., and MAEHLY, A.C.: Poisoning by volatile compounds; chlorinated aliphatic hydrocarbons. *J For Sci, 11*:495, 1966.

CABANA, B.E., and GESSNER, P.K.: The determination of chloral hydrate, trichloroacetic acid, trichloroethanol and urochloralic acid in the presence of each other and in tissue homogenates. *Anal Chem, 39:*1449, 1967.

GARRETT, E.R., and LAMBERT, H.J.: The gas chromatographic analysis of trichloroethanol, chloral hydrate, trichloroacetic and trichloroethanol glucuronide. *J Pharm Sci, 55:*812, 1966.

GETTLER, A.O., and BLUME, H.: *Arch Path, 11:*554, 1931.

GETTLER, A.O.: *J For Sci, 1:*15, 1956.

HALL, F.B., and HINE, C.H.: Trichloroethane poisoning, a report of two cases. *J For Sci, 11:*404, 1966.

JAIN, N.C.; KAPLAN, H.L.; FORNEY, R.B., and HUGHES, F.W.: A rapid gas chromatographic method for the determination of chloral hydrate and trichloroethanol in blood and other biological materials. *J For Sci, 12:* 497, 1967.

KAPLAN, H.L.; FORNEY, R.B.; HUGHES, F.W., and JAIN, N.C.: Chloral hydrate and alcohol metabolism in human subjects. *J For Sci, 12:*295, 1967.

MOSS, M.S., and RYLANCE, H.J.: The Fujiwara reaction: some observations on the mechanism. *Nature, 210:*945, 1966.

REHLING, C.J.: Poison residues in human tissues (17 cases of chloral hydrate poisoning). In Stolman, A. (Ed.): *Progress in Chemical Toxicology,* vol. 3. New York, Academic, 1967.

TURNER, L.K.: Searching for drug metabolites in viscera. In Curry, A.S. (Ed.): *Methods of Forensic Science,* vol. 4. New York, Interscience, 1965.

WEINIG, E.: *Deutsch Z Gerichtl Med, 47:*410, 1958.

xi. Fluoride

Fluoride is not a common poison but it is available to the general public in several forms — as a remover of iron mould as a liquid and paste; as solid sodium fluoride for use as a pesticide, and as hydrofluoric acid as an etching fluid or as a glass cleanser in horticulture.

The promise of a rapid quantitative screening procedure using diffusion from acidified blood direct into alizarin complexone reagent has not been fully realised because of the difficulty of diffusing the hydrofluoric acid within the stability life of the colour reagent. However, as a screening test, i.e., to detect unsuspected fluoride poisoning, the procedure has proved itself to the author.

Screening Test and Assay (Frere, F.J.:*Anal Chem, 33:*644, 1961. Frere, F. J., and Rieders, F.: *Amer Acad Forensic Sci Toxicol,* Feb. 1961 [slightly modified]). Blood, 1 ml, and 1 ml of 80%

v/v sulphuric acid containing 0.25% Tergitol are put without mixing in the outer compartment of an Obrink polypropylene diffusion vessel.* Into the centre compartment are mixed 0.25 ml each of an aqueous solution of cerous nitrate (43.2 mg/100 ml Ce $(NO_3)_3.6H_2O$) and alizarin complexone (38.5 mg/100 ml in pH4.3 acetate buffer: 4.2 ml glacial acetic acid + 2.2 g anhydrous sodium acetate or 5.3 g of trihydrate). The sealing compartment is filled with 1.5 ml of 80% sulphuric acid containing 0.25% Tergitol and the blood and liberating acid are mixed. Diffusion at room temperature of the hydrofluoric acid into the colour reagent is complete in about three hours. The colour of the reagent is blue if fluoride is present. This test should be done in parallel with positive and negative controls at the same time so that direct comparison of the colours is possible.

For quantitative assay, see Part II.

Interpretation of Results. Normal levels of fluoride in blood, that is the amount to be found in a healthy adult, are of the order $0-50\mu g/100$ ml and soft tissues may contain up to $80\mu g/100$ g. In fatal cases of poisoning blood levels rise to about $200-300\mu g/100$ ml. Urinary output in a normal individual is said to be up to 1 mg per day.

Teichman, Dubois and Monkman reporting at the 1st International Meeting in Forensic Toxicology, London, 1963, surveyed the literature on urinary excretion in persons not exposed to abnormal fluoride and gave mean concentrations of the order of 0.3-0.4 ppm ($30-40\mu g/100$ ml). In poisoning cases, high concentrations which can be of the order of several milligrams per 100 ml are found.

REFERENCES

GOLDSTONE, N. I.: The microchemical detection of fluorides by the sodium fluorosilicate crystal test. *Anal Chem, 27:*464, 1955.
LINDE, H.W.: The estimation of fluoride in body fluids. (An enzymatic method) *Anal Chem, 31:*2092, 1960.
STEWART, C.P., and STOLMAN, A.: *Toxicology, Mechanisms and Analytical Methods.* New York, Academic, 1960, vol. I, p. 222.

*Arthus H. Thomas, Philadelphia, U.S.A., Catalogue No. 4472S.

B. BLOOD ANALYSIS — SECOND STAGE

The clinical biochemist requires tests for the detection of poisoning that can give an answer to the clinician to help him in the diagnosis and treatment of his patient. This information must be available either before the patient recovers or death occurs. Time is, therefore, very much at a premium. A large-scale routine screen for all common drugs on 5 ml or so of blood takes a considerable amount of time and it is doubtful whether, except for barbiturates and glutethimide, further blood analyses will result in a worthwhile return of effort. Larger quantities of more readily identifiable material will in all probability be found from an extraction of a larger volume of urine. If the gas chromatographic examination or the simple colour test for barbiturate has given a positive result for barbiturate, a confirmation or check of the quantitative result can be obtained by extraction, ultra-violet spectrophotometry followed by paper or thin layer chromatography. Several authors prefer to extract the blood sample (5 ml) direct with chloroform (50 ml) and perform ultra-violet spectrophotometry on the sodium hydroxide extract (5 ml 0.5N) of the separated chloroform. This technique is adequate provided the barbiturate concentration is high, but the nonspecific background absorption that is found often interferes when low concentrations are met. Under these conditions glutethimide is incompletely extracted from the chloroform which, therefore, should be evaporated and examined separately.

As far as the carbamates (e.g., meprobamate) are concerned it is probably easier to extract a larger volume of urine as high concentrations are found in it (see Chap. 4). They are, however, considered here as urine may not be available.

The forensic toxicologist will not wish to use the irreplaceable blood with further screening tests, but will turn to the analysis of liver (see Chap. 7).

The schematic diagram (Fig. 4) gives a breakdown of the extraction. The recovery of barbiturates by the tungstic acid precipitation method is approximately 70 per cent.

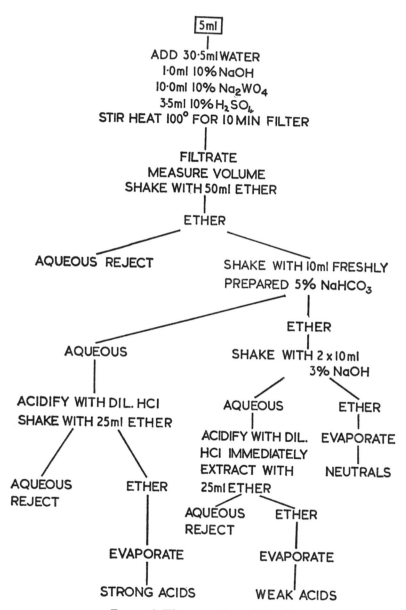

FIGURE 4. The extraction of blood.

i. Method

Blood, 5 ml, is mixed in a 100 ml beaker with 1 ml of 10% sodium hydroxide, 30.5 ml of water and 10 ml of 10% sodium tungstate (premixed in bulk if a number of analyses are done routinely) ; 3.5 ml of 10% sulphuric acid are then added with stirring. The beaker is immersed in a boiling water bath for ten minutes after which the precipitated protein is filtered off through a fluted filter paper; the filtrate is cooled and its volume measured. Because the original volume was 50 ml the proportional recovery is therefore known and the loss corrected for when quantitating. The filtrate is extracted with 50 ml of ether by vigorous shaking in a separating funnel. After separation this ether is shaken with firstly 10 ml of 5% freshly prepared sodium bicarbonate which removes the organic acids, then with two portions of 10 ml of 3% sodium hydroxide, which remove glutarimides and barbiturates and, finally, is evaporated after drying with a little solid sodium sulphate to give the neutral fraction in which the carbamates will be found.

The bicarbonate extract is acidified with dilute hydrochloric acid and extracted with 25 ml ether which is separated, dried with solid sodium sulphate and carefully exaporated to give the "strong acid" fraction. Because salicylic acid, which appears in this fraction, sublimes easily, the last few drops of ether must be blown off at room temperature.

Similar treatment to the sodium hydroxide extract gives the "weak acid" fraction which is usually examined first because of the popularity of barbiturates as poisons. This extract must not be allowed to remain alkaline during the extraction for longer than is absolutely necessary.

Care must be taken to ensure the purity of the organic solvent because of its relative large volume compared to the quantity of drug (dioctyl phthalate is a common contaminant if the ether has been in contact with plastic) ; purified ether must not be stored and any anti-oxidant must be removed immediately before use. This warning especially applies to laboratories not using ether routinely. The ether should be shaken with freshly prepared ferrous suphate solution immediately before use and great care taken in subsequent evaporation to ensure the absence of lighted cigarettes, naked flames, electrical sparks and static. Evaporation must be done in a fume cupboard.

ii. Identification and Assay

(a) *Strong Acid Fraction*

This is dissolved in 5 ml (more if necessary) of 0.45N sodium hydroxide and its ultra-violet absorption spectrum measured from 220 mμ to 320 mμ. Control spectra are essential in any toxicological laboratory but the most common poison in this fraction is salicylic acid with an absorption peak at 295 mμ and $E_{1cm}^{1\%} = 250$. A rapid spot test for salicylate is to test an aliquot of the extract, evaporated to dryness on a filter paper spot, with ferric chloride solution with which it gives a violet colour.

Even if the screening test for salicylate has proved negative the isolation of this fraction should not be ignored. Besides acting as a means of separating interfering acids from the other fractions, sometimes unusual poisons appear; 2,4-dichlorophenoxyacetic acid is one example which has an absorption maximum at 280 mμ with $E_{1cm}^{1\%}{}' = 110$.

A list of peaks that can be found in this fraction is shown in Table VII which also gives the names of acids not showing significant ultra-violet absorption.

Intrepretation of Results. Salicylic Acid: See p. 46.

2,4-Dichlorophenoxy Acetic Acid: This is a relatively nontoxic compound; ingestion of ounces of liquid weed-killer does lead

TABLE VII
ABSORPTION MAXIMA OF "STRONG ACIDS"
(Solvent 0.5N NaOH)

226	Acetylsalicylic acid	273	{ Hydrochlorthiazide { Bendrofluazide
228	Chlorpropamide		
233	Benzoic acid	274	Hydroflumethiazide
235	p-chlorobenzoic acid		
238	β-p-hydroxphenylpropionic acid	280	{ p-hydroxybenzoic acid { 2,4-dichlorophenoxyacetic acid
255	2,4-dinitrophenol		
263	Nicotinic acid	292	Chlorthiazide
265	p-aminobenzoic acid	295	Salicylic acid

(The figures shows absorption maxima in mμ)
No Absorption Peak
succinic acid

however to severe poisoning and death. In such cases, levels of about 30 mg/100 ml in the blood are found. The free acid is also found after ingestion of the ethyl ester.

(b) Weak Acid Fraction

This is dissolved in 3 ml of 0.45N sodium hydroxide and the ultra-violet absorption spectrum measured immediately from 220 to 320 mμ. Any visible colours are noted — red indicates phenolphthalein, or phenothiazine metabolites, yellow, p-nitrophenol from parathion. After ten minutes at room temperature the readings are taken again. If there has been a change in reading at 235 mμ α-phenyl α-ethyl glutarimide (glutethimide Doriden®) may be present. This compound has a maximum at this wavelength with $E_{1cm}^{1\%} = 1000$. Glutethimide, although it forms a sodium salt is an extremely weak acid and is therefore not quantitatively extracted in the weak acid fraction. If this drug is suspected, or if a change in reading is noted at 235 mμ in alkali, then the neutral fraction, should also be examined. Hydrolysis in 0.45N sodium hydroxide is very rapid (50% loss in five minutes). If the stimulant drug β-ethyl-β-methyl-glutarimide (Megimide®) has been administered, an overriding peak at 230 mμ will be present. This compound is also hydrolysed by alkali but much more slowly than glutethimide; 5,5-disubstituted barbiturates have an absorption maximum at 255 mμ and salicylamide at 241 and 323 mμ: 0.5 ml of 16% ammonium chloride* is then added to both the sample and the compensating cell and the ultra-violet spectrum re-read from 220 to 320 mμ at this lower pH of 10. Interference from the glutarimides is removed and any barbiturate can be detected by a peak at 240 mμ. Quantitative assay is achieved by adding a few drops of 50% sulphuric acid to both cells to give pH 2 when the absorption of the barbiturates at this wavelength is reduced almost to zero. (The optical density difference at 240 mμ between pH 10 and pH 2 approximates 1.0 when 1 mg of barbiturate is dissolved in 45 ml of solution.) (See Fig. 5.)

When a clear barbiturate curve has been obtained the approximate concentration present in the blood is calculated as follows:

---

*For each 3 ml of 0.45N sodium hydroxide.

$$\text{Concentration in mg/100 ml} = \frac{100 \times OD \times V_1}{3 \times V_2}$$

Where OD = optical density difference reading between
          pH 10 and pH 2
V_1 = volume of pH 10 buffer used to
          dissolve extract
V_2 = volume of tungstic acid filtrate

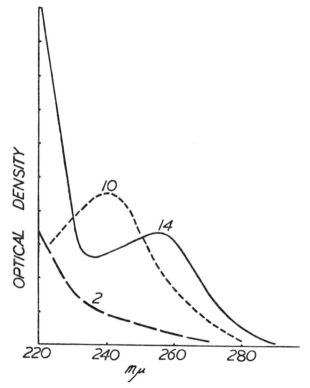

FIGURE 5. The ultra-violet curves of 5.5-disubstituted barbiturates at three pH values.

Glutethimide and megimide have no significant absorption at acid pH, but salicylamide shows peaks at 235-237 mμ and 299 mμ wtih $E^{1\%}_{1cm}$ values of 590 and 280 respectively.

The thiazide diuretic drugs will also be found distributed between the weak and strong acid fractions and have absorption maxima at 264-300 mμ in alkali and 310-315 mμ in acid. They can be detected on paper chromatograms by a spray of 1.0N sodium hydroxide followed by a saturated solution of 1,2-naphthaquinone-4-sulphonic acid, sodium salt, in 50% aqueous ethanol. Red spots are observed in ten minutes. Pilsbury and Jackson report their separation using Street's well-known reversed phase system. A list of peaks that can be found in this fraction is shown on Table VIII, which also gives the names of drugs not showing significant absorption.

TABLE VIII
ABSORPTION MAXIMA OF "WEAK ACIDS"
(Solvent 0.5N NaOH)

225	Coumarin	265	Phenylbutazone
226	Tolbutamide	286	Phenols
230	Bemegride	295	p-cresol
235	Glutethimide		Methyl-p-hydroxybenzoate
240	Salicylamide	296	Vanillic acid diethylamide
	Chloroxylenols	305	Thiobarbiturates
245	1,5,5-Trisubstituted	310	Warfarin
	barbiturates	315	Dicoumarol
255	5,5-Disubstituted barbiturates	325	Pentachlorophenol
260	Stilboestrol		

(The figures shows absorption maxima in mμ)
Not Detected by uv
Hydantoins (e.g., phenytoin)

It is stressed that it is essential to read the ultra-violet spectra from 220 mμ to 320 mμ in every case at the three pHs, 13.5, 10 and 2. Normally, no trouble will be experienced with any clouding when the solution is acidified but if this does occur, re-extraction into ether followed by evaporation after triturating with a little charcoal should overcome the problem. If a manual instrument is used readings should be taken at 5 mμ intervals. If a high background is found, then difference curves should be calculated and plotted for the readings pH 14 – pH 2 and pH 10 – pH 2. In old, decomposing blood, inflections at 240 mμ, not changing between pH 14 and pH 10 will be found and Leach (personal communication) has also observed this following the administration of mustard as an emetic.

Pentachlorophenol, a widely used herbicide, has caused death when taken in high doses. It also appears in the weak acid fraction and is excreted mainly in the urine.

Chromatographic Methods for Identification. After the ultra-violet curves have been read, the acidified solution from the cuvette is re-extracted into 5 ml of ether which is separated, dried with a little anhydrous sodium sulphate, decanted, and evaporated. If barbiturate has been found by ultra-violet spectrophotometry an estimate of its total weight in the extract can be made. The amount necessary for good results in the chromatographic identification depends on the particular technique that is to be used. For paper $10\mu g$ should be put on one spot; for TLC, about $5\mu g$; for Eastman Chromatogram sheet, $0.5\mu g$; for GLC, about 10 nanograms. Full details on GLC are given in Part II. The most common other drugs to be sought are glutethimide and phenytoin. Recommended systems for paper, TLC, and Eastman sheet follow.

Paper. Systems are as follows:

1. Whatman No. 4 paper: solvent, n-butanol:880 ammonia: water (100:33:66). Use the top layer.

2. (R.H. Fox, personal communication.) Whatman No. 1 paper is pretreated by dipping in 10% w/v trisodium phosphate, blotted and dried. Before use dip in acetone:water (75:25), blot, and in the two to three minutes during which time the acetone evaporates at room temperature, apply the spots. Run either for a four-inch run ascending in a beaker, or for a ten-inch descending run in a tank using ethylene dichloride as the developing solvent with water in the bottom of the tank.

3. (R. Abernathy and E.B. Hensel, personal communication.) Whatman No. 1 paper pretreated by dipping in 5% sodium silicate, blotted and dried. The paper is run in the bottom layer of chloroform:880 ammonia (100:50) after equilibrating the paper for forty-five minutes in the vapour of the top layer. The developing solvent must be introduced without disturbing the atmosphere; a symmetrical paper arrangement is best.

Systems 2 and 3 are recommended but system 1 is useful for the beginner. Rfs are given in Table IX but the values are not absolute ones and control spots should be run on all occasions. Practice is needed, during which the reader will obtain his own values.

If there is any yellow colour in the ether extract in this fraction, system 1 should be used. Control spots of DNOC and p-nitrophenol should be run as well. Sometimes decomposing blood and tissue contains a yellow phenolic impurity which is separated in this system from these poisons.

TABLE IX
RF VALUES OF BARBITURATES ON PAPER CHROMATOGRAMS

System (1)	System (2)	System (3)	Compound	Melting Point
.43	.02	.05	Barbitone	188 – 190
.50	.05	.05	Phenobarbitone	193 – 195
.58	.20	.22	Cyclobarbitone	171 – 174
.69	.30	.36	Butobarbitone	127 – 130
.73	.65	.66	Amylobarbitone	152 – 156
.73	.75	.66	Pentobarbitone	122 – 130
.77	.85	.77	Quinalbarbitone (Secobarbital)	96 – 100
.75	.45	.44	Nealbarbitone	155 – 157
.60	.65	.65	Phenytoin	295 – 298
.75	.90	.90	Glutethimide	87

Detection is achieved by one of the following methods: (a) Inspect the paper under 254 mμ light; alkaline papers used in solvents 2 and 3 enables the barbiturate spots to be seen without prior treatment. In the case of solvent 1 the paper is inspected before and after exposing the paper to ammonia fumes. Phenobarbitone and cyclobarbitone can be seen before exposure to ammonia because they exhibit slight absorption at this wavelength in neutral conditions. Glutethimide is decomposed if solvents 2 or 3 are used and is not detected by this method.

(b) Dip the paper in 5% mercuric oxide dissolved in 20% sulphuric acid; wash well with three rinses of distilled water and then dip in 0.1% diphenylcarbazone in ethanol. The spots are coloured various shades of purple.

(c) Spray with saturated aqueous mercurous nitrate solution. The spots are black. Not suitable for system 1.

(d) Spray with 0.1% aqueous potassium permanganate solution. Those compounds with allyl groups in the molecule (neal-

barbitone, quinalbarbitone) give immediate yellow colours. Cyclobarbitone gives a yellow colour in about thirty seconds.

(e) Expose the paper to chlorine or bromine fumes for five
minutes. Aerate for fifteen minutes; spray with 1% w/v potassium iodide containing freshly boiled starch solution to reveal
blue-black spots.

Thin Layer Chromatography. Solvent systems are as follows:

1. Chloroform:acetone (9:1) on Silica-Gel G plates.
2. (Richardson, S.J.: *Proc Ass Clin Biochem, 3*:140, 1964.)
   Chloroform:isopropanol (8:2) on Silica-Gel G plates in an
   atmosphere of ammonia.
3. (R.H. Fox and A.S. Curry.) Merck cellulose coated plates
   (with fluorescent indicator) GF254 pretreated by dipping
   in 10% w/v trisodium phosphate aqueous solution, blotting
   and drying for twenty minutes at 80°C. Before applying
   the spots dip in acetone:water (75:25) and aerate for two
   to three minutes for the acetone to evaporate. Run in
   methyl n-amyl ketone.
4. (R.H. Fox, personal communication.) Treat Eastman
   Chromatogram Sheet Cellulose No. 6065 and run in the
   same way as the Merck plates in system 3 in the Eastman
   Chamber No. 104 or the 20 x 20 cm size.

As for the paper systems, the reader should obtain his own Rf
values running controls on every occasion. Systems 3 and 4 are
recommended but require practice. See Table X for typical
values.

For detection use the methods as for paper except that the
mercury/diphenylcarbazone treatment is modified as follows:
Spray with 5 g mercuric oxide in 100 ml of 20% sulphuric acid
diluted to 250 ml. Barbiturates are seen as white spots. Overspray
with .01% diphenylcarbazone in chloroform to reveal blue spots.
To see spots on Silica-Gel G plates in 254 mμ light, spray with
.04% fluorescein in 4% w/v aqueous sodium hydroxide.

An alternative method for the chlorine/starch iodide method
is to spray with commercial sodium hypochlorite diluted x 20;
after five minutes spray with ethanol, and after one minute with a

solution of 0.5% amidon in 0.5% potassium iodide: 0.2μg of barbiturates can be detected on the Eastman sheet with the mercurous nitrate spray.

TABLE X
RF VALUES OF BARBITURATES ON THIN LAYER CHROMATOGRAMS

System (1)	System (2)	System (3)	System (4)	Compound
.20	.47	.20	.20	Barbitone
.24	.33	.30	.30	Phenobarbitone
.24	.62	.38	.38	Cyclobarbitone
.33	.67	.70	.70	Butobarbitone
.33	.74	.82	.82	Amylobarbitone
.33	.74	.85	.85	Pentobarbitone
.44	.77	.90	.90	Quinalbarbitone
.38	.68	.75	.75	Nealbarbitone
.00	.62	.00	.00	Phenytoin
.75	.97	.99	.99	Glutethimide

Gas Chromatography. Experimental details are given in Part II, Barbiturates.

Interpretation of Results. Barbiturates. It is always difficult to accurately relate blood levels and the probable effect of a drug; the following however provides a guide for relating them in the living patient:

Short acting barbiturates : blood levels over 0.8 mg/100 ml will account for coma.

Intermediate acting : blood levels over 2-3 mg/100 ml will account for coma.

Phenobarbitone : blood levels over 5 mg/100 ml will account for coma.

Barbitone : blood levels over 8 mg/100 ml will account for coma.

Recovery of consciousness following an overdose can be expected at about these levels.

Rough estimates of the length of time in days that the patient will remain in coma, provided an adequate airway is maintained and infection does not supervene, can be found by subtracting from the observed blood level the level at which consciousness is expected and dividing by two. This is because blood levels of most barbiturates *in toxic doses* fall by about 2 mg/100 ml in twenty-four hours.

The above figures apply to cases in which other depressant drugs are not present. If lower levels are found and the patient is in deep coma then the ingestion of other poisons must be considered. Alcohol, carbamates, phenothiazines, and morphine are the most frequently found drugs.

Addiction to the barbiturates can be diagnosed from a consideration of blood levels: for example in the case of amylobarbitone when the patient is taking normal therapeutic doses the blood level is unlikely to exceed 0.5 mg/100 ml but if a dose of 2-3 g per day is reached the blood level rises to 3-4 mg/100 ml. Although there is no accumulation in the body of the shorter acting barbiturates in therapeutic dosage, normal doses of phenobarbitone as taken by epileptics will, taken over a long period, result in stationary blood levels of about 5 mg/100 ml. Similarly barbitone accumulates and levels of about 8 mg/100 ml are to be expected in the blood of normal, conscious patients on continuous therapy.

For several hours following ingestion the concentration in the liver is many times that in the blood and the ratio can be helpful in estimating the time between ingestion and death. Even when the patient has been in coma for several days the liver concentration is usually twice that in the blood. It is for this reason that the toxicologist is advised always to perform the tungstic acid isolation process on 100 g of liver rather than on blood or on any other organ. The interpretation of tissue levels is discussed in more detail in Chapter 7A (i).

Primidone. This is metabolised to phenobarbitone, and in fatal cases, correspondingly high levels of the barbiturate are found.

Glutethimide. Deep unconsciousness can be expected at blood levels over about 3 mg/100 ml. Finkle reports a blood level of 0.75 mg/100 g after ingestion of 1 g. At this level definite symptoms of intoxication were apparent.

Diphenyl Hydantoin. Plaa and Hine found blood levels of hydantoins between 0.9 and 5.7 mg/100 ml in patients receiving diphenylhydantoin and mesantoin therapy for epilepsy. At doses of 14 mg/kg blood levels are held at about 4 mg/100 ml. A 30 to

55 per cent loss per twenty-four hours after cessation of therapy has been found.

A fatal case, dying fourteen days after ingestion, reported by Laubscher had a blood level of 9.4 mg/100 ml and a liver level of 27 mg/100 g. In another case, dying after three days, the brain and kidney levels were 7.8 and 11 mg/100 g respectively.

Pentachlorophenol. Comstock *et al.* report urine levels up to 3.5 mg/100 ml in workers exposed to pentachlorophenol.

(c) Neutral Fraction

The carbamates, 3-carbamoyloxy, 3-methylpentyl, 1-carbamyloxy-methyl 2-o-tolyloxyethanol, 2-2-dicarbamoyloxymethylpentane, and 1-ethynyl cyclohexyl carbamate are the most commonly sought drugs in this fraction. A simple method for their detection is to transfer an aliquot of the extract in ethereal solution to a spot on a filter paper. A drop of 10% furfural in ethanol is carefully run onto the extract spot and after evaporating the solvent at room temperature the paper is stood in fumes of hydrochloric acid. A deep purple spot indicates the presence of a carbamate of which $1\mu g$ can be detected.

Positive and negative controls should be done at the same time. The neutral extract should also be dissolved in 5 ml ethanol and examined by ultra-violet spectrophotometry (see Table XI for interpretation).

A colour test for meprobamate is to heat an aliquot of the evaporated extract with 3 ml of a solution of 2% hydroquinone in 85% v/v sulphuric acid for 25 minutes at 100°C. A rose fluorescence is seen on inspection under Wood's light (365 mμ).

Chromatographic Methods for Identification. Paper. A paper chromatographic separation enables identification to be achieved while the acetylenic linkage in ethinamate and methyl pentynol carbamate provides another centre for attack by ammoniacal silver nitrate. Solvent systems recommended for this fraction are (a) isoamyl alcohol:water (190:10); (b) glacial acetic acid:water (100:100) on Whatman No. 1 paper that has been impregnated with 20% olive oil in acetone and dried; (c) methanol:water (180:20) also on olive oil paper.

TABLE XI
ABSORPTION MAXIMA OF "NEUTRALS"
(SOLVENT ALCOHOL)

220	α-Naphthyl thiourea	265	Methaqualone
236	DDT	269	Phenylindanedione
240	(Methyltestosterone*	270	Approx: many sulphonamides; Benzocaine
	(Ethisterone*		(Mephenesin
	(Santonin	273	(Chloromycetin
241	Acetanilide		(Caffeine
245	(Progesterone*	275	Theophylline
	(Testosterone*	276	Parathion
	(Prednisolone*	288	α-Naphthyl thiourea
250	(Phenacetin		
	(Khellin		

(The figures shows absorption maxima in mμ)

Not detected by UV

Meprobamate	Methyprylone
Bromvaletone*	Sedormid*
Carbromal*	Sedulon
Mephenesin carbamate	Styramate
Methylpentynol carbamate	

*Unlikely to be present in blood but relevant to tissue extracts.

Detection is achieved by exposing the paper to chlorine gas for ten minutes and then spraying with a 2% starch solution containing 1% potassium iodide after a period of aeration sufficiently long so that the background is nearly colorless.

Thin Layer Chromatography. The thin layer chromatography of neutral drugs has been reported by Haywood, Horner and Rylance using three solvent systems — ethyl acetate; dioxan:methylene chloride:water (1:2:1); and chloroform:acetone (9:1). Detection is achieved by inspection in 254 mμ light or by the chlorine-starch-potassium iodide reaction. Several drugs, notably meprobamate, methylpentynol carbamate, methyl-prylone and Sedulon® are not detected in uv light. The procedure for the chemical detection is as follows.

The plates are exposed to chlorine gas for a few seconds, left in air for fifteen minutes and sprayed with 2% starch solution containing 1% potassium iodide. In ethyl acetate solvent using Merck Kieselgel GF254, TCL plates the following Rf values are found:

Meprobamate 0.48	Glutethimide 0.68
Methylpentynol carbamate 0.66	Mephenesin 0.48
Amidopyrine 0.25	Mephenesin carbamate 0.50

For a full list of twenty urea and other derivatives in the three systems see Haywood *et al.*

A solution of p-dimethylaminobenzaldehyde in 2% hydrochloric acid can also be used as a chromogenic spray to detect meprobamate on paper and thin layer chromatograms.

For the colorimetric assay of meprobamate, see Part II.

Gas Chromatography. For experimental conditions see Part II.

It is strongly stressed that for routine screening of toxicological extracts by gas chromatography, it is essential to use one type of column for acidic and neutral drugs and another for basic drugs. No attempt should be made to use one column for both classes. This is because the acid fraction always contains nonvolatile acidic material and this sits at the top of the column; injection of a base causes salt formation with the risk of the nonappearance of the base in the effluent. The reverse base-acid situation can also occur.

Because blood concentrations of such common basic drugs as the amphetamines, imipramine, phenothiazines, chlordiazepoxide, etc., are low, procedures like those described for barbiturates in blood will not normally detect their presence. For routine screening the extraction of urine in which they, or their metabolites appear in much higher concentrations is mandatory if detection is to be ensured. Details of this procedure are described in Chapter 4.

Interpretation of Results. *Meprobamate.* Therapeutic levels after the consumption of 1,600 mg are about 1-2 mg/100 ml in the blood. At the higher level the patient is difficult to rouse. In a case of poisoning reported by Bedson consciousness was regained about thirty-five hours after the blood level was 21.5 mg/100 ml.

Maddock and Bloomer suggest that plasma levels approaching 20 mg/100 ml indicate very profound intoxication. These workers note that urinary excretion is considerable and say that haemodialysis appears to be the most efficient method for removing meprobamate. Marck reported a case (personal communication) in which after a dose of 24 g there was 145 mg of the drug in 30 ml of urine!

There have been other reports of nonfatal poisonings with

blood levels as high as 25 mg/100 ml, but patients are usually comatose with levels over 5 mg/100 ml. However, patients taking 0.8-4.8 g per day for periods of four months were found to have plasma levels of 2.3-6.3 mg/100 ml, with virtual disappearance of the drug in ninety-six hours after cessation of intake.

Finkle reports normal therapeutic blood levels up to 1.5 mg/100 g but notes that with simultaneous alcohol ingestion, levels of 50 mg/100 ml ethanol and 0.4 mg/100 ml meprobamate, the subject was "very drunk." His series give results for combinations of meprobamate, glutethimide, barbiturate, benactyzine, dexedrine, etc., found in road accident cases.

REFERENCES

ALGERI, E.J., and WALKER, J.T.: Paper chromatography for identification of the common barbiturates. *Amer J Clin Path, 22:*37, 1952.

BLADH, E., and NORDEN, A.: A method for determining 1-butyl-3 p-tolyl sulphonylurea (Tolbutamide) in human blood serum. *Acta Pharmacol Toxicol, 14:*188, 1958.

BOGAN, J.; RENTOUL, E., and SMITH, H.: Fatal poisoning by primidone. *J For Sci Soc, 5:*97, 1965.

BOGAN, J., and SMITH, H.: Analytical investigations in barbiturate poisoning. *J For Sci Soc, 7:*37, 1967.

COMSTOCK, E.G.; COMSTOCK, B.S., and ELLISON, K.: A turbidimetric method for the determination of pentachlorophenol in urine. *Clin Chem, 13:* 1050, 1967.

CURRY, A.S.: The interference of β methyl-β ethyl glutarimide in the determination of barbiturates. *J Pharm Pharmacol, 9:*102, 1957.

CURRY, A.S., and SUNSHINE, I.: The liver/blood ratio in cases of barbiturate poisoning. *Toxicol Pharmacol, 2:*602, 1960.

CURRY, A.S.: The barbiturates. In Stewart, C.P., and Stolman, A. (Eds.): *Toxicology, Mechanisms and Analytical Methods.* New York, Academic, 1961, pp. 153-158.

FINKLE, B.S.: The identification, quantitation, determination and distribution of meprobamate in biological material. *J For Sci, 12:*509, 1967.

GOLDBAUM, L., and WILLIAMS, M.A.: The determination of glutethimide in biological fluids. *Anal Chem, 32:*82, 1960.

HAYWOOD, P.E.; HORNER, M.W., and RYLANCE, H.J.: Thin layer chromatography of neutral drugs. *Analyst, 92:*711, 1967.

HOLLISTER, L.E., and GLAZENER, F.S.: Withdrawal reactions from meprobamate. *Clin Res, 8:*98, 1960.

JACKSON, J.V., and Moss, M.S.: In *Chromatographic and Electrophoretic Techniques,* 2nd. ed. New York, Interscience, 1960, vol. 1, Chaps. 20, 21 and 22, pp. 379-409.

LAUBSCHER, F.A.: Fatal diphenylhydantion poisoning. *JAMA, 198:*194, 1966.

MADDOCK, R.J., and BLOOMER, H.A.: Meprobamate overdosage; evaluation of its severity and method of treatment. *JAMA, 201:*123, 1967.

MOSS, M.S., and JACKSON, J.V.: A furfural reagent of high specificity for the detection of carbamates on paper chromatograms. *J Pharm Pharmacol, 13:*361, 1961.

OLSEN, O.V.: A simplified method for extracting phenytoin from serum and a more sensitive staining reaction for quantitative determination by TLC. *Acta Pharmacol Toxicol, 25:*123, 1967.

PILSBURY, V.B., and JACKSON, J.V.: The identification of the thiazide diuretic drugs. *J Pharm Pharmacol, 18:*713, 1966.

PLAA, G.L., and HINE, C.H.: A method for the simultaneous determination of phenobarbital and diphenylhydantoin in blood. *J Lab Clin Med, 47:* 649, 1956.

PLAA, G.L.; HALL, F.B., and HINE, C.H.: Differentiation of barbiturates for clinical and Medico-legal purposes. *J For Sci, 3:*201, 1958.

REHLING, C.J.: Poison residues in human tissues (report of 150 barbiturate and 90 barbiturate/alcohol combinations). In Stolman, A. (Ed.): *Progress in Chemical Toxicology.* New York, Academic, 1967, vol. 3.

SCHREINER, G.E.; BERMAN, L.B.; KOVACH, R., and BLOOMER, H.A.: Acute glutethimide poisoning. *AMA Arch Intern Med, 101:*899, 1958.

STONE, H.M., and HENWOOD, C.S.: The spectrophotometric determination of low levels of barbiturates in blood. *J For Sci Soc, 7:*51, 1967.

STREET, H.V.: The separation of barbiturates by reversed phase paper chromatography at elevated temperatures. *J For Sci Soc, 2:*118, 1962.

TURNER, L.K.: Some applications of acceleration thin layer chromatography in toxicology. *J For Sci Soc, 5:*94, 1965.

Chapter 4

URINE ANALYSIS

Hensel (*Methods of Forensic Science,* vol. 3, edited by A. S. Curry. New York, Interscience 1964) has provided much useful warning information on the need for care in the collection of urine samples. Most of this is pertinent to police investigations but, as the hospital biochemist may be involved at an early stage in criminal cases, Hensel's points are worth repeating. They are for the collecting personnel to use new, unused screw-capped wide-mouthed jars with 1 g of sodium benzoate as a preservative; as much urine as is available should be collected; to stay with the subject while he is providing the sample and to seal and label the sample properly; finally, the analyst should be provided with as much information as possible concerning the circumstances and clinical history of the case.

A tremendous amount of information can be obtained very quickly from the analysis of a few millilitres of urine and in a case of suspected poisoning the tests described below should be done at the very first stage of the analyses.

It is not often possible to interpret urine concentrations of drugs in terms of probable ingested dose and the tests should be looked upon as merely providing evidence of ingestion. This, coupled with the clinical condition of the patient, is usually sufficient to assist in providing a firm diagnosis. In investigating a sudden death, the rapidity and ease with which the tests can be completed means that many of them are even suitable for use in the mortuary. A special section is included for the screening of urine for narcotics. The tests are described in detail below.

It is stressed that normally blood and urine are needed for efficient screening. If only urine is available the other preliminary tests described for blood, i.e., for alcohols and fluoride with a GLC screen should also be done on the urine.

A. SPOT TESTS

Special Reagents (except where stated, these are stable at room temperature):

1. **Fluorescein reagent:** a saturated ethanolic solution of fluorescein sodium.
2. **Gold chloride reagent:** a mixture of equal volumes of 20% w/v trichloroacetic acid and 0.25% w/v gold chloride.
3. **FPN reagent** (Forrest and Forrest, 1960) : a mixture of 20% v/v perchloric acid: 50% v/v nitric acid: 5% w/v ferric chloride (9:10:1, by vol.) .
4. **Reagent for imipramine** (Forrest *et al.*, 1960b) : a mixture of one volume each of 0.2% w/v potassium dichromate, 30% v/v sulphuric acid, 20% v/v perchloric acid and 50% v/v nitric acid.
5. **α-Naphthol reagent:** approx. 100 mg α-naphthol dissolved in 5 ml 2 N-sodium hydroxide solution. Make up fresh.
6. **Reagent for thioridazine** (Forrest *et al.*, 1960a) : 1 vol 5% w/v ferric chloride added to 49 vol. 30% v/v sulphuric acid.
7. **Diphenylamine-sulphuric acid reagent:** 0.5% w/v diphenylamine in concentrated sulphuric acid.
8. **Furfural reagent:** a fresh 10% v/v solution of furfural in absolute ethanol.

Reagents for Alkaloids and Bases:

1. **Potassium iodobismuthate (Dragendorff's spray):** (a) 2 g bismuth subnitrate and 25 ml glacial acetic acid in 100 ml water. (b) 40 g potassium iodide in 100 ml water. Before use mix 10 ml of A, 10 ml of B, 20 ml of glacial acetic acid and 100 ml of water. The spots on TLC plates can be enhanced by overspraying with 5% sodium nitrite solution.
2. **Potassium iodoplatinate spray** (for paper chromatograms) : Add 10 ml of 5% platinum chloride solution to 240 ml of 2% potassium iodide solution, and dilute with an equal volume of water. Iodoplatinate solution (acid, for thin layer chromatograms) Add 10 ml of 5% platinum chloride solution and 5 ml of concentrated hydrochloric acid to 240 ml of 2% potassium iodide solution.

REFERENCES

FORREST, I.S., and FORREST, F.M.: *Clin Chem, 6*:11, 1960.

FORREST, I.S.; FORREST, F.M., and MASON, A.S.: *Amer J Psychiat, 116*:928, 1960a.

FORREST, I.S.; FORREST, F.M., and MASON, A.S.: *Amer J Psychiat, 116*:1021, 1960b.

Urine

(Minimum volume required 8 ml)

Test	*Remarks*
1. Dip a Clinistix® briefly in urine and read after one minute.	Correlate with blood sugar results.
2. Dip a Phenistix® briefly in urine and read immediately. Alternatively, add one drop 5% w/v ferric chloride to one drop of urine.	A violet colour indicates salicylate, salicylamide or chlorpromazine. If the colour remains or is intensified by a drop of 50% v/v sulphuric acid, chlorpromazine is indicated. If the colour disappears it is probably from salicylate.
3. Put a drop of urine on an Acetest® tablet: observe the colour after thirty seconds.	A violet colour indicates acetone bodies.
4. Mix a drop of urine with a drop of gold chloride reagent on a white tile. To obtain a known positive for phenothiazines, grind one tablet of 25 mg chlorpromazine hydrochloride with 10 ml water. Use one drop.	A red colour indicates chlorpromazine or other phenothiazine tranquillizer. A brown colour indicates bromide; if positive, check for bromide by using the fluorescein test— 0.2 ml urine is mixed with two drops of fluorescein reagent, four drops of glacial acetic acid and four drops of 100 volumes hydrogen peroxide and heated to dryness in a boiling water bath: a red colour is obtained if bromide is present.

Place 1 ml urine in each of six test tubes.

5. To 1 ml of urine add 1 ml 20% w/v sodium hydroxide and 1 ml pyridine; heat in a boiling water bath for one minute. To obtain a known positive, grind one half tablet of dichloralphenazone in 10 ml water. Take 0.1 ml diluted to 1 ml.	A red colour in the pyridine layer indicates chloroform, chloral hydrate, dichloralphenazone or trichloroethylene. (Chlorodyne should also be considered as well as other medicines containing chloroform water.) Perform in parallel with negative and positive controls.

Test	*Remarks*
6. To 1 ml urine add 1 ml FPN reagent. To obtain a known positive, grind one tablet of 25 mg chlorpromazine hydrochloride with 10 ml water. Use 1 ml.	A violet colour indicates high dosage of chlorpromazine or other phenothiazine drugs. Pink colours may also be obtained—colour depends on dose and metabolites.
7. To 1 ml urine add 1 ml imipramine reagent. To obtain a known positive, grind one tablet of 25 mg imipramine hydrochloride or 25 mg desipramine hydrochloride with 10 ml water. Take 0.1 ml diluted to 1 ml.	Green or blue colours indicate imipramine or desipramine ingestion. If the patient has hyperpyrexia, dilated pupils and is "drunk" or in coma, consider the possibility of imipramine interaction with a monoamine oxidase inhibitor such as phenelzine.
8. To 1 ml urine add 1 ml thioridazine reagent. To obtain a known positive, grind one tablet of 25 mg thioridazine with 10 ml water. Take 0.1 ml diluted to 1 ml.	A pink to blue colour indicates thioridazine ingestion. The colour depends on the dose and metabolites.
9. To 1 ml urine add two to three drops dilute hydrochloric acid and cool in ice. Add two to three drops freshly prepared 1% w/v sodium nitrite solution followed by 2-3 drops α-naphthol reagent. Aqueous p-aminophenol (2 mg/ml) may be used as a known positive.	A red colour indicates excretion of p-aminophenol following ingestion of paracetamol or phenacetin.
10. Consider tests for heavy metal poisoning.	See Index for arsenic, mercury, lead, and thallium.
11. To 1 ml urine add 20 mg sodium hydrosulphite and 20 mg sodium bicarbonate.	A blue colour indicates Paraquar-intoxication (see Part II).

B. EXTRACTION PROCEDURES

After these very simple rapid screening tests have been completed, the extraction of poisons soluble in organic solvents can be started. If possible, at least a 25 ml sample of urine should be used, but if this volume is not available, 5 ml can provide much useful information. Because the urine contains drug metabolites instead of, or in addition to, unchanged drug, and because metabolites are usually more polar, the technique of examining urine must take this into account. It is stressed that the aim is to isolate and identify drugs; quantitative procedures, with few exceptions, are of limited value because of the difficulties of interpretation. It is well established that excretion of both acidic and basic drugs (e.g., salicylates and amphetamines) vary with the pH of the urine and little useful data is available to enable one to deduce the probable dose *when only a single urine sample has been voided.* The following procedure is suggested for a drug screen; if GLC is available then the direct injection techniques for barbiturates and amphetamines are suggested. The warnings about the uselessness of trying to "make do" with only one column are reemphasised. In the absence of GLC, then paper and TLC techniques are used.

It may be that the analyst is asked to "screen for narcotics" or to "check this for amphetamine" — in my opinion there is still a strong case for extracting first with organic solvent from acidic solution before making alkaline and extracting the organic bases from alkaline solution. This preliminary extraction from acid, as well as providing additional drug extracts (the suspect may have been smoking mixed barbiturate/heroin mixtures, or taking "purple hearts" containing both barbiturate and amphetamine) has an additional advantage that the purity of the subsequent basic extract is enhanced. Prior hydrolysis of the urine either with β-glucuronidase or with concentrated hydrochloric acid, is advised to hydrolyse morphine glucuronides: acid hydrolysis can be done on a separate aliquot or on the residue from the original extraction.

There are about as many variants regarding extraction techniques, solvents and pHs used for extraction, paper and TLC systems as there are authors of published papers. An authoritative review of some is given in the *Psychopharmacology Bulletin* of December, 1966. It must be noted that sulphuric acid and ether are recommended for the acid and basic extractions. Hydrochloric acid and chloroform are specifically not recommended because many base hydrochlorides are soluble in chloroform. The warning (page 57) about the dangers of ether is repeated.

Methods

(a) For barbiturate only — using GLC — see Part II.
(b) For amphetamines only — using GLC — see Part II.
(c) General method — see Figure 6.

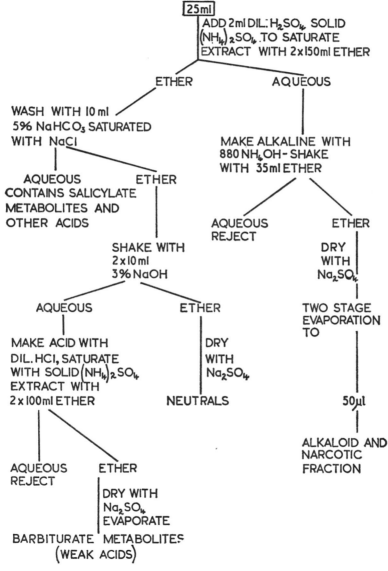

FIGURE 6. The extraction of urine.

Urine, 25 ml, is made acid to pH 2 with dilute sulphuric acid and sufficient solid ammonium sulphate to make a saturated solution is added. The solution is extracted with 2 x 150 ml of ether which are separated. The aqueous phase is retained. The combined ether layers are washed with 10 ml of a freshly prepared solution of 5% sodium bicarbonate in saturated salt (sodium chloride) solution. This aqueous layer is rejected: if necessary, it can be examined for salicylates. Barbiturate and glutethimide metabolites are next extracted from the ether by 2 x 10 ml extractions with 3% w/v sodium hydroxide. The aqueous alkaline layers are combined, made acid with dilute hydrochloric acid to pH 2, saturated with solid ammonium sulphate and re-extracted with 2 x 100 ml portions of ether. The ether layers are combined, dried with 2 g of solid anhydrous sodium sulphate, separated and evaporated. This gives the barbiturate extract, the "weak acid" fraction.

The ether fraction remaining after the bicarbonate and alkali extractions is dried with solid sodium sulphate, poured off and evaporated to give the "neutral" fraction.

i. Acid Extracts

Identification

Provided it is required to detect toxicologically significant amounts of glutethimide or barbiturate, the "weak acid" extract can be examined directly by ultra-violet spectrophotometry at three pHs as described for blood see Chap. 3 Bii (b)). Metabolites retain the chromophoric ring intact and an obvious positive can be obtained. When it is required to detect the residues of therapeutic doses a high background absorption interferes and the prior purification of the extract by a paper chromatographic separation as described for blood is necessary. Absorbing spots under 254 mμ light are cut out, eluted with 0.45N sodium hydroxide and individually read from 220-320 mμ at not more than 5 mμ intervals. A piece of "blank" paper from the same chromatogram is similarly eluted and put in the reference beam. Normally 3.5 ml of sodium hydroxide are used for elution, but if the absorption under 254 mμ is only weakly seen, then a microcell and 0.7 ml can be used.

Identification of the particular barbiturate or barbiturates from the metabolic excretion chromatographic pattern may be possible if only one drug is involved. Experience with barbitone, phenobarbitone (and p-hydroxyphenobarbitone), amylobarbitone (which gives 3-hydroxyamylobarbitone) is readily acquired. Other barbiturates tend to give complex patterns.

Glutethimide (Doriden®) gives 2-phenylglutarimide in the urine which is slowly hydrolysed at pH 13-14, losing its 235 mμ peak. The procedures described above for ultra-violet spectrophotometry should, therefore, be closely followed.

As far as the neutral fraction is concerned, I have no doubt that unless large quantities of visible crystals can be seen, the routine procedure of choice is to sublime this extract at 100°C at 10^{-2} mm for two to three hours. I realise this is probably too time-consuming for use in a hospital laboratory, but the appearance of beautiful sublimed crystals from an extract that would otherwise have been consigned to the sink has on so many occasions convinced me that this must be done routinely in systematic toxicology. Carbromal, phenacetin, and meprobamate are but a few examples. Identification can proceed by a determination of micro melting points, a TLC examination, (see p. 68) or best of all, by infra-red spectroscopy comparing the curve with knowns.

Over 2000 infra-red spectra of toxicologically important compounds and 700 ultra-violet spectra of alkaloids have been prepared on microfilm together with a film feature card system for retrieving an "unknown" curve by the Home Office, Central Research Establishment, Aldermaston. Details of availability and cost are obtainable from the Director.

ii. Narcotics and Bases

The acidified aqueous urine remaining after the ether extraction above, is made alkaline with 880 ammonia and extracted with 35 ml of ether. The ether is separated and dried by triturating with solid anhydrous sodium sulphate. It is then decanted and evaporated in two stages; firstly, to approximately a 3 ml volume by heating over a boiling water bath in a fume cupboard (beware cigarettes, etc.) and secondly, the final stage is accomplished in a

15 ml Quickfit test tube with a finely tapered base, at 40°C on a water bath, to reduce the volume to 40μl; 10μl of ethanol are then added. The extract must *not* be allowed to dry. The tube should be glass-stoppered.

Identification

In this extract there can appear drugs of nearly all types of pharmacological action. The most comprehensive list has been given by Dr. E. G. C. Clarke in *Methods of Forensic Science*.* Clarke resolved these compounds in one paper chromatographic system and with three provisos there is, in my view, no doubt that for the identification of an unknown alkaloid this system is still the best approach. The provisos are as follows:

1. If a stimulant drug of the amphetamine type is suspected, then use the TLC systems described below.
2. The cellulose/citrate system modified to work on TLC plates enables the bulk of Clarke's work to be done more quickly, with greater sensitivity on TLC plates: this can be used, therefore, as a suitable alternative.
3. When the analyst is asked to look for a basic drug for which either specific colour tests can be applied, or a well-tried alternative paper or TLC system utilised.

Even direct ultra-violet spectrophotometry *may* be of use in these cases and, if a 25μl portion of the ether extract is dissolved in 3 ml O.1N H_2SO_4, useful information can often be obtained. However, in my experience it is usually a waste of time to do this before a chromatographic examination. Nicotine is frequently found in the urine and often, quinine. This latter alkaloid has a special significance in narcotic cases as it is sometimes an adulterant of heroin. Both nicotine and quinine have high ultra-violet absorption which can completely swamp that from other potent drugs which may be in the urine. It is for this reason that I consider ultra-violet spectrophotometry of this fraction prior to chromatography a waste of time. In order to get good chroma-

---

*Clarke, E. G. C.: In Lundquist, F. (Ed.) : *Methods of Forensic Science*, vol. 1. New York, Interscience, 1961.

tographic spots it is necessary to test a 1μl portion of the 50μl extract to estimate, roughly, the aliquot that is to be put on a chromatogram. This is done by running the 1μl on a piece of filter paper. A micro drop of potassium iodobismuthate (Dragendorff's reagent) is run onto it and the depth of any deep orange colour observed. Experience soon enables one to judge the required volume to put on the chromatogram. The inexperienced analyst can prepare 1, 5, 10 and 50μg standards (say 1, 5, 10 and 50μl of a 0.1% solution of quinine in alcohol). This test will *not* detect amphetamine and here the analyst is in something of a dilemma. The 50μl extract must be put onto a chromatogram before the ether evaporates and it must be divided in such a way that there is the maximum chance of detecting a wide variety of drugs; at the same time, overloading the chromatogram must not occur so that the results become uninterpretable. It is for this reason that a GLC screen (see Part II) on a 1μl injection is so valuable. Subnanograms of amphetamines can be detected within a few minutes and the very high sensitivity ensures detection of therapeutic doses even on 1 ml samples of urine. However, a TLC screen for amphetamine type drugs on 10μl takes only little longer, but care in stoppering the extract and storing it in the refrigerator must be observed.

Chromatographic Methods for Identification. Paper (Clarke, E. G. C.; *J For Sci Soc, 7:*46, 1967, based on Curry, A. S., and Powell, H., *Nature, 173:*1143, 1954). Whatman No. 1 paper is dipped in 5% sodium dihydrogen citrate solution, blotted and dried. It can be stored. The solvent is 2.4 g citric acid in 65 ml of water with 435 ml of n-butanol. About 10-20μg spots are applied to the paper. Detection is achieved by spraying with iodobismuthate or iodoplatinate. It is useful to note that with the latter reagent amphetamine gives a slowly developing white spot at Rf 0.45. It is impossible here to give a complete list of Rf values for about 1,000 alkaloids and basic drugs that can appear in this fraction, and identification can only be achieved by inspection of the chromatogram under 254mμ light before spraying; the colour and Rf of the coloured spots; elution and ultra-violet or infra-red spectrophotometry, and comparison of all the results with published or self-determined data. As was indicated above, the only really useful other chromogenic agents, which should also be used on cut-out strips from the chromatogram, are the phenothiazine reagents (tests 6, 7, 8 on urine) and Marquis reagent (2% of 40% formalin in concentrated sulphuric acid) (see Table XII). Other useful Rf values with uv data are given in Table XIII. The rationale of

TABLE XII*
ALKALOIDS LISTED AS GIVING STRONG REACTIONS WITH MARQUIS REACTION

Alkaloid	Rf	λ Max	Colour with Marquis
Pseudomorphine	0.02	231 262	Red
Morphine	0.14	285	Purple
Codeine	0.16	284	Purple
Dihydromorphine	0.16	283	Red-purple
Apocodeine	0.18	280	Purple
Neopine	0.18	284	Blue-purple
Norcodeine	0.18	N/A	Blue-purple
Dihydrocodeine	0.20	283	Purple
Boldine	0.23	282, 301	Green-purple-green
Methyldihydromorphine	0.23	281	Purple
Mescaline	0.24	269	Orange
Protopine	0.24	240, 288	Blue-green
Prochlorperazine	0.24	253	Purple
Sinomenine	0.26	263	Orange-green-blue
Cryptopine	0.27	236, 283	Blue-green
Mepacrine®	0.27	279, 222	Bright yellow
Thenyldiamine	0.27	239 315	Black-violet
Tripelennamine	0.28	239, 315	Red brown
Ethyl morphine	0.30	285	Yellow-purple-black
Heroin	0.30	279	Purple
Apomorphine	0.32	273	Purple-black
Methapyrilene	0.32	237, 313	Black-violet
Thebaine	0.32	284	Red-orange
Desomorphine	0.35	277	Purple
Harmine	0.38	247	Orange-grey
Lachesine	0.39	258, 261, 251	Orange-green-blue
α-allo cryptopine	0.40	N/A	Purple
Pipamazine	0.40	255 306	Purple
Narcotine	0.42	312 290	Blue-purple (fading)
Methyldesorphine	0.44	283	Purple
Narceine	0.46	276	Brown-green
Pipenzolate	0.46	258, 252	Orange-green
Benzyl morphine	0.47	284	Red-purple
Chloropyrilene	0.49	238, 314	Purple
Diphenylpyrilene	0.50	258, 253	Yellow
Detigon®	0.55	260	Red-purple-brown
Diphemanil	0.56	231	Orange-red
Ethyl narceine	0.57	277	Brown-green-blue
Piperoxane	0.58	274	Deep purple
Pyridium®	0.58	405 238, 277	Red
Phenindamine	0.59	260	Grey-green

*CLARKE, E.G.C.: In LUNDQUIST, F. (Ed.): *Methods of Forensic Science*, Vol. 1, Interscience, 1962, and personal communication.

the approach with suggested standards is discussed in the next
section.

TABLE XII (continued)
ALKALOIDS LISTED AS GIVING STRONG REACTIONS WITH MARQUIS
REACTION

Alkaloid	Rf	λ Max	Colour with Marquis
Dimenoxadol	0.60	259, 263, 270	Orange-greenish blue
Dimethythiambutane	0.60	281, 269	Purple-brown
Bephenium	0.62	269, 263, 275	Red-purple
Linadryl	0.62	258, 252	Yellow
Neobenodine	0.62	259, 264	Yellow
Phenyltoloxamine	0.62	269, 276	Purple
Antadril	0.63	220	Yellow
Medrylamine	0.63	273	Yellow
Diphenhydramine	0.64	258, 253	Yellow
Bromodiphenhydramine	0.65	230	Yellow
Chlorpromazine	0.65	255	Purple
Methotrimeprazine	0.65	250 301	Blue-purple
Promethazine	0.65	250 297	Purple
Reserpine	0.65	270	Blue-grey-green-brown
Diethylthiambutene	0.67	287, 269	Purple-brown
Phentolamine	0.67		Yellow
Allylprodine	0.69	258, 252, 264	Blackish-blue
Pecazine	0.69	252 301	Purple
Ethylmethylthiambutane	0.71	268, 285	Purple-brown
Captodiamine	0.73	266	Bright purple
Octaverine	0.75	248 321, 357	Green-brown
Alphameprodine	0.75	257 251, 263	Brown-red
Diethazine	0.75	250	Purple-brown
Ethylisobutrazine	0.82	250	Purple
Trimetozine	0.84		Red-brown
Oxethazaine	0.87	258 252, 264	Red-brown
Clomiphene	0.88	233, 288	Purple-brown
Bisacodyl	0.90	264	Purple

Solvent 0.1N H_2SO_4 for uv spectrophotometry.
N/A Sample not available for uv spectrophotometry.
Rf values in Curry-Powell system.

Thin Layer Chromatography. (a) *Amphetamines.* (Beckett,
et al.: *J Pharm Pharmacol, 19:273,* 1967): Silica-Gel G (Merck)
plates are prepared mixing 30 g with 50 ml water containing
0.04% sodium fluorescein and spread at 250μ thickness on 20 x 20
cm glass plates. The plates are allowed to dry in air for fifteen
minutes and then for two hours at 80°C. Cool in a dessicator and
run at room temperature. Beckett and his co-workers give details
for eleven stimulants and nicotine in ten solvent systems with
three chromogenic agents. For screening purposes my preferred
solvent is chloroform:methanol (50:50) in which the following

TABLE XIII

BASES AND NARCOTICS
Absorption Maxima
(In 0.1N H_2SO_4)

	Rf	λ Max.			Rf	λ Max.
Morphine	0.14	285		Chlorpromazine sulphoxide	0.65	240, 273,
Codeine	0.16	284				300, 340
Pholcodine	0.05	282		Tripelennamine	0.28	240, 315
Dextromethorphan	0.65	280		Mepyramine	0.32	240, 315
Diamorphine	0.30	279		Amitriptyline	0.65	240
Zoxazolamine	0.89	277		Nortriptyline		240
Pyrimethamine	0.45	275 287		Anthisan®	0.32	240, 315
Isoniazid	0.22	265		Methaphenilene	0.61	240
Iproniazid	0.72	265		Halopyramine	0.44	238, 312
Brucine	0.17	265, 300		Methapyrilene	0.32	237, 313
Iodoantipyrine	0.90	265		Thenylpyramine	0.50	237, 313
Parabromdylamine®		265		Persantin®	0.70	235, 283
Pheniramine	0.25	264		Methaqualone	0.93	235 270
Coramine® (nikethamide)	0.83	265		Thonzylamine	0.48	237 316,
Bisacodyl®	0.90	264				275
Thioperazine		264		Cocaine	0.42	235 275
Thioridazine	0.83	261 313		Amylocaine	0.62	232
Nicotine	0.07	260		Chlorcyclizine	0.68	232 264
Perphenazine	0.20	257 306		Piperocaine	0.64	231
Pyridine		256		Phenazone	0.81	231
Pyrrobutamine	0.68	255		Cytisine	0.03	230, 300
Stelazine®	0.36	255		Hydroxyzine	0.66	231 263
Chlorpromazine	0.65	255 305		4-Bromobenzhydryloxy-		
Fluopromazine	0.68	255 304		ethyl dimethylamine	0.65	230
Amidopyrine	0.54	255		Amethocaine	0.48	229 312
Fluphenazine	0.65	255 306		Amiphenazole	0.42	229, 265
Pecazine	0.69	254 301		Dimethisoquin	0.63	228
Diethylpropion	0.52	254		Primaquine	0.39	224, 265,
Thiopropazate	0.47	253 307				285
Prochlorperazine	0.25	253		Procainamide	0.19	225
Strychnine	0.24	255		Procaine	0.27	227, 280
Pipamazine	0.40	253 307		Methoxamine	0.42	225, 290
Quinine	0.50	2.52 347		Buclizine	0.94	225 261
Promazine	0.58	251 301		Dimethoxanate	0.47	225, 253
Trimeprazine	0.66	250		Ergometrine	0.24	225, 312
Promethazine	0.65	250 298		Isopropyl phenazone	0.89	225–245
Ethopropazine	0.64	250 294		Tetrabenazine	0.80	225, 282
Imipramine	0.66	250		Cyproheptadine	0.70	223, 285
Diethazine	0.65	248 299		Amodiaquine	0.19	222 340
Harman	0.45	245, 300		Naphazoline	0.50	220 275
Chlordiazepoxide		245, 308		Chloroquine	0.21	221, 235,
Nupercaine®	0.65	245, 315				255, 330,
Antazoline	0.70	243				343
Acepromazine	0.50	242, 270		Hydroxychloroquine	0.12	220, 233,
Amplicaine	0.50	240				255, 330,
Propiomazine	0.60	241, 275				343
Tacrine	0.55	240, 325,		Chlorpheniramine	0.39	220, 265
		335		Etryptamine	0.57	218, 275
Thenyldiamine	0.27	240, 315				

Rf values in Curry-Powell system.

Rfs are found: p-hydroxyamphetamine, 0.16; norephedrine, 0.19; methylamphetamine, 0.30; strychnine, 0.21; ephedrine, 0.23; amphetamine, 0.29; methylephedrine, 0.30; phenmetrazine, 0.52; nicotine, 0.72; diethylpropion, 0.81; caffeine, 0.86; and nikethamide, 0.89.

Chromogenic sprays are as follows:

1. 3 ml 10% solution of chloroplatinic acid with 97 ml water and 100 ml 6% potassium iodide. Reference spots give pale yellow or brown spots, except for strychnine and nicotine which give deep violet; p-hydroxy amphetamine and caffeine are not detected. Sensitivity about 5μg.

2. 0.4% ninhydrin in acetone prepared within thirty minutes of use. Warm under an ultra-violet lamp. Amphetamine, ephedrine and norephedrine give violet spots, the others pale blue except strychnine and caffeine. The presence of phenothiazine metabolites may give false positives.

(b) *Other Bases:* as was indicated above, there are a very large number of published papers concerning the TLC separation of alkaloids and other bases. Many of these papers describe several solvent systems for perhaps over a hundred compounds. To the newcomer or the inexperienced worker in this field there exists the problem of how to identify an "unknown," positive iodobismuthate or iodoplatinate reacting material in a urinary or tissue extract. To set up perhaps four or five different solvent systems and try and deduce from a combination of Rf values a possible identification is one approach. It does, however, involve a vast amount of work — both experimental and literature studying — and involves loss of material. It also involves a lot of preliminary work ensuring that, for a chosen selection of alkaloids, the published Rf values are reproducible in the workers own laboratory. R. H. Fox has studied the translation of the well known Curry and Powell paper system on which Dr. Clarke has done so much valuable work (*vide supra*) to TLC. The success of this approach means that the vast list of known Rf values on paper can be justifiably extended to the TLC system.

METHOD. Cellulose 20 x 20 cm plates (Merck) are dipped in 5% sodium dihydrogen citrate solution, drained and dried at 80°C for twenty minutes. The plates are run in n-butanol:citric acid: water (435 mls: 2.4 g: 65 mls). Detection is as for paper and useful Rf values are in Tables XII and XIII.

The control spots applied for comparative purposes are best, nicotine, codeine, quinine and phenazone. As seen from Table XIII these are widely separated and give useful comparative spots for unknowns. It is fortunate and noteworthy that nicotine, which is commonly found in urine is not confused with any common drug in this system. The plates are inspected in 254mμ light and sprayed with iodoplatinate.

Gas Chromatography. Although gas chromatography is the method of choice for rapid screening of urine for amphetamines, there is a grave doubt whether it is yet the best method for detecting and identifying unknown alkaloids in urine or tissue.

There is no universally accepted column suitable for all bases and the sensitivity of detection is not significantly higher than that obtainable by thin layer chromatography. Street, who has done a very great deal of research in this field, claims no more than 0.1μg as the acceptable detection limit, and the majority of published work refers to experiments at well above the microgram level. If a laboratory decides to use GLC it must face the prospect of a considerable amount of development work before it will achieve acceptable results.

Firstly, the choice of column filling must be made; this is indeed a field where even angels fear to tread. Street has described in detail how even new stainless steel columns have to undergo a lengthy pretreatment before they are filled: his column is home-made and it requires very considerable experimental expertise before satisfactory results can be obtained. Columns age and new columns have to be recalibrated before even the simplest identification can be made. It would be more satisfying if GLC could be classed as a procedure suitable for deciding whether there was a toxic alkaloid present or not present in the extract, but two difficulties arise — firstly, the fact that normal urine can contain bases which give peaks of no toxicological significance, and secondly, some alkaloids either decompose on the column or have such long retention times that even with temperature programming each urine analysis can take over an hour. If a peak is obtained its identification becomes a matter of inspired guesswork, even if a good reference map has been previously made, before one can decide on the best potential derivative formation. To equip with collector stream splitting, and to trap the bulk of the effluent for infra-red spectroscopic identification requires 10μg of most alkaloids at the present time. This quantity is relatively so large that paper and TLC separations, on which very much more knowledge and experience are available, are much quicker and simpler to use.

The appearance of spots in 254 mμ light coupled with Rf values and chromogenic sprays soon sorts out the unknown alkaloid into a very small number of significant compounds. In addition, the material is not destroyed and can be eluted from the paper or TLC plate. In the case of tissue extracts, the number and size of GLC peaks become intolerably large and overshadow traces of significant poisons. The location of iodoplatinate reacting spots on paper or TLC plates is the overriding advantage which, at the present time, inhibits a full experimental description of a GLC method for this fraction. The collection of GLC peaks, using a stream splitter, direct onto a TLC plate is possible, but the profit from the extra work involved is only one retention time. If manpower and expertise are available this may be worthwhile. Let the beginner realise the amount of work he is letting himself in for.

REFERENCES

MANNERING, G., and ANDERS, M.: Application of gas chromatograph to toxicology. In Stolman, A. (Ed.) : *Progress in Chemical Toxicology.* New York, Academic, 1967, vol. 3, p. 121.

STREET, H.V.: GLC of submicrogram amounts of drugs, III. Analysis of alkaloids in biological media. *J Chromat, 29:*68, 1967.

iii. Morphine

As was indicated above, morphine is excreted unchanged and as the glucuronide. Strong hydrochloric acid digestion can be used to liberate morphine from its conjugate; there is little experimental data on the simultaneous decomposition during the hydrolysis but most authorities suggest that the procedure is worthwhile. Enzymatic treatment with glucuronidase is undoubtedly preferable. A 10 ml sample of urine is normally ample. Conditions for the acid hydrolysis are to heat with one tenth the urine's volume of concentrated hydrochloric acid at 100°C for one hour; for the enzyme to incubate with 4,000 Fishman Units at pH 5.2 in 0.2M sodium acetate at 37°C overnight. The acid hydrolysis can be done on the residue from the previously described ether extractions. After the hydrolysis the solution is made to pH 1 and extracted with 30 ml of ether, which is rejected. The aqueous layer is carefully neutralised with sodium bicarbonate (beware frothing) and made to pH 8-9. It is then extracted with 2 x 50 ml of a chloroform:isopropanol (4:1) solution. The combined organic solvent layers are filtered through a fluted Whatman No. 1 paper and evaporated. Few authors acknowledge the brown gum that invariably is found in the extract after an acid hydrolysis. The extract is redissolved in 0.1 ml of ethanol and examined by paper chromatography and/or TLC. Clarke's and Fox's systems are recommended respectively (see above). The maximum quantity is put on the chromatogram consistent with minimal interference from the brown colour (normally, $20\mu l$ spots can be accommodated). A general chromogenic spray (e.g., iodoplatinate) can be used but, in my opinion, a much greater degree of specificity is achieved by the beautiful violet colours seen on dipping the dried paper or TLC plates in 2% formaldehyde in concentrated sulphuric acid. Control spots ($5-10\mu g$) of codeine and morphine are put on the same plate or paper.

iv. Other Narcotics and Hallucinogens

(a) Cannabis

At the time of writing there is no published method known to me that will detect cannabis products in blood or urine, although it is very likely that a technique for this is not far away. For the identification of cannabis in plant or smoking material see Part II.

(b) LSD

There is no method that can be recommended that will, for certain, detect LSD in urine. An effort may be made by examining the ethereal extract from alkaline aqueous salt solution as described for LSD in Part II. The identification as LSD of any compound exhibiting the expected spectrofluorimetric curve must be rigorous as similar fluorescent compounds are normally found in urine. The paper chromatographic system is especially recommended. In rats, LSD is said to be best detected in lung blood and has a half-life of 175 minutes.

C. OTHER TESTS ON URINE

i. Coproporphyrinuria

Urinary Porphyrins

Method (Scott, C.R., Labbe, R.F., and Nutter, J.). Urine, 8 ml, is placed in a 12 ml centrifuge tube; 0.2 ml of 8N HCl are added and the pH adjusted to pH 3 with saturated sodium acetate (0.2-0.3 ml) as determined by pH paper. Then 2 ml of n-butanol are added and the mixture is shaken vigorously and then centrifuged. Examination of the upper butanol layer under ultra-violet light indicates the presence of abnormal porphyrins and is useful as a screening test. For the rapid assay of individual porphyrins by a TLC separation, the reader is referred to the original paper.

Coproporphyrin III. A screening test for excessive excretion of Coproporphyrin III is as follows.

Method (Blanke, R. V.: *J Forensic Sci, 1:5*, 1956). Urine, 5 ml is made to below pH 4.1 by addition of a little glacial acetic acid. Five drops 3% hydrogen peroxide are then added and the urine is shaken with 5 ml of ether. The layers are separated and the water layer is discarded. The ether layer is then shaken with 1 ml 1.5N hydrochloric acid. The acid layer is separated and observed under ultra-violet light from a lamp having a Wood's filter. If the fluorescence is blue or blue green then there is no excessive excretion of corproporphyrin, if the fluorescence is pink or red then the test is positive.

Interpretation of Results. Excessive excretion has been noted in poisoning by lead, arsenic, mercury, bismuth, copper, iron, gold, silver, zinc and phosphorus. Barbiturates, sulphonal as well as sulphonamides, alcohol, TNT, chloroform and carbon tetrachloride have also been noted as causing coproporphyrinuria. Many diseases involving hypermetabolism, hepatitis, hematological conditions and hypovitaminoses also result in this condition.

REFERENCES

Chu, T.C., and Chu, E.J.H.: Rapid TLC of porphyrins and related compounds and its application to the study of porphyrias. *J Chromat, 28:*475, 1967.

Scott, C.R.; Labbe, R.F., and Nutter, J.: A rapid assay for urinary porphyrins by TLC. *Clin Chem, 13:*493, 1967.

Chapter 5

ANALYSES OF OTHER SAMPLES FROM THE LIVING PATIENT

A. STOMACH WASH AND ASPIRATE

T HE EXAMINATION of this material by the hospital biochemist should be compared with the analysis of the contents of the alimentary tract by the toxicologist which is described in detail in Chapter 6.

Method.

Put aside one third of the stomach aspirate in reserve.
The aspirate should be taken before washing out the stomach; it should be uncontaminated by administered antidote.

Test	*Remarks*
1. Smell the stomach aspirate; at this stage also carefully smell the urine.	Obvious smells such as those due to *Lysol,* camphor and methyl salicylate should be noted. Methyl salicylate may indicate ingestion of surgical spirit. Phenelzine has its own peculiar odour and this should be checked by smelling a crushed tablet. The drug is readily available and interaction of even therapeutic doses with imipramine, pethidine and dexamphetamine, etc., can cause serious reactions.
2. Measure the pH of the stomach aspirate with a piece of Universal Indicator paper. Note also the colour of the aspirate.	If neutral or slightly alkaline, ingestion of sodium barbiturate should be considered. Any colour may derive from a tablet or capsule—or from a dye used to colour a rat poison. Blue ferrous phosphate following ingestion of "anaemia pills" is usually obvious. Normal pH of aspirate is 3-4.
3. Perform the test for chloroform-like compounds described under urine test No. 5.	Tests are necessary on both body fluids, as the concentration in each is altered by absorption and excre-

4. Perform FPN test for chlorpromazine as described under urine test No. 6.

5. Perform imipramine test as described under urine test No. 7.

6. Put a quarter of the total stomach aspirate in a conical flask with an equal volume of 2N-hydrochloric acid and a 0.5 cm square of copper foil. Boil for five minutes.

7. Treat a few drops of the aspirate with 1 ml concentrated ammonia.

8. Extract one third of the total stomach aspirate after acidification with 2N-hydrochloric acid, with four times its volume of chloroform. Separate and evaporate off the organic solvent. Dissolve the residue in 0.5 ml ethanol. Take about 0.01 ml and evaporate it on to a small spot on a filter paper. Superimpose 0.01 ml furfural reagent and allow to dry. Expose to the fumes of concentrated hydrochloric acid in a beaker.
To obtain a known positive, extract one tablet of 400 mg meprobamate with 5 ml chloroform. Separate, evaporate and dissolve the residue in 50 ml ethanol. As with the unknown, evaporate 0.01 ml as a small spot on a filter paper and treat with furfural reagent and hydrochloric acid fumes as described.

9. Heat 0.01 ml of the alcohol extract, obtained in test 8, to dryness on a white porcelain dish with two drops 2N-sodium hydroxide using a microburner. Cool; add two drops fluorescein

tion factors, depending on the time which has elapsed between ingestion and obtaining the sample.

Observe colour of the foil; a film of metallic mercury is obvious and arsenic, antimony, and bismuth give black stains. Confirmatory tests are essential.

Deep blue colour indicates copper salts. Red indicates phenolphthalein.

A purple-black colour in about one minute indicates a carbamate, most probably meprobamate. A negative and a positive control on the same piece of filter paper are essential for purposes of comparison. Meprobamate is excreted in the urine and therefore 10 ml of urine can be used instead if the aspirate is very fatty or otherwise unsuitable.
(Furfural reagent — see p. 73.)

A red colour indicates carbromal or bromvaletone which are the most common bromoureides. The red colour obtained is eosin.
(Fluorescein reagent — see p. 73.)

reagent, four drops glacial acetic acid and four drops 100 volume hydrogen peroxide. Evaporate to dryness on a boiling water bath.

10. To two drops of aspirate add two to three drops 2N-hydrochloric acid and one drop 1% w/v potassium ferricyanide solution.

Blue precipitate indicates ferrous iron from anaemia pills and "female correctives." Confirm by serum iron estimation. — see Part II.

11. Repeat 10 using 1% w/v potassium ferrocyanide solution.

Blue precipitate indicates ferric iron —iron salts have been used as abortifacients. Confirm by serum iron estimation.

12. Add 1 ml diphenylamine-sulphuric acid reagent to two drops of aspirate.

A blue colour indicates nitrite, chlorate or bromate. Nitrate ingestion will also give a positive result. (See p. 73 for reagent.)

B. FAECES

Examination of faeces from the living patient is sometimes worthwhile. Mushrooms often resist digestion and I have found excellent specimens in faeces; this could be of great help in cases of suspected ingestion of toxic fungi and presumably for other botanical debris. For the identification of *Amanita phalloides,* see Part II.

Administration of powdered glass can be established by destroying all the organic material by a nitric-sulphuric acid digestion, dissolving any natural calcium sulphate and any barium sulphate that may have been given as an x-ray contrast medium in sodium ethylenediamine tetra-acetate and examining the centrifuged residue microscopically in polarised light to distinguish the glass from naturally occurring sand. Extreme precautions must be taken to exclude accidental contamination from laboratory glassware: normal faeces contain a few microscopic particles of glass, presumably from the glaze on cups and from cracked glasses and bottles. These, in experiments that I did, did not exceed eight per normal passage of faeces.

Yellow phosphorus is excreted unchanged in the faeces and this may be important in diagnosing a case of poisoning when the secondary phase involving liver failure is reached. The micro test described in Chapter 7A (iv) is suitable, but distillation in the dark in a current of nitrogen, admitting air at the moment distillation starts, when the brilliant Mitscherlich phosphorescence can be most readily seen, is more satisfying. Quantitative determination is described on page 100. In the United Kingdom the most common form of phosphorus used to be from rat or beetle poison which also contained bran. This can also be separated from faeces and the exact nature of the ingested poison determined from an examination of bran size. It is rare for more than 1 or 2 mg of yellow phosphorus to be found in faeces, but even this quantity will give a phosphorescence on distillation lasting several minutes and occasionally over an hour.

An x-ray examination of faeces often enables lead paint to be localised.

C. HAIR AND NAILS

These are usually only examined in cases where it is desired to determine whether arsenical compounds have been administered to the patient over a period of time. The point of maximum concentration is related to its distance from the point of growth. In many cases the clinician will not want to arouse the patient's suspicions and will obtain samples of hair from a comb. There is insufficient hair obtainable in this way for classical analyses but activation analytical techniques can succeed as was demonstrated on less than 2 mg of Napoleon's hair by Smith and his co-workers. Generally at least 100 mg for each analysis is necessary because normal levels in hair are about 0.1μg in this weight. Levels of 0.2 μg/100 mg and over merit further examination. If the hair is cut in lengths of half an inch this means that about 1 g of hair is necessary in a complete lock. This is about 3,000 hairs.

The analyses are discussed in Part II.

D. AIR FROM THE LUNGS

The air exhaled by a living person can be examined by gas chromatography. The recent work on anaesthetic technique has shown that this can be done relatively easily and it has been described in a review by Hill. Carbon monoxide can be detected in the breath using the Siebe Gorman potassium pallado-sulphite tubes (see Part II).

REFERENCES

HILL, D.W.: The application of gas chromatography to forensic science. *J Forensic Sci Soc, 2:*32, 1961.

FORSHUFRUD, S.; SMITH, H., and WASSEN, A.: Arsenic content of Napoleon I's hair probably taken immediately after his death. *Nature, 192:*103, 1961.

SMITH, H.: The interpretation of the arsenic content of human hair. *J For Sci Soc, 4:*192, 1964.

Chapter 6

ANALYSIS OF THE CONTENTS
OF THE ALIMENTARY TRACT

INTRODUCTION AND DIVISION

A T THIS STAGE OF THE analysis the toxicologist usually pays close attention to the details of the case submitted on the form shown in Table I. Screening tests on blood and urine will have been completed and the first simple tests on the liver for arsenic, zinc phosphide, phenothiazines and the many organic solvent soluble poisons that can be isolated following the easy quick tungstic acid protein precipitation such as the barbiturates glutethimide and meprobamate, and some alkaloids including morphine (see Chap. 7) will have been done. He will therefore be approaching the alimentary tract either to confirm positive findings or to search for further poisons.

It is desirable to analyse the section of the alimentary tract which is likely to contain the highest concentration of poison.

If death has been established to have been relatively rapid then the stomach contents will obviously be chosen; when death has not occurred for several days the intestinal contents will be taken. Fluoride is sometimes localised as the calcium salt in the wall of the stomach so the wall should also be analysed. Barbiturate sometimes crystallises under the stomach mucosa and can be seen microscopically as a pin point appearance looking rather like a mould growth.

The stomach contents can be easily separated from the wall and, after noting their weight, it is convenient to wash the wall and add this to the contents. The separation of the intestinal contents is sometimes a tedious procedure if the pathologist has not separated the intestines from adherent fat. This must be done so the contents can be squeezed into a previously weighed beaker. The wall then can be opened, inspected and washed. The washings are added to the beaker.

The contents and washings after weighing should be carefully inspected, smelt and their pH taken. If any abnormal degree of acidity or alkalinity is noted this lead should be followed. Sodium barbiturates give an alkaline reaction and irritate the mucosa. Tablets generally resist disintegration better than capsules and often can be picked out from the stomach contents in a relatively fresh condition; enteric-coated tablets are very stable and clinicians would be well advised to consider performing stomach washes not only on the admission on the patient to hospital but also if the clinical condition suddenly deteriorates, several hours later because this often coincides with the solution of the enteric coating. The mucosa should be inspected for signs of corrosion or irritation or in the intestines for pathological changes associated with salmonella infection. Toxicologists who are not medically qualified should make sure of this facet of their training by instruction from a pathologist. Recognition of normal and abnormal conditions comes only from experience.

If an adequate time chart has been obtained the chosen contents and washings are taken, their volume is measured and their weight taken. They are divided as described below. If a time chart is not available the stomach contents, the small intestines contents and the large intestine contents are separately isolated and measured. One third of each is bottled and put into reserve. The other aliquots are combined, diluted if necessary to give fractions that can be easily handled and divided into the following fractions — one third, which is put into a flask ready for distillation, one ninth, put into dialyser, and two ninths of the total, put into a beaker ready for isolation of organic poisons; with the one third in reserve this accounts for the total.

The following tests are then made.

A. TESTS ON ONE THIRD

i. Distillation from Acid Solution

This fraction is made to pH 2 with dilute hydrochloric acid and distilled: 25 ml of distillate are collected; if any test on the distillate is positive the distillation is continued to completion.

The first test on the distillate is that of smell: cyanide is one obvious example that makes its presence obvious to those blessed with the hereditary ability to smell it, but there are many other poisons that can be detected in very small amounts by this very simple and important test.

(a) 1 ml of distillate is tested for volatile reducing substances by heating with 5 ml of dilute sulphuric acid and a few crystals of potassium dichromate. Any alcohols or aldehydes will turn the orange colour to green and ethanol which is oxidised to acetaldehyde can be detected by smell and by heating the condensed products with pellet sodium hydroxide to give the characteristic colour and smell of aldehyde resin. Methanol, ethanol, isopropanol, ethylene glycol, acetaldehyde, paraldehyde are the common poisons found in this fraction and their identification and assay must follow. Isopropanol is oxidised to acetone by acid dichromate and this can be detected by Rothera's reagent or by an Acetest® tablet.*

If the test is positive, gas chromatography is the obvious choice for separating and identifying the members of this group and even aqueous solutions can be put directly onto the column. The column and technique are described on p. 33.

(b) 1 ml of distillate is added to 2 ml of Schiff's reagent with which formaldehyde and acetaldehyde react to give a violet colour. Formaldehyde can be identified by the chromotropic acid test (see p. 36) and acetaldehyde by the aldehyde resin test described above.

(c) 1 ml of distillate is heated in a test-tube in a boiling water bath with 1 ml of pyridine and 2 ml of 20% sodium hydroxide for one minute. Colours in the pyridine layer are noted. Red indicates halogenated hydrocarbons while yellow results from p-nitrophenol, from the insecticide parathion or aldehyde resin from acetaldehyde or paraldehyde. This is a very sensitive test; 1μg of chloroform can be detected. Parathion itself also distils in steam readily and can be extracted from the distillate with benzene. The paper chromatographic identification of this very important insecticide is considered in Table XVII and Part II because it also appears in the neutral organic solvent soluble poisons with other organo-phos-

*Ames Co., Ltd., Miles Laboratories, Stoke Poges, Slough, U.K.

phorus compounds. Parathion and p-nitrophenol have distinctive ultra-violet absorption spectra; blood cholinesterase levels should be depressed if an organo-phosphorus compound has been absorbed.

(d) 10 ml of distillate are extracted with 10 ml of ether which are separated and carefully evaporated. The residue is examined and smelt. A large number of compounds can be detected by this simple test: camphor, methyl salicylate, cresols, chlorinated phenols, benzene and nitrobenzene are but a few. This method of concentrating the smell often enables the poison to be detected when the original distillate has such an objectionable odour that it overpowers the senses.

Pentachlorophenol is one of the compounds that will readily crystallise in the distillate; when this occurs identification is easy by comparison of melting points.

(e) several other simple tests should be done. These are as follows:

1. Cyanide: This should be a routine test and the methods described in Chapter 3A (ix) are suitable.

2. Acetone: This can be detected in trace amounts by putting a drop of distillate on an Acetest tablet.

3. Phenols: If there is any suggestion of a smell of phenols in the ether extraction test described above, a drop of bromine water acts as a suitable chemical screening test. Brominated phenols are precipitated from solution. Salicylic acid will steam distil and give a faint positive in this test.

4. Methylpentynol: This hypnotic is detected by adding 1 ml of distillate to 1 ml of ammoniacal silver nitrate. A white precipitate of a silver acetylide is a positive result. Care must be taken to ensure that the precipitate is not silver chloride from distilled hydrochloric acid by making sure that the ammonia is in excess.

5. Yellow Phosphorus and Phosphides: As was described above, the distillation is done in the dark under nitrogen if yellow phosphorus is suspected. Distillation in the dark must be done if the screening test for phosphorus and phosphides that is always done beforehand on the liver (see Chap. 7Aiv) is positive. Phosphine and yellow phosphorus are distilled from the contents and collected in silver nitrate solution from which they are oxidised to phosphate by boiling aqua regia and quantitatively determined.

Alternative Method (Oliver, W. T., and Funnel, H. S.: *Anal Chem, 33:434*, 1961). The distillate (45 minutes) is cleansed from sulphide by a lead acetate trap and then collected on a plug of 0.3 g of powdered mercuric bromide. The plug is then washed with 4x2 ml portions of 0.003N iodide solution and 1 ml of ammonium molybdate solution (14 ml concentrated sulphuric acid added to 60 ml of water and 1 g of ammonium molybdate added. The solution is then made up to 100 ml) added to the washings together with 0.5 ml of freshly prepared 0.15% aqueous hydrazine sulphate solution. The mixture is then put in a boiling water bath for ten minutes. After cooling the volume is made up to 10 ml and the optical density measured at 710 mμ. Calibration measurements are made with standards from 0-50μg of phosphorus.

6. *Ultra-violet Spectrophotometry.* Normal aqueous distillates of intestinal contents usually show absorption peaks in the region 270-280 mμ and the optical density reading is up to about 1.0 when the volume of distillate is 25 ml. Phenols and parathion increase the readings in this region. If additional peaks are found they should be investigated. Aromatic compounds such as benzene show fine structure bands about 240-270 mμ and use of a recording spectrophotometer is advantageous.

Interpretation of Results

The presence of ethanol in the gastrointestinal tract does not necessarily mean that it has been ingested. This particular alcohol is a fairly common artefact, usually in trace quantities. I have also had positive tests for traces of isopropanol when none had been ingested. The presence of alcohols should always be fully investigated, however, as they are common constituents of many medicines, liniments and household commodities.

Chloroform is the most common halogenated hydrocarbon to be found as it is often present in medicines. As with the alcohols, gas chromatography is the best method of differentiating these halogenated hydrocarbons. Carbon tetrachloride is a common household cleansing agent of high toxicity with a fatal dose of the order of 5 ml; cases of death from the inhalation of the vapours of halogenated hydrocarbons are known and even in the absence of a positive test in the gastrointestinal tract the brain should always be examined (Chap. 8).

Ethyl salicylate with a smell reminiscent of methyl salicylate can be found as a result of esterification in the post-mortem stomach contents of ethanol and salicylic acid. Camphor is difficult to detect in trace quantities other than by smell; a common liniment contains aconite, belladonna and camphor, and the importance of smelling a carefully evaporated ethereal extract of the distillate cannot be overemphasised. A fatal dose of camphor for a one year old child is probably about 1 g.

Cyanide is extremely toxic with a fatal dose of about 60 mg of the acid. Alkali cyanides are rarely pure but are generally toxic in doses of this magnitude.

Methylpentynol and similar alcohols either free or as their carbamates are generally of relatively low toxicity with therapeutic doses in the order of about 100 mg or slightly higher.

In the case of yellow phosphorus poisoning, on many occasions no unchanged poison can be detected in the alimentary tract. It is rare for more than 1 or 2 mg to be found in any case. Phosphorus has, however, been found in a body exhumed after thirteen months and generalisations are difficult. A negative result in the alimentary tract does not exclude phosphorus as the causative agent in a case of acute fatty degeneration of the liver.

ii. Dialysis for Anions

After distillation the volume of the residue in the flask is measured and a division is made into four equal parts. Two parts are combined, made to pH 7 and, after concentration by evaporation to approximately 20 ml, are dialysed. It is usual for the dialysis of this extract, which is one sixth of the total stomach or intestine content, to *follow* the dialysis of the untreated one ninth portion of the content described on page 107. The only reason for this second dialysis is to check the dialysis of the untreated fraction. If the analyst is certain of his initial findings it can be ignored but often it is extremely useful to have a separate fraction for confirmation.

Dialysis can be performed against about 300 ml of distilled water either through the conventional Visking or by stirring in a bag of cellophane. Two hours are usually sufficient for thin grade cellophane but checks should be made routinely. The dialysate is concentrated by boiling to 2 ml to give a clear brown solution; the following tests are then made:

1. Silicofluoride: 0.5 ml is made acid with hydrochloric acid and 0.5 ml of 10% barium chloride is added. Sulphate and silicofluoride are precipitated as barium salts. There is usually a faint positive result at this point, from sulphate normally present from foods. This can be distinguished from silicofluoride by an examination of the centrifuged, washed, crystals. Barium sulphate is usually amorphous while those from barium silicofluoride are boat shaped. The well known hanging drop test for silicofluoride can also be used in which fluorosilicic acid is liberated by concentrated sulphuric acid and captured in a hanging drop of sodium chloride solution to give characteristic crystals of sodium fluorosilicate. Goldstone has reinvestigated this reaction and recommends the following procedure.

Method (Goldstone, N. I.: *Anal Chem, 27:*464, 1955). Approximately 0.5 mg of powdered calcium carbonate are placed with the fluorosilicate in a 10 ml crucible and dried on a hot plate. After cooling, two small drops of concentrated sulphuric acid are added and the crucible is placed on a hot plate at 170°C. A glass slide on the underside of which has been placed a small drop of sodium chloride solution is quickly placed over the crucible and a 50 ml beaker containing an ice cube is put on top of the slide to prevent evaporation of the drop during the twenty minutes required for the distillation. The sodium chloride solution is made by dissolving 1 g of sodium chloride with 3 g of glycerol in water and two drops of 40% of formaldehyde and making the volume up to 100 ml. When the liberated fluorosilicic acid has all been collected by the sodium chloride the slide is removed, the top surface blotted and then the drop is dried out by placing the slide in a warm place for a few minutes. A microscopic examination shows the sodium fluorosilicate as faintly pink hexagonal or six-pointed stars at the peripherary of the drop amongst the well known and easily recognisable sodium chloride crystals: $1\mu g$ of fluorosilicate is easily detectable; the limit is about $0.2\mu g$.

2. Hypophosphite: 1 g of granulated zinc and 10 ml of dilute hydrochloric acid are added to 0.5 ml of dialysate in a Gutzeit apparatus where phosphine is liberated. The paper in the Gutzeit holder is soaked in alcoholic silver nitrate or mercuric bromide. A black or yellow-brown stain depending on which paper is used can be converted to reduced phosphomolybdate blue (see p. 137).

Hypophosphite is not itself particularly toxic but it is a metabolic product of the rat poison, zinc phosphide, and may be ingested as hypophosphite in the form of "tonics" containing strychnine or quinine.

3. Bromide: The simple fluorescein test described in Chapter 5, Test No. 9 is most suitable; $1\mu g$ can be detected. Bromide is found not only from the ingestion of bromide sedatives but also as a metabolite of organo- bromo sedatives and of bromate which is used in "home perm" capsules. Large quantities of chloride interfere in this test and when bromide is present in trace amounts this test may be negative because of interference by the hydrochloric acid added in the distillation stage; a similar test on the untreated one ninth dialysate may be positive.

4. Oxalate and Fluoride: 0.5 ml of dialysate is acidified with dilute acetic acid and calcium chloride solution is added dropwise. Any calcium oxalate is precipitated; this reaction can be assisted by heating slightly. The precipitate is removed by centrifuging and examined microscopically and by classical techniques. Calcium fluoride may also be precipitated and sulphate if present in large amounts. Fluoride may not have survived the distillation however but differentiation of the ions is possible by testing portions of the isolated precipitate in the alizarin-complexone diffusion test for fluoride (see . 53) and by warming the washed precipitate with very weak acid permanganate to indicate oxalate. The crystal form of calcium oxalate is distinctive. Traces of fluoride can also be detected by Goldstone's hanging drop technique; 2 mg of powdered silica are added to the dried calcium salt before carrying out the test described under fluorosilicate on page 102.

Interpretation of Results

Silicofluoride is very toxic, a dose of 1 g of the sodium salt can be fatal. If more than a few milligrams of sulphate have been detected then the metal from whose salt they have been derived must be considered. Magnesium sulphate is one example but ferrous and zinc sulphates are of more toxicological significance.

The detection of hypophosphite may lead to the discovery of the medicine whose other constituents are responsible for the illness or death of the patient.

If a positive bromide test is obtained then blood and tissue levels must be determined (see Part II).

Both oxalate and fluoride are toxic ions and ingestion in both cases leads to gastrointestinal disturbances. The fatal dose of oxalate is usually about 10 g while fluoride can kill in doses of about 5 g. In both cases death may be delayed for several hours and the toxicologist must be prepared to detect milligram or even less quantities. Oxalate occurs in several plants, for example rhubarb, and a full history of what the patient has eaten in the forty-eight hours prior to the illness or death is therefore desirable coupled with a close examination of the vomit and the contents of the alimentary tract.

iii. Tests for Metals

The remaining portions after distillation, i.e., one sixth of the total amount, are examined for metals.

The Reinsch test (boiling a small copper foil in dilute hydrochloric acid on which metallic arsenic, antimony, bismuth or mercury is deposited) is a worthwhile test because it is so quick to perform. It is therefore done on the quarter aliquot remaining after distillation which is boiled for five minutes with an equal volume of dilute hydrochloric acid and a piece of acid cleaned copper about 0.5 cm x 0.5 cm in area. If no stain is seen on the copper in this time the flask is put on a boiling water bath for a further period of one hour when, if the foil is still bright, the test is considered negative. Black stains indicate arsenic, antimony or bismuth. Arsenic can be sublimed off and recognized as crystals of arsenic trioxide. Mercury also is obvious and the shiny deposit can be sublimed off the foil by heating.

The last quarter of the residue remaining after distillation is examined comprehensively for metals. This can be done in many ways and new techniques appear regularly. Destruction of organic matter by a nitric-sulphuric acid digestion can be followed by the classical metal Group separation. After centrifuging off any insoluble chlorides or sulphates (Group I), this involves passing hydrogen sulphide gas through the solution firstly at pH 3-4 (Group II), then in ammoniacal solution (Groups III and IV) and finally precipitating magnesium with warm ammonium phosphate solution (Group V). Twenty-four hours are recommended for sulphide precipitations; it must be remembered that although mercury will have been lost in the wet digestion its detection should have been ensured by the Reinsch test which, because the interfering sulphides have been removed during the distillation, is usually very sensitive.

The group precipitates are centrifuged off and examined by arc emission spectroscopy, by paper chromatography or by specific spot tests. The first is a specialist technique requiring experience but is most useful in detecting and identifying all the toxic metals. Paper chromatography is also valuable because it can separate those metallic ions which often mutually interfere in colour tests. The sulphides and any magnesium salt from Group V are dissolved in a drop of hot dilute hydrochloric acid before application to the paper. Rf values, coupled with colour tests on the purified ions, are criteria of identification. There are many papers published on this aspect of analysis but a solvent consisting of the top layer of n-butanol: 3N hydrochloric acid (1:1) is suitable as demonstrating the method. To detect copper, lead, zinc, iron, bismuth, tin, mercury and many other metals, the paper is dipped in a solution of 0.005% dithizone in chloroform, then removed to allow the chloroform to evaporate when the multicoloured dithizonates are visible. Prior inspection in 254 mμ light detects lead as a brilliant green fluorescence and some other metals as absorbent

spots (see Table XIV) . If a particular metal is being sought, tests
for it are applied directly on the paper and any spot can be examined by arc emission spectroscopy. Magnesium which is commonly taken as the sulphate must not be forgotten and is precipitated by warming with alkaline ammonium phosphate solution
after the acid and alkaline sulphides. It is detected on paper by
dipping in a 0.01% solution of titan yellow, in 1N sodium hydroxide; excess reagent is removed by washing in water when
magnesium can be seen as red spots on a yellow background. The
very toxic metal, thallium, should be detected by precipitation as
the insoluble thallous iodide. A portion of the original digest
should be reduced by passage of sulphur dioxide and potassium
iodide solution added. A green-yellow precipitate is obtained. For
quantitation see Part II.

TABLE XIV
PAPER CHROMATOGRAPHY OF METALS

Appearance in Daylight		Appearance in uv* Acid Conditions	Appearance in uv* (Ammonia Fumes)	Colour with Dithizone	Rf
Pb	Nil	Green	Fades to negative	Pink	0.29
Cu	Green	Strongly Absorbs	No change	Brown	0.19
Bi	Nil	Strongly Absorbs	No change	Pink	0.63
Hg	Nil	Weakly absorbs	No change	Orange	0.83
Fe	Yellow	Very strongly absorbs	No change	Brown	0.28
					0.42
Cr	Green	Strongly absorbs	No change	Slowly grey/blue	0.11
As	Nil	Nil	Nil	Nil	—
Sb	Nil	Absorbs	No change	Pink-orange	0.78
Sn	Nil	Orange-red	No change	Red	0.78
Ni	Green	Absorbs	Intensified	Weak red	0.12
Co	Blue-red	v.weak absorbs	Intensified	Red-magenta	0.20
Mn	Nil	Nil	Absorbs	Pink	0.19
Zn	Nil	Yellowish	No change	Scarlet	0.78
Cd	Nil	Yellowish	No change	Yellow-orange	0.78
Tl	Nil	Absorbs	No change	Weak red	0.00

*254 mμ radiation.
System: n butanol 100: 3N hydrochloric acid 100 (top layer) .

In my view, although examination of the alimentary tract contents for metals is most useful and obviously necessary, a negative
result should not weigh too heavily. It is advisable to cross check
by analyses of liver tissue for the main toxic metals such as arsenic,

antimony, mercury, lead and thallium, and these are considered under the relevant sections.

B. DIALYSIS

i. Dialysis of One Ninth Aliquot

This aliquot of the alimentary tract contents untreated in any way is dialysed through cellophane or Visking against 2 x 250 ml portions of distilled water: the dialysate is then exactly neutralised and concentrated to 2 ml and the following spot tests are performed:

1. Nitrate, Chlorate and Bromate: One drop of dialysate is mixed with five drops of a 0.5% solution of diphenylamine in concentrated sulphuric acid. A blue colour indicates the presence of one of these ions which are not present in normal extracts. They can be distinguished by the following additional tests. A solution of indigo carmine is made in dilute sulphuric acid and diluted to a very pale blue colour. A few crystals of sodium sulphite are added followed by one or two drops of dialysate. Microgram quantities of chlorate or bromate will completely decolourise the solution. Green colours indicate a negative reaction. Confirmation of chlorate and bromate can also be accomplished as follows: silver nitrate solution acidified with nitric acid is added to an aliquot of the dialysate until completion of the precipitation of silver chloride; the precipitate is removed by filtration and a weak solution of sodium nitrite added dropwise: any silver chlorate or bromate in the filtrate (both are soluble) is thus reduced to chloride or bromide and can be seen as a further precipitate.

Nitrate may be found after the ingestion of nitrite.

2. Bromide: Recheck for bromide as described above.

3. Oxalate and Fluoride: Precipitation of the respective calcium salts as described above is the screening test. If milk of lime has been given as an antidote no free ions will be detectable until a second dialysate is made from acid solution as described below.

4. Thiocyanate and Thioglycollate: Thiocyanate may occasionally be ingested by laboratory workers and by schoolboys who mistake it for cyanide; thioglycollate is used in hair setting. Both can be detected by the formation of colours with a drop of ferric chloride solution on a drop of dialysate. Often a violet colour is noticed and this usually results from the salicylate following ingestion of aspirin.

5. *Fluoracetate and Fluoroacetamide:* This ion and compound are of great toxicological importance because of their availability as rat poisons. Rodenticides seem to be specially favoured by criminal poisoners and methods for their detection should be reliable. Fluoracetamide, which is a volatile compound, will most probably be hydrolysed to the ion *in vivo* or during the concentration of the dialysate. The GLC separation of these compounds is described in Part II.

6. *Borate:* This ion does not normally dialyse, even if present in stomach contents, presumably because of the formation of sugar complexes. This is why the determination of total boron in blood or tissue is advisable in any general search. If large excesses of borate are present a positive test may be obtained but it should be remembered that evaporation of the dialysate in borosilicate glass can give a positive result in the test. A x 10 dilution if still positive indicates a positive result from the content and not from the glass. The test consists of evaporating to dryness on a tile on a water bath a drop of dialysate with a turmeric paper wetted with dilute hydrochloric acid. A red colour turning blue on wetting with dilute ammonia is a positive.

In borate deaths, which occur sometimes in young children accidentally given boric acid solutions, the blood is frequently a bright red colour.

7. *Nitrite:* A drop of dialysate is put on a powder made by mixing 6.2 g of α-napthylamine, 1 g of sulphamic acid and 25 g of citric acid and drying the powder in a dessicator. Although this is a very sensitive test, controls should be done at the same time to show that deterioration of the stored powder has not occurred.

In deaths from nitrites the blood is usually a chocolate colour.

8. *Iodide:* A drop of dialysate is acidified with dilute sulphuric acid and a drop of copper sulphate solution added. Free iodine is liberated if iodide is present which can be detected as a violet colour in a chloroform extraction or by the blue of a starch iodide reaction.

Iodide is another ion which is bound in some way to protein and if there is any suspicion of ingestion of iodide, blood or tissue should be ashed as described in Part II. Iodide does not appear in deproteinised filtrates of blood and there is a grave doubt as to whether it will always dialyse from stomach contents.

9. *Thiosulphate:* A drop of dilute sulphuric acid and a weak solution of iodine in potassium iodide is added to a drop of dialysate. Decolourisation indicates thiosulphate which photographers and laboratory workers might ingest.

10. *Ferrous and Ferric Ions:* These ions will not dialyse if the contents were neutral or alkaline: if acid, they may be found. Spot tests with potassium ferrocyanide and ferricyanide acidified with dilute hydrochloric acid are suitable and sensitive tests.

11. *Check Tests:* Chloride and phosphate are normally present in the stomach and intestine contents and serve as an internal control; tests for their presence should always be done to check the efficiency of the dialysis.

ii. Dialysis from Acid Solution

After the dialysis of the one ninth part of the content the contents of the cellophane or visking are made acid with hydrochloric acid and a second dialysis made again against 2 x 250 ml portions of distilled water. After evaporation, tests for ferrous, ferric, oxalate and fluoride ions are repeated. In deaths from ferrous sulphate in young children tests for ferrous ions are often obtainable before evaporation and, in this way, any oxidation during evaporation does not complicate the interpretation. The dialysate should be neutralised before concentration to 2 ml by evaporation so that loss of hydrogen fluoride does not occur.

Interpretation of Results

Nitrate and chlorate will cause serious symptoms of poisoning and sometimes death in doses of about 15 g of their sodium or potassium salts. Bromates are said to be slightly more toxic. Nitrates are found in fertilisers, chlorates in weedkillers and also as an ingredient of mouthwashes and throat lozenges, and bromate is a very common ingredient of "home perm" kits. All may therefore be encountered. In the complete analysis for these ions it is likely that their presence will be detectable in the alimentary tract in only milligram amounts and the inference that they were responsible for the poisoning must rest, to some extent, on the circumstantial evidence coupled with the clinical history and the findings at the post-mortem examination.

The very high toxicity of the fluoroacetates, 50-100 mg being a lethal dose, means that the detection of microgram quantities in the alimentary tract is of great significance. Because of the way in which interference with the tricarboxylic acid cycle manifests itself, death may be delayed for many hours or even days and there is often an early quiescent period. Reported cases of poisoning by these compounds are, to some extent, complicated by the fact that inorganic fluoride was present in many early commercial samples.

Borates are found in most households either as boric acid or as borax. The interpretation of tissue levels of boron is discussed in Part II.

Nitrite and nitrate can be found in some water supplies and can cause poisoning of children and animals; methaemoglobin-aemia is an outstanding clinical finding. Nitrite is used as a rust preventative and also in the chemical industry. Very small amounts are used to preserve the colour in pickled or salted meats. Death has resulted in an adult from the ingestion of 2 g sodium nitrite, but the more usual fatal dose is about 10 g.

Ferrous sulphate is commonly taken by young children by accident because parents underestimate the climbing capabilities of the young child. Anaemia tablets hidden in a cupboard or drawer are attractive sweets to a youngster. In such cases the intestine contents are frequently blue in colour from the formation of iron phosphates and tests for ferrous ion can often be obtained by a direct test on the faeces. The ingestion of five to ten tablets, each containing an adult therapeutic dose of ferrous sulphate, by a young child can be expected to lead to poisoning. Ferrous phosphate is also encountered in "tonics." Ferric salts cause irritation of the gastric mucosa and like ferrous sulphate have been taken in attempts to procure an abortion. Traces of ferric ion are sometimes found in normal intestinal contents and faint positive tests on a drop of solution from a 2 ml sample of evaporated dialysate of one ninth of the alimentary tract contents should be ignored.

REFERENCES

BURDEN, E.H.W.J.: The toxicology of nitrites with particular reference to the potability of water supplies. *Analyst, 86:*429, 1961.

JACKSON, R.C.; ELDER, W.J., and McDONNELL, H.: Sodium chlorate poisoning complicated by acute renal failure. *Lancet, ii:*1381, 1961.

POLSON, C.J., and TATTERSALL, R.N.: *Clinical Toxicology.* London, English Universities Press, London, 1959, p. 140—Fluorides; *ibid. idem:* page 274, Boracic acid (Boron®).

SAWYER, R.; GRISLEY, L.M., and COX, B.G.: Separation and determination of fluoroacetamide residues in water, biological materials and soils. *J Sci Fd Agri, 18:*283, 1967.

C. EXAMINATION OF THE TWO-NINTHS ALIQUOT FOR ORGANIC SOLVENT SOLUBLE POISONS

i. Extraction

Which method to use to extract these poisons? This is a difficult question to answer but four are commonly used. They are as follows:

1. Direct extraction without prior treatment.
2. Protein precipitation by ammonium sulphate.

Method (Nickolls, L. C.: *The Scientific Investigation of Crime.* Butterworth, London, 1956, p. 382). The content is diluted to a gruel consistency and sufficient dilute hydrochloric or acetic acid is added to make the pH approximately 2-3. Solid ammonium sulphate is then added to make a saturated solution and the digest is warmed without stirring in a boiling water bath for fifteen minutes. Filtration without suction through a paper pad on a sintered glass Buchner funnel gives a clear, protein-free filtrate suitable, after cooling, for extraction with an equal volume of ether. The solid on the paper pad is washed with warm acid water and then with ether and all the extracts are combined.

3. Continuous extraction by acid ethanol.
4. Prior treatment of the content in 40% hydrochloric acid at 100° C for five minutes.

The above processes are not put forward as being the only or the best methods; no single method can guarantee efficient extraction for all compounds. They do however provide a guide.

In all the processes the extraction is made with an organic solvent firstly from acid solution and then from alkaline solution and subsequently divided into the strong acid, weak acid, neutral, alkaloid and morphine fractions. Evaporation of the alkaline ether fraction must be done very carefully so that such volatile alkaloids as nicotine are not lost. If the presence of an unstable alkaloid such as atropine is suspected very mild extraction procedures must be used; continuous extraction with alcohol under reduced pressure is suitable.

If screening tests on liver for phenothiazines have been positive the toxicologist may consider it advisable to hydrolyse half of this aliquot by method four to free protein bound drug. Apart from a few acid labile alkaloids the method does not result in the loss of many compounds and, as usual, extraction from acid solution should precede that from alkaline solution. Filtration after the acid treatment gives a clear solution which does not usually emulsify when shaken with organic solvent.

Direct extraction of the content or diluted content preferably with a large excess of solvent may be the easiest method but often emulsions occur and protein precipitation is obviously necessary if the content is thick or bulky. Methods two or three may be used as experience indicates.

The aim of these extraction procedures is to produce firstly an aqueous acidic phase and an organic solvent phase. If chloroform is used as the organic phase, then the aqueous acid should be sulphuric acid. This is because many base hydrochlorides are soluble in chloroform and in the subsequent division into strong acids, weak acids, neutrals and bases, they would be lost. The separation is as shown in schematic outline in Figure 6, with the additional extraction at pH 8 after the addition of a little sodium sulphite with chloroform:isopropanol (4:1) to isolate morphine.

The extracts will contain between them the possible presence of a very large number of poisons together with coextracted fat, cholesterol and other natural products.

A really comprehensive list of compounds to be sought in these fractions would contain many hundreds, possibly thousands, of substances covering the whole range of chemicals in use in every branch of life. The toxicologist must consider the weed killer or insecticide in the same fraction as the medicament and household poisons. Several screening tests are necessary to detect any abnormal compound amongst those occurring in the normal stomach or intestines.

There are four stages in the approach to these analyses: these are considered in order below.

ii. Analyses

(a) Spot Tests

These consist of (1) a drop of 5% ferric chloride solution is spotted on an evaporated one per cent aliquot of the weak and strong acid fractions on a filter paper or test tile. This will detect salicylic acid and salicylamide by the production of a violet colour.

If salicylic acid is found it may be desirable to show unchanged aspirin in the contents: infra-red spectroscopy is the easiest method provided the instrument is available. If not, separation by electrophoresis and paper chromatography should be attempted: aspirin gives a violet colour with a mixture of 1% ferric chloride and 1% potassium ferricyanide, but not with ferric chloride itself.

(2) One per cent of the neutral fraction dissolved in alcohol is evaporated in a small spot on a filter paper. A drop of 10% furfural in alcohol is allowed to run carefully onto the spot and is dried. The paper is then exposed to fumes of hydrochloric acid in a beaker for several minutes when any carbamate will reveal its presence as a blue-purple spot. Common carbamates are meprobamate and ethinamate.

(3) One per cent of the neutral fraction is boiled over a microflame with two drops of 10% sodium hydroxide solution to dryness on a white tile. One drop of 50% saturated fluorescein solution, six drops of glacial acetic acid and six drops of 100 volume hydrogen peroxide are added and evaporated to dryness on a boil-

ing water bath. A red colour of eosin indicates the presence of an organo-bromo compound such as carbomal.

(4) Test for DDT (Irudayasamy, A., and Natarajan, A. R.: *Anal Chem, 33:*630, 1961). An alcoholic aliquot of the neutral fraction is evaporated to dryness and treated with 10 ml of a chilled nitrating reagent consisting of 1:1 v/v nitric acid and sulphuric acids. It is then transferred to a 8 x $\frac{3}{4}$ test tube and heated in a boiling water bath for one hour. If any carbonaceous material remains heating is continued for a further half an hour. After cooling, dilute with 50 to 100 ml of ice cold water and extract with 20 ml and then 10 ml of chloroform. Wash the combined chloroform extracts with 50 ml of 1% potassium hydroxide solution and then with 3 x 50 ml portions of water. Dry the separated chloroform with anhydrous sodium sulphate and evaporate to dryness. Transfer the residue in chloroform to two separate spots on a white tile and evaporate off the solvent. To one spot add one drop of a 20% alcoholic potassium hydroxide solution (made by dissolving 5 g potassium hydroxide in 2.5 ml of water and diluting with 22.6 ml of ethanol). A positive reaction of colours going from rose to bright blue to green to yellow is obtained if DDT, DDE, DDA, DDD, DFDT or methoxychlor in even 1μg quantity is present. To the other spot, addition of one drop of the alcoholic potassium hydroxide solution is followed by addition of one to two drops of acetone. A positive result is bright blue colour changing to bright purple to grey to yellow.

(5) Test for α-naphthyl thiourea (Dybing, F.: *Acta Pharmacol Toxicol, 3:*184, 1947. An aliquot, one per cent, of the neutral fraction, is dissolved in chloroform and shaken for thirty seconds with a few drops of bromine water. Excess sodium hydroxide solution is then added and the whole shaken again. A positive result sensitive to 1μg or 50μg/ml is obtained if a blue colour is seen in the chloroform layer which is unchanged by shaking with 60% sulphuric acid.

(6) An aliquot, one per cent, of the neutral fraction in alcohol is carefully evaporated. 1 ml of 20% sodium hydroxide solution and 1 ml of pyridine are added and the reaction test tube is immersed in a boiling water bath for one minute. A red colour in the

pyridine layer indicates the presence of chloral hydrate or chlorbutol in the neutral fraction. This is a very sensitive reaction and chloroform must be absent from the environment. Positive tests should also be obtained in the volatile fraction.

(7) One per cent (10% if a 1% fraction gives a negative reaction) of the alkaloid fraction in ethanol is spotted on a filter paper and a drop of potassium bismuth iodide solution (Dragendorff's reagent) allowed to run into it. An orange colour indicates the presence of an alkaloid. Three positive reacting aliquots are examined by paper chromatography. The solvent system consists of the top layer of n-butanol:water:citric acid (100:100:2 g). The paper is Whatman No. 1 which has previously been dipped in 5% sodium dihydrogen citrate solution (23.5 g $Na_3C_6H_5O_7$. $2H_2O$ + 30.4 g citric acid dissolved in 1024 ml of water) and dried at 60°C for twenty minutes. The aliquots are dissolved in ethanol for application to the paper and suitable control spots of nicotine, morphine, strychnine, quinine, phenazone and any other alkaloid that may be involved in the enquiry are also applied to serve as comparison spots: 2μl of 2% solutions are suitable for these standards. After running and drying, the paper is inspected in 254 $m\mu$ light and any fluorescent or absorbent spots are ringed. One of the aliquots is sprayed with Dragendorff's reagent and positive reacting spots are noted.

Colour tests such as Marquis and the p-dimethylaminobenzaldehyde reagents should be applied to 2 mm squares cut from the similar spots which have not been sprayed; the alkaloid can be also recovered from the Dragendorff spot by adding successively one drop of 10% sodium sulphite solution, one drop of 10% barium chloride and one drop 880 ammonia and drying between each application. The free alkaloid is eluted from the paper with chloroform. Colour and crystal tests, a consideration of Rf values, and appearances in ultra-violet light as well as ultra-violet and infra-red spectroscopy on the eluates are all criteria leading to identification. Details of Rf values and ultra-violet absorption maxima for many common alkaloids are shown in Tables XII and XIII. The use of TLC and GLC in these identifications was discussed in Chapter 4.

(8) The procedure followed for the detection of an unknown alkaloid in the alkaloid fraction is followed with the morphine fraction. Detection of any morphine is accomplished either by spraying with Dragendorff's reagent or by dipping the dried chromatogram in a 2% solution of 40% formaldehyde in concentrated sulphuric acid (Marquis reagent). Full identification follows the line suggested above.

(9) One per cent of the alkaloid fraction is spotted on a filter paper and a drop of FPN reagent is allowed to flow onto it. This reagent is made as follows: five parts 5% ferric chloride, forty-five parts 20% perchloric acid, fifty parts 50% nitric acid. It gives a variety of colours with different phenothiazines. If the test is positive it is necessary to differentiate the many drugs that have the phenothiazine nucleus. Chlorpromazine is the most commonly found but several of the others are very popular in medicine. Techniques available for their separation and identification are paper electrophoresis in 6% w/v acetic acid and paper chromatography as described above. After partially drying the electrophoretogram, exposure to 254 mμ light for several minutes converts many of these drugs to coloured derivatives. Table XV gives details.

TABLE XV
PAPER CHROMATOGRAPHY OF PHENOTHIAZINES

Compound	Rf Value*	Colour of Spot** on Exposure to 254 mμ Light	Colour with FPN Reagent
Perphenazine	.50	yellow/grey	red
Prochlorperazine	.50	—	red
Trifluoperazine	.55	—	orange
Fluphenazine	.64	—	orange
Promazine	.71	orange	orange
Notensil	.72	—	orange-red
Thiopropazate	.73	—	red
Pecazine	.74	salmon	orange
Veractil	.77	violet	violet
Chlorpromazine	.77	yellow/green	red
Promethazine	.78	—	pink-red
Trifluopromazine	.81	—	orange-yellow
Ethopropazine	.81	—	red
Diethazine	.81	—	orange-red brown
Imipramine	.81	—	turquoise
Thioridazine	.81	green	blue

*In butanol 100: water 100: citric acid 2 g top layer on Whatman No. 1 paper impregnated with 5% sodium dihydrogen citrate and dried.
**After electrophoresis

Additional methods involving a TLC separation and sulph-oxide formation for the identification of phenothiazines are described in Chapter 7A (ii).

(b) Ultra-Violet Spectrophotometry

The second stage consists of measuring the ultra-violet absorption spectra for every fraction between 220 and 320 mμ. It is usual to take 10 per cent aliquots and use the following solvents:

1. Strong acid fraction — 0.45N sodium hydroxide.
2. Weak acid fraction — this fraction is read at three pHs; 0.45N sodium hydroxide is followed by 0.45N sodium hydroxide + 16% ammonium chloride (3 ml + 0.5 ml; pH = 10) then after adding 50% sulphuric acid to the pH 10 solution to change it to pH = 2.
3. Neutral fraction — alcohol.
4. Basic fraction — 0.1N sulphuric acid.

Normally, 5 to 10 ml is a suitable volume to dissolve each aliquot for taking the readings. In the absence of poison there are normally no inflexions in the curves whose optical density decreases slowly as the wavelength increases. If poison is present then considerable dilution may be necessary.

Barbiturates in the weak acid fraction form the most common group of poisons and their spectral changes with pH are illustrated in Figure 5. Normally the presence of barbiturate will have been established by the first stage of the liver analysis which precedes that described here. In the neutral fraction, phenacetin, with an absorption maximum at 245 mμ, is common; most of the carbamates do not show inflexions although mephenesin peaks at 270 mμ. Caffeine may be found in both the neutral and the alkaloid fraction and has a peak at 273 mμ. It does not react with Dragendorff's reagent. In the case of the alkaloids a routine examination by ultra-violet spectrophotometry and if possible infra-red spectroscopy is worthwhile because such common drugs as benzocaine and theobromine also do not react with the common general alkaloid reagents and spectroscopy is the only method for their easy detection.

The alkaloids show a great variety of absorption spectra with

$E_{1cm}^{1\%}$ values ranging from over 1,000 to less than 5 with wavelength maxima from below 220 mμ to above 360 mμ. Comparison of the observed spectrum with known spectra enables identification to be easily and rapidly achieved if the curves are sufficiently characteristic. Often a chromophoric group is common to a series of drugs; for example, the phenothiazines show similar spectra with a maximum at 255 mμ, and in my opinion, a chromatographic separation using paper, thin layer or gas chromatography is a valuable, and in many cases an essential, additional tool for identification. If infra-red is available only a few micrograms are necessary for absolute identification to be achieved but purity is, again, most important, and prior chromatography is of the greatest value. Details of the absorption peaks to be commonly found in each extract are given in Tables XII and XIII.

It is obvious that the toxicologist must characterise for himself the poisons and drugs that are common in his area and also study such collections of data that are published. Any abnormal curve or chromatographic spot must be tracked to its source. A visit to the scene of the poisoning may be a great help.

(c) Sublimation

Many compounds will sublime provided a sufficiently low pressure is used, 10^{-2}mm is essential, preferably lower. A temperature of 100°C is used. Crystals are characterised by melting points (see Table XVI) or by any of the other available methods, x-ray diffraction or infra-red spectroscopy, for example. If any of the tests described above have given a positive result, sublimation is worthwhile trying. Even in negative cases its use is recommended. Cantharidin and the halogenated insecticidal compounds form examples which are detected most simply by the isolation of crystalline material.

(d) Determination of Elements

Four elements, bromine, chlorine, phosphorus and nitrogen are usually sought in the various fractions. Bromine has been considered in test Aiii above and will not be discussed further here. Paper chromatography is a useful step prior to the tests because they can all be carried out on the paper for the detection of

TABLE XVI
MELTING POINTS

Melting Point (°C)	Substance	Melting Point (°C)	Substance
41– 43	Phenyl salicylic acid	163	Rotenone
46	Trimethadione	165	Methyl testosterone
48– 50	Urethane	165	Sulphanilamide
51	Thymol	168	p-Acetamidophenol
		169–172	Stilbestrol
69	Coumarin	170–173	Santonin
72	Antabuse	171	isonicotinyl hydrazide
74– 76	Sulphonethylmethane	175	Sulphathiazole
75	Noludar	179	Camphor
87	Glutethimide	184	Sulphacetamide
91	Persedon	185–187	Succinic acid
97	Chlorbutanol (sublimes)	185–188	Hexestrol
97	Ethinamate	186	Hexachloroethane
100–102	Aldrin	190–191	Pentachlorophenol
103	Isopropylphenazone	190	Sulphaguanidine
104–106	Meprobamate	191	Oxalic acid
109	DDT	192	Sulphapyridine
109–110	TDE	193	Pregnelone
111–113	Antipyrine	194	Sedormid
113–115	Acetanilide	198	α Ethylcrotonyl
114	Hexachlorcyclohexane		carbamate
116–118	Carbromal	199	Sulphamethazine
122	Benzoic acid (sublimes 100)	203	Picrotoxin
		209	Phenylacetyl urea
124–126	Sulphonmethane	212–216	Phenurone
130	Nicotinamide	219	Irgafen
131	Progesterone	228	Saccharin
134–135	Phenacetin	237	Nicotinic acid
135	Aspirin	238	Caffeine (sublimes 178)
136–137	Methylphenylethyl hydantoin	238	Sulphamerazine
140	Salicylamide	256–257	Digitoxin
145–153	Bromvaletone	258	Phenolphthalein
148	Cholesterol	262	Sulphadiazine
151	Chloramphenicol	265	Digoxin
153	Khellin	270–274	Theophylline
155	Testosterone	295–298	Diphenylhydantoin
157–159	Salicylic acid (sublimes)	357	Theobromine (sublimes 290–295)
161	Warfarin		

microgram quantities of the organically combined element. The solvents and sprays for use are detailed in Tables XVII and XVIII.

Details for the further investigation of organo-chloro, organo-phosphorus and nitrogen containing compounds are given in Part II. The continued use of a paper chromatographic examination at this stage instead of going direct to TLC systems is justified on the grounds that the neutral extract, in which the bulk

TABLE XVII
SOLVENT SYSTEMS FOR ELEMENT PAPER CHROMATOGRAPHY

Element	Refs.	Solvent	Paper Treated with	Compounds Detected
Chlorine	1,2	Pyridine + water (3 + 2)	Soya bean oil at 2 mg per square inch	Aldrin, Dieldrin BHC
Phosphorus	3	Light petroleum + 10% aqueous solution of acetonitrile (3 + 1)	Saturate paper and chamber with vapour	p-nitro phenol Paraoxon, Parathion
Phosphorus	4	Chloroform Carbon tetrachloride	Nil	try for organo phosphorous compounds
Nitrogen	5	Glacial acetic acid + water (1 + 1)	20% olive oil in acetone and dried	Carbromal Bromvaletone Sedormid
Nitrogen	5	Methanol + water (18 + 2)	20% olive oil in acetone and dried	Methyprylone Glutethimide Thalidomide Bemegride Sedulon Persedon all carbamates

1   MITCHELL, L. C., and PATTERSON, W. I.: *J Assoc Agric Chem, 36*:553, 1953.
2   MITCHELL, L. C.: *ibid*, 1183.
3   KARLOG, O.: *Acta Pharmacol Toxicol, 14*:92, 1957.
4   OTTER, I. K. H.: *Nature, 176*: 1078, 1955.
5   JACKSON, J. V., and MOSS, M. S.: In Smith, I. (Ed.) : *Chromatographic and Electrophoretic Techniques*, 2nd ed. New York, Interscience, 1960, vol. 1, p. 404.

of the toxicologically significant compounds of these groups occur, often contains a lot of fat. In my experience paper is a far better medium than TLC in these particular circumstances.

If a positive result is obtained, and the amount of drug responsible for it is present in only trace quantities, then this is another occasion when a visit to the scene will probably produce more worthwhile results than days of semi-inspired guessing in the laboratory.

Interpretation of Results

These can be divided into three main categories as follows:

1. When a toxic dose of a particular poison can be isolated from the alimentary tract. In such cases the interpretation is straightforward.

2. When the presence of a highly toxic material is established, even in trace amounts, the inference that poisoning is the cause of death is also usually wholly justified.

3. When a small quantity of drug is found in the alimentary tract and the question arises as to whether it is the residue of a toxic or a therapeutic dose.

TABLE XVIII

SPRAY REAGENTS FOR ELEMENTS

Element	Ref.*	Spray for Chromatography
Chlorine	1,2	0.5N silver nitrate in ethanol: air dry for 30 minutes. Spray with 37% formaldehyde; air dry 30 minutes. Spray 2N potassium hydroxide in methanol. Heat at 130°C for 30 minutes; cool; spray concentrated nitric acid + 30% hydrogen peroxide (1 + 1); air dry overnight; expose to sun. Alternatively — Spray with 0.5% ethanolic silver nitrate containing 1% phenoxyethanol. Expose to ultraviolet radiation.
Phosphorus	3	1.0N ethanolic sodium hydroxide
Phosphorus	4	1% N-bromosuccinimide in acetone; dry; then spray with molybdate reagent and dry in the oven at 70°C. for 8 minutes. Remove and expose to ultra-violet light for 10 – 20 minutes. Molybdate reagent is made by mixing 15 ml 72% perchloric acid, 25 ml 5% ammonium molybdate, 10 ml N hydrochloric acid and 55 ml distilled water.
Nitrogen	5	Expose paper to chlorine vapour for 10 minutes; suspend in a current of air. Spray with 2% starch + 1% potassium iodide when paper itself does not give a deep stain. An alternative to exposure to chlorine is to dip the paper in sodium hypochlorite solution with 2.5% available chlorine.

*Refs. as in Table XVII.

The question of the time interval that has elapsed between ingestion and death may also be posed.

In all cases the amount remaining in the stomach at death is what remains of that ingested after vomiting and absorption have occurred. If both of these two unknowns can be established by other analyses the total ingested can be determined; if not, the calculation is, at best, a guess. The experience of the toxicologist is then the overriding factor and it would be foolish here to indulge in generalisations. It is sufficient to say that 50 mg of barbiturate can be found in the stomach of a person who died less than an hour after the ingestion of a large overdose, and in another case the same quantity may be found after a period of forty-eight hours spent in coma. Simultaneous ingestion of alcohol can increase the absorption rate very considerably because of the dilation of the stomach's vascular system. It has often been put to me that the small intestine is the main site for the absorption of many poisons; in my opinion, as far as large overdoses are concerned, this is not so — it is, in fact, the stomach. On many occasions it is possible to show by analysis that the poison has not reached the small intestine, yet the concentration of drug in the tissues is at a fatal level.

General principles hold relating the position of maximum concentration of drug in the alimentary tract to the time of ingestion although there are two complications. Firstly, diffusion of toxin after death and during the post-mortem examination and, secondly, secretion of some drugs by the bile. Unless the content is highly fluid the first is usually unimportant but the second is of some significance — drugs which have been injected may be only demonstrable in the intestines; for example, nalorphine. On such occasions the interpretation becomes very much a guess based on experience.

Chapter 7

THE ANALYSIS OF LIVER

In the United Kingdom four tests are conveniently done early in the investigation because they are designed to detect poisons common in that geographical area. These will be considered first. They usually follow, the simple tests on blood and urine and precede the tests on the alimentary tract described in Chapter 6. The second stage in the analysis of the liver follows the tests on the tract although it is often convenient to cut the portions of tissue required for all these analyses at the one time.

In all, the following weights are required: 2 g, 2 x 10 g, 2 x 50 g, 2 x 100 g and 250 g. It is also a convenient moment to weigh the whole organ. The tissue and any fluid in the jar should be macerated together before the weights are taken. This applies for all analyses on liver.

The weight amounts to approximately one third of a normal liver and the same proportion should apply in the case of young children. If acute necrosis has been noted the liver should be examined by x-ray to determine whether the damage is from Thorotrast which was used about twenty years ago as an x-ray contrast medium and which causes death by the radiation from thorium dioxide. The pathologist will usually have remarked on the macroscopic appearance of the liver but the toxicologist should be capable of recognising gross pathological changes and of searching first for those poisons which interfere with the metabolism of this very important organ.

A. THE FIRST STAGE

i. The Sodium Tungstate Precipitation

Method (Fox, R.H., personal communication) . Tissue (100 g), 430 ml water and 100 ml 25% w/v sodium tungstate solution are thoroughly homogenised in an electric blender. The contents of the blender are washed into a 2 litre stainless steel beaker with a further 300 ml of water. The beaker is placed in a boiling water bath, 100 ml of 50% w/v sodium bisulphate solution added, and rapidly stirred electrically for ten minutes. This gives an excellent precipitation of granular material which can be easily removed by filtering through a 40 cm Whatman No. 114 paper. No suction is required and about 850 ml (85% recovery) of filtrate is obtained in only two to three minutes.

After cooling, the filtrate is extracted with 1 litre of ether which has previously been freed from antioxidant and stored over ferrous sulphate solution. The subsequent treatment of this ether and the acid aqueous solution for the strong acid, weak acid, neutral, alkaloid and morphine fractions follows that described in Figure 6 and Chapter 4, with the volumes of extracting and re-extracting solutions suitably scaled up to deal with the larger volumes. For the morphine fraction, for example, 240 ml chloroform and 60 ml isopropanol are suitable volumes. It is again emphasized that the evaporation of ether in such large volumes requires the greatest care and laboratory discipline. Amphetamine is not lost to a significant degree if evaporation of the alkaloid fraction is done in two stages — firstly, reduction of the 500 ml volume to 5 ml by normal evaporation, and secondly, from 5 ml to 50μl in the special tube with drawn-out base on a 40°C water bath. The 5 ml volume is redried with solid anhydrous sodium sulphate before the second evaporation. The extracts from the acidic extractions should be allowed to cool and then carefully inspected for any crystalline product. Examination follows the general procedure suggested for the blood and urine samples described in Chapters 3 and 4 with the following additional notes.

(a) Strong Acid Fraction

As with the blood extract, salicylic acid is the commonest encountered acid. However, mandelic acid may be found if mandelamine has been taken, and succinic acid is commonly found as a natural product.

For this fraction, the weak acid fraction and neutral fraction, references to Tables VII, VIII and XI to identify ultra-violet peaks will be useful.

(b) Weak Acid Fraction

This extract is dissolved in 10 ml of ether and the following divisions are made:

1. 1 ml, which is evaporated and examined by ultraviolet spectrophotometry at pH 13.5, pH 10 and pH 2. The characteristic absorption maxima illustrated in Figure 5 are found if barbiturate is present. As was indicated in relation to blood in Chapter 3, glutethimide must also be sought by observing the reading at 235 mμ in 0.45N sodium hydroxide (pH 13.5) for several minutes. A diminution in reading indicates the opening of the glutarimide ring. Bemegride gives a peak at 230 mμ at this pH. The amount in the extraction, and then by simple arithmetic the amount in 100 g of liver, can be calculated roughly at first by using an $E_{1cm}^{1\%}$ value of 450 at 240 mμ for pH 10 − pH 2, then exactly when full identification of the barbiturate or barbiturates has been achieved. The volume of solvent used for spectrophotometry depends on the amount of drug present; therapeutic amounts need only 5 ml of sodium hydroxide, or even less, but toxic doses may take over 100 ml to bring the reading within the range of the instrument. Visible examination of the extract gives a rough guide of the volume to be used, but it must be found by experiment. $E_{1cm}^{1\%}$ values for the common barbiturates are shown in Table XIX. The values shown are for the maxima; when an optical density difference between pH 10 and pH 2 is to be taken the $E_{1cm}^{1\%}$ values are slightly less.

2. 1 ml is evaporated in a test tube and 1 ml of concentrated sulphuric acid added. A cotton wool plug is placed in position at the mouth of the tube which is then immersed in a boiling water bath for exactly one hour. The acid is then poured into 25 ml of water, cooled, and extracted with 20 ml of ether. The ether is separated, evaporated and dissolved in 0.5N ammonia solution. The volume should equal that used above for the reading taken at pH = 10. The ultra-violet absorption spectrum is measured between 220 and 320 mμ. 5,5 disubstituted barbiturates substituted in the alpha position

TABLE XIX

E1% VALUES OF COMMON BARBITURATES
1cm

| *E1% values at 240 mμ in 0.05 M borax buffer** | | | |
1cm			
Phenobarbitone	431	Quinalbarbitone Secobarbital	374
Barbitone	538	Hexethal	400
Methylphenobarbitone	458	Sigmodal	271
Dial	442	Butallyonal	280
Vinbarbitone	446	Allyl, sec-butyl barbiturate	401
Cyclobarbitone	423	Sandoptal	415
Cycloheptenyl, ethyl, barbiturate	400	Nostal	301
Amylobarbitone	424	Aprobarbital	438
Butobarbitone	453	Probarbital	452
Butabarbitone	439	Allyl, phenyl, barbiturate	401
Pentobarbitone	411		

*Stevenson, G. W.: *Anal Chem, 33:*1376, 1961.

to the ring undergo attack and Table XX shows typical results of the acid treatment.

3. The 8 ml of ether remaining are evaporated to near dryness and suitable aliquots are examined by paper, GLC or TLC chromatography.

Details of three recommended paper and four TLC systems with methods of detection are given in Chapter 3. GLC separations are described in Part II. The trapping of GLC effluents prior to micro infra-red spectroscopy is discussed in more detail below.

If chromatography has shown only one barbiturate to be present, sublimation will usually give a crystalline product which can be characterised by melting points, x-ray diffraction and by inspection with comparative infra-red curves. Occasionally, it may be necessary to run all the extract on a number of paper chromatograms and elute the purified barbiturate before sublimation will give crystalline material.

Interpretation of Results. An opinion can be given from a consideration of the concentration of the barbiturate in the liver as to whether a therapeutic or a toxic dose had been ingested; by comparison with the blood concentration it is possible to give an estimate of the time interval between ingestion and death.

Therapeutic levels of the rapid acting barbiturates in the liver rarely exceed 0.5 mg/100 g; in cases of poisoning levels as high as 30 mg/100 g may be found although Bonnichsen and his co-workers in a review of 600 cases showed that for amylobarbitone and pentobarbitone the average figures were 6.7 and 8.5 mg/100 g respectively. In the case of phenobarbitone and barbitone the possibility of accumulation from therapeutic dosing is possible and this has been discussed earlier in relation to blood.

TABLE XX
EFFECT OF CONCENTRATED SULPHURIC ACID ON
BARBITURATES

Barbiturate	Wavelength Maximum of Product at pH 10.
Barbitone	240 mμ
Amylobarbitone	240 mμ
Butobarbitone	240 mμ
Pentobarbitone	268 mμ
Cyclobarbitone	268 mμ
Quinalbarbitone (Secobarbital)	weak peaks at 240, 266 and 315 mμ
Phenobarbitone	completely destroyed
Nealbarbitone	240 mμ major peak and 315 mμ as minor peak

The concentration ratio of the liver/blood can be as high as 20/1 if death follows within a few minutes of ingestion, and this usually occurs when large doses of sodium barbiturates, especially quinalbarbitone, are taken with alcohol on an empty stomach. However, Moghrabi (personal communication) has found that a liver left in a jar experiences depletion of fluid because of drainage. When this happens, a very significant rise in the tissue concentration occurs because the drained fluid is relatively free of barbiturate. Incorrect conclusions could be drawn from liver/blood concentration ratios if the tissue and fluid are not maccrated together before the weighed tissue is processed.

Blood levels may even be less than 1 mg/100 ml when death occurs rapidly. The ratio falls slowly until after twenty-four hours has elapsed between ingestion and death it is usually about 2/1.

Figure 7 shows a review of cases from Dr. Irving Sunshine and my own records. Bonnichsen's figures showed that, at death, the average blood levels for amylobarbitone and pentobarbitone were 2.7-2.8 mg/100 ml and this should be contrasted with the much higher figures experienced in living patients. Death occurs more readily in some individuals if the airway is in any way restricted either by the mouth being partially blocked by a pillow or if the head falls forward.

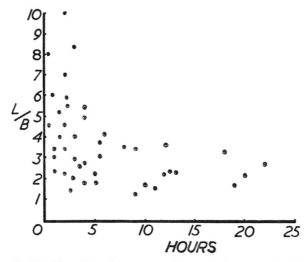

FIGURE 7. The liver/blood concentration ratio in cases of poisoning.

Bogan and Smith in a review of eighty-five cases give an average liver concentration of 9.6 mg/100 g with blood concentrations from 0.7-9.6 mg/100 ml. They also note that brain concentrations are lower, averaging 3.5 mg/100 g. Rehling, reporting on the experiences of the members of the American Academy of Forensic Sciences, also gives comprehensive lists of analytical results.

REFERENCES

BONNICHSEN, R.; MAEHLY, A.C., and FRANK, A.: *J Forensic Sci, 6:*411, 1961.

BOGAN, J., and SMITH, H.: Analytical investigations of barbiturate poisoning. *J For Sci Soc, 7:*37, 1967.

REHLING, C.J.: Poison residues in human tissues (report of 150 barbiturate and 90 barbiturate/alcohol combinations). In Stolman, A. (Ed.): *Progress in Chemical Toxicology.* New York, Academic, 1967, vol. 3.

(c) Neutral Fraction

This is examined by ultra-violet spectrophotometry using alcohol as solvent and then by the spot tests for carbamates. On many occasions sublimation can provide crystalline products suitable for infra-red spectroscopy and gravimetric assay. In deaths from bromo-ureides the corresponding compound with a hydrogen replacing the bromine atom may be found.

(d) Alkaloids

As was noted above, the extraction by ether from ammoniacal solution is done in two stages finishing with a final volume of 50 μl. The rationale of the examination of this fraction has been discussed in relation to the urine and alimentary tract fractions and there is no difference in principle here. The preferred method is to use paper or TLC using the butanol-citric acid system on either buffered paper or cellulose TLC plates. Rf values are the same whichever system is used; TLC gives higher sensitivity and can be conveniently used as a relatively rapid screening procedure.

The total extract is divided into three 30μl alcoholic aliquots which are run separately on the chromatogram. After inspection in 254 mμ light one extract is sprayed with Dragendorff's or iodoplatinate reagents leaving the other two extracts for other tests. If a positive reacting spot is obtained on spraying with iodoplatinate, elution of the spot from the chromatogram for ultraviolet spectrophotometry is probably the next simplest approach. When a base has been localised by iodoplatinate or Dragendorff reagents, it can be eluted by shaking the cut out spot with chloroform (5 ml) after wetting the paper with 880 ammonia and adding a drop of 5% sodium sulphite. Separation and evaporation of the chloroform, after filtering through a fluted filter paper, gives a clean extract suitable for ultra-violet spectrophotometry in 0.5 ml 0.1N H_2SO_4.

It is emphasized that both paper and TLC plates are suitable media to perform colour tests based on concentrated sulphuric acid. The purification of the unknown alkaloid by paper, TLC, or GLC can also be followed by an infra-red examination. GLC is the best purification system and excellent infra-red curves can be obtained on 10μg of trapped effluent. Using 0.5 mm discs, curves on as small a quantity as 200 nanograms can be obtained. In this technique a 1:10 splitter is used and the larger effluent trapped in a small glass tube to which it is carried by means of a heated line. The tube is cooled in liquid nitrogen and the geometry is important to avoid fog formation. The trapped extract is dissolved in $25\mu l$ chloroform which is taken up into a repeating Hamilton Syringe; $0.5\mu l$ aliquots are dispensed onto 0.5 mg potassium bromide allowing the chloroform to evaporate between each dispensation. When all $25\mu l$ have been transferred the micro disc is made with the KBr in the usual way. This method is most useful for nonvolatile acidic, neutral and alkaloid fractions. (Curry, A.S.; Read, J.F.; Brown, C., and Jenkins, R.W.: Infra-red of gas chromatographic fractions. *J Chromat, 38:*200, 1968.)

The paper or TLC chromatogram, on spraying with Dragendorff's solution or iodoplatinate, will show a positive reacting spot at Rf 0.05; it does not absorb or fluoresce in ultra-violet light. This alkaloid serves as an internal marker and should be obtained from all livers. Table XIII gives the Rf values and ultra-violet maxima for a number of common alkaloids and Table XII gives Rf values for alkaloids reacting with Marquis reagent.

This particular examination is only one of the three designed to detect alkaloids in the liver in a comprehensive analysis. The other two, using hydrochloric acid digestion and continuous extraction with alcohol are described below. Each has its separate function: none must be missed in a complete analysis.

(e) Morphine Fraction

Morphine may be found in the alkaloid fraction because it can be salted out into ether. It is for this reason that the extract is redissolved in ethanol prior to chromatography. An extraction with chloroform + isopropanol (4 + 1) serves to complete the extraction. Morphine is detected by the use of paper chromatography or TLC on the evaporated extract. The solvent system of butanol/citric acid on citrated paper, as described above, will separate morphine not only from codeine and other opium alkaloids but also from nalorphine which may have been given to counteract the poisoning. When 2% formaldehyde in concentrated sulphuric acid (Marquis reagent) is poured onto the dried paper chromatogram side by side with control spots of morphine the beautiful violet spots that appear coupled with the Rf value provide criteria of identity that, as far as I am aware, are not paralleled by any other compound. However, further criteria can be obtained by the use of crystal tests on the eluate when even 0.025μg will give characteristic shaped crystals with potassium cadmium iodide solution. This reagent is made by mixing 1 g of cadmium iodide with 2 g of potassium iodide in 100 ml of water. The volume of alkaloid and reagent solutions can be made as low as 0.1μl by using the capillary rod technique for transfer (Clarke, E. G. C., and Williams, M.: *J Pharm Pharmacol, 7:255,* 1955).

Interpretation of Results. The recovery of alkaloids by the tungstic acid method is not uniformly good, in fact, in some cases it is nil. Notwithstanding this drawback a sufficient number of common alkaloids and basic drugs do show a good enough recovery — strychnine, nicotine, diphenhydramine, codeine, quinine, orphenadrine, and morphine, for example — to make the little extra time that it takes after the extraction of acidic poisons worthwhile. General considerations apply as indicated in Chapter 1C.

ii. Hydrochloric Acid Digestion

Phenothiazines

These drugs are very popular in the field of psychiatric medicine and severe side effects following therapeutic doses as well as poisoning following large overdoses have been noted for most if not all of the members of this group. Their popularity results in a need for consideration at this early stage of the analysis.

Normal extraction procedures do not recover the phenothiazines from blood or tissues samples but Dubost and Pascal (1953, 1955) found that a strong hydrochloric acid treatment would release bound chlorpromazine and the other phenothiazines will respond to the same treatment. This preliminary hydrolysis also often gives greatly increased yields of other alkaloids, for example, quinine and imipramine, over more conventional extraction procedures such as those using ethanol, and detection following isolation should include tests, not only for the phenothiazines, but also for other alkaloids.

Method. All Phenothiazines: 10 g of liver are macerated with 10 ml of water and 13.5 ml of concentrated hydrochloric acid are added. If the test is being done by the clinical chemist, 10 g of blood are mixed with 2 ml of water and 8 ml of hydrochloric acid. The acid digest is then heated in a beaker in a boiling water bath for five minutes after which time it is removed and placed in an ice bath; 12 ml of 60% potassium hydroxide (previously washed with ether) are added with stirring and the pH is checked to ensure alkalinity. If acid, more alkali is added. When cool the solution is shaken with 150 ml of purified ether. Any emulsion is broken by centrifuging and the ether is removed. A further portion of 50 ml of ether is used for extraction and the ether extracts are combined. These are shaken with 10 ml of 2.5% sodium hydroxide followed by 10 ml of water, and 5 ml of water. Finally the ether is extracted with 5 ml of 0.1N sulphuric acid which is separated and, after blowing off the ether is examined by ultraviolet spectrophotometry from 220 to 320 mμ.

Provided the hydrochloric acid is distilled before use and adequate precautions are taken about the purity of the other reagents the background absorption from normal blood and brain can be made very low. The detection and estimation of toxic doses of the phenothiazines in such samples by ultraviolet spectrophotometry therefore is possible, and in any case the detection of other alkaloids and basic drugs with high absorption is also ensured. The phenothiazines show an absorption maximum at approximately 255 mμ with $E_{1cm}^{1\%}$ values about 1,000. Any chlorpromazine sulphoxide present is converted to chlorpromazine by the strong acid treatment. The sulphoxide with absorption peaks at 240, 275, 300 and 340 mμ will be found in the urine.

Nikethamide with a maximum about 260 mμ may often be encountered. The background absorption in liver extracts, however, tends to rise about the wavelength maximum shown by the phenothiazines and even if a good curve suggestive of a phenothiazine is obtained further confirmatory tests must be applied. The quickest of these is to re-extract the alkaloid fraction into ether after making the sulphuric acid solution alkaline with ammonia, dry with a little sodium sulphate and evaporate to about

0.1 ml. About 1μl is then allowed to dry on a filter paper and a drop of FPN reagent is allowed to flow into it. Positive results in the form of red, purple, blue or green colours indicate the presence of a phenothiazine. These compounds can be rapidly separated from impurities by paper electrophoresis on Whatman 3 mm paper at 200 volts in 6% acetic acid in about two hours. A strongly reacting aliquot is applied to the paper which is exposed to 254 mμ light for three minutes after partially drying off the acetic acid on completion of the chromatogram. It is finally sprayed with FPN reagent. Colour comparisons with standards give estimates of quantity. Further results are obtained by paper chromatography and Table XV shows the results with a number of common phenothiazines.

It is also worthwhile testing an aliquot of the extract with Dragendorff's reagent because of the increased yield of many alkaloids in this extraction process. If positive, paper chromatography is used as described in Chapter 4.

If blue colours are noted on exposure to ultra-violet light or with the spray, thioridazine or imipramine are indicated (see Part II for quantitative assay).

The TLC separation of forty phenothiazines and their sulphoxide derivatives has been studied by Lucas and his co-workers. Silica-Gel GF 254 (Merck) is used with a solvent of 1.5 g ammonium acetate, water 10 ml, methanol to 50 ml. The phenothiazine is converted to the sulphoxide by treatment on the plate with 10-20% hydrogen peroxide with hot air to dry the spot. Elution with water is followed by ultra-violet spectrophotometry. Their results are shown in Table XXI.

These authors have used 60 cm x 7 mm 3% SE30 on Gas Chrom. Q 80/100 mesh at 210-250°C for the separation of phenothiazines.

Interpretation of Results. If a phenothiazine can be detected in a 10 ml sample of blood using ultra-violet methods then considerably more than a normal therapeutic dose has been ingested. As indicated above, concentrations in liver may be much higher than those in blood. In a case in which 2 g of thioridazine had been taken the blood level was only 0.18 mg/100 ml although

8 mg/100 g were found in the liver (author). In general, levels in excess of 0.1 mg/100 ml in the blood indicate large doses. A single dose of 1 g of chlorpromazine can be expected to lead to blood levels of about 0.1-0.2 mg/100 ml. Imipramine (Tofranil®) and

TABLE XXI*
TLC OF PHENOTHIAZINE SULPHOXIDES

Generic Name	Rf Value Original Drug	Sulfoxide	λMaxima of the Sulfoxides Obtained in the Manner Described
Acetophenazine	0.69	0.16	251–274S–310
Acetopromazine or acetylpromazine	0.58	0.39	251–272S–310–343
Aminopromazine or proquamazine	0.60	0.28	232–266–295–333
Carphenazine	0.71	0.16	246–277S–310
Chlorpromazine	0.62	0.48	238–273–298–340
Chlorproethazine	0.69	0.49	238–250S–273–298–340
Chlorprothixene	0.66	0.45	255–302
Cyamepromazine	0.61	0.39	243–274S–304–340
Diethazine	0.69	0.44	233–268–293–338
Dimethoxanate	0.56	0.41	240–274–295
Ethopropazine or prophenamine	0.70	0.47	233–267–292–336
Fluphenazine	0.75	0.59	232–273–304–343
Isopromethazine	0.63	0.39	233–267–291–336
Isothipendyl	0.64	0.41	238–273–336
Levopromazine	0.87	0.59	250–276S–296–333
Mepazine	0.58	0.39	231–272–299–342
Methdilazine	0.64	0.43	232–272–298–342
Methopromazine or methoxypromazine	0.67	0.35	244–274S–294–330
Methylpromazine	0.62	0.40	238–272–299–340
Perphenazine or chlorpiprozine	0.65	0.45	240–250S–274–342
Phenothiazine or fenethazine	0.69	0.37	232–266–294–334
Pipamazine	0.83	0.53	239–274–300–342
Prochlorperazine	0.55	0.15	238–274–300–340
Promazine	0.51	0.37	231–271–299–342
Promethazine	0.66	0.38	232–270–297–340
Propiomazine	0.77	0.54	246–265S–304–360
Prothipendyl	0.69	0.48	238–276–340
Pyrathiazine or pyrrolazate	0.64	0.43	232–269–295–336
Thiazinamium	0.53	0.33	232–269–294–336
Thiethylperazine	0.47	0.28	238–272–301–350
Thiopropazate	0.77	0.25	238–274–300–340
Thioproperazine	0.43	0.26	245–262S–275–304–342
Thioridazine	0.71	0.46	237–273–302–340
Transergan	0.53	0.33	225–266–291–330
Trifluoperazine	0.63	0.41	233–273–302–343
Triflupromazine	0.69	0.50	233–274–301–343
Trimeprazine or alimemazine	0.71	0.50	232–297–340
No. 6710 Rhône-Poulenc	0.63	0.46	251–273–298–332
No.9260 Rhône-Poulenc	0.85	0.59	240–274–305
No. 7261 Smith Kline & French	0.78	0.27	233–272–302–340

*KOFOED, J.; FABIERKIEWICZ, and LUCAS, G. H. W.: A study of the conversion of phenothiazine derivatives to the corresponding sulfoxides on thin-layer plates. *J Chromat, 23*:410, 1966.

desipramine (Pertofran®) when taken in gram quantities also give concentrations in the blood of about 0.1 mg/100 ml although the liver may contain several milligrams/100 g.

Many psychotic patients take very considerable doses of these drugs — sometimes of the order of grams per day: withdrawal symptoms when these are suddenly stopped may be alarming: tests on the urine will indicate the probable dosage.

REFERENCES

ALGERI, E.J.; KATSAS G.C., and McBAY, A.J.: The toxicology of some new drugs; glutethimide, meprobamate and chlorpromazine. *J Forensic Sci,* 4:111, 1959.

ANDERS, M.W., and MANNERING, G.J.: Gas chromatography of some pharmacologically active phenothiazines. *J Chromat, 7:258,* 1962.

BRAMLETT, C.L.: Determination of phenothiazine and several of its derivatives by GLC. *JAOAC, 49:857,* 1966.

DUBOST, P., and PASCAL, S.: *Ann Pharm Franc, 11:*615, 1953. *idem. ibid: 13:* 56, 1955.

FORREST, I.S., and FORREST, F.M.: A colour test for all phenothiazines (F.P.N. reagent) *Clin Chem, 6:*11, 1960.

KOFOED, J.; FABIERKIEWICZ, C., and LUCAS, G.H.W.: A study of the conversion of phenothiazine derivatives to the corresponding sulphoxides on thin layer plates. *J Chromat, 23:*410, 1966. *idem, Nature, 211:*147, 1966.

TURNER, L.K.: Sulphoxides of the phenothiazine drugs. *J For Sci Soc, 4:*39, 1963.

iii. Tests for Arsenic

Arsenious oxide is one of the classic poisons in the long history of toxicology. In many parts of the world it is still a common poison although it is slowly being displaced by chemotherapeutic agents or by insecticides. Because it holds a foremost place in the minds of most clinicians and some murderers, its inclusion in a systematic search for poison is obvious. Blood levels are low even in cases of acute poisoning and it is more convenient to take a 2 g sample of liver at this stage in the analysis. In the living patient, however, analysis of vomit, blood and urine are often all undertaken; 10 ml of urine is a convenient volume.

The Marsh test is not described here because I have been advised by toxicologists fully conversant with its use that it requires great skill, technical experience and continual use in order to get reliable reproducible results. In my opinion, although this great test may still have a place in analyses for arsenic where poisoning is a common occurrence, other simpler and equally reliable tests are to be preferred in the average European laboratory.

Full experimental details are given in Part II.

iv. Test for Yellow Phosphorus and Phosphides

If a fatty, yellow, liver is found at autopsy four poisons must be considered immediately; these are arsenic, carbon tetrachloride, *Amanita phalloides,* and yellow phosphorus. I have also seen a liver of this type in a young child following ingestion of ferrous sulphate. The circumstances of the death will undoubtedly be closely investigated in such cases and enquiries will have been started at the instigation of the pathologist.

In children, there is a condition characterised clinically by repeated vomiting and increasing drowsiness preceding the onset of coma by intervals of a few hours to three days. Wild delirium may also be seen. The usual provisional diagnosis is encephalitis but, at autopsy, the characteristic finding is a uniformly bright yellow or orange-yellow liver with fat distribution in small vacuoles within the parenchymal-cell cytoplasm. Despite reports of this condition from Australia (Reye and Morgan), Czechoslovakia (Stejskal and Kluska), Jamaica (Hill *et al.*), New Zealand (Becroft) and England (Curry *et al.*), whether it is a disease or a toxin-induced illness has not been established. The presence of an "alkaloid" in urine fluorescing blue under 254 mμ light having an Rf = 0.45 in the butanol/citrate system (see Chap. 4) with λ max in 0.1N sulphuric acid = 255 and 330 mμ and λ min = 280 mμ, has been the only potentially significant finding. The "alkaloid" has not been identified but, on the basis of microbiological activity, it has been tentatively classed as a pteridine (Curry, Guttman and Price).

Notwithstanding this special enquiry, the following test should be done routinely in areas where yellow phosphorus is available to the general public. Its most common form in the United Kingdom used to be as a sugar paste containing bran sold as a rodenticide.

Method (Schwartz, H., Posnick, D., and Schenkel, S.: *Exper Med Surg, 13:*124, 1955, modified by Curry, A. S.; Rutter, E. R., and Lim, C. H.: *J Pharm Pharmacol, 10:*635, 1958). From the centre of the liver 50 g are cut into small pieces and covered with water in Tube B of the apparatus shown in Figure 11. Tube A is used as a water bubbler to show the flow rate of nitrogen which is passed slowly through the apparatus. The Gutzeit holder shown in Figure 3 is placed at the exit with a filter paper which has been soaked in a saturated methanolic silver nitrate solution and dried. The head is filled with glass wool that has been soaked in lead acetate solution and dried. Nitrogen is passed through the apparatus for thirty minutes. A black stain on the filter paper indicates the presence of phosphine in the liver. Any stain is oxidised to phosphate by exposing it to chlorine vapour (made in a small generator by dropping concentrated hydrochloric acid onto solid potassium permanganate) for five minutes. The stain should be completely decolourised. A cold air stream, which is conveniently obtained from a hair dryer, is then blown over the paper for five minutes to remove excess chlorine.

The phosphate is converted to phosphomolybdaté by dropping on one drop of ammonium molybdate solution (5 g ammonium molybdate dissolved in 100 ml of water and mixed with 35 ml of concentrated nitric acid) and after standing at room temperature for three minutes is evaporated to dryness on a Petri dish or white tile over a boiling water bath. It is then removed and allowed to cool. When absolutely cold one drop of benzidine solution (0.05 g benzidine in 10 ml glacial acetic acid is diluted to 100 ml with water) is dropped on the centre of the paper which is then very carefully exposed to the fumes of ammonia. A positive result is shown as a blue colour which is not stable and which, in the lowest range of detection—about $0.1\mu g$ phosphorus—is very transient.

The same procedure is repeated after adding 10 ml dilute sulphuric acid to the liver and again after surrounding the tube B with a heating jacket and raising its temperature to 100°C. The second passage of nitrogen liberates phosphine which may be present from any unchanged phosphide — the rodenticide zinc phosphide is the only one that need be considered or from a yellow phosphorus metabolite which is as yet still uncharacterised. The third passage of nitrogen distils out any unchanged yellow phosphorus.

The oxidation and production of reduced phosphomolybdate blue is exactly the same in each case; the paper may have to be changed several times if large quantities of poison are present. Fatty livers and intestine walls not containing poison produce a yellow stain on the silver nitrate paper which is of no significance. A silvery sheen to a faint stain should also be regarded with suspicion; in all cases it is essential to confirm by the phosphomolybdate test.

Interpretation of Results. The test is very sensitive and has detected phosphorus in a liver exhumed after thirteen months burial. In other cases positive results have been obtained even though eight days elapsed between ingestion and death. Artefacts have not been reported.

No quantitative estimate of the ingested dose can be given from the result of this test on the liver. If no phosphorus can be detected in the intestinal tract a positive test on the liver is the only available chemical evidence for poisoning and, even then, only the metabolite may be present. In my opinion, this is sufficient: it must be admitted, however, that in putrefied tissue there is the possibility of phosphine production from bacterial reduction of phosphate. This might cause difficulty in interpretation if it was suspected that zinc phosphide had been ingested because phosphine is the major metabolite of this rodenticide.

REFERENCES

BECROFT, D.M.O.: *Brit Med J, 2:*135, 1966.
CURRY, A.S.; GUTTMAN, H.A.N., and PRICE, D.E.: *Lancet, i:*885, 1962.
HILL, K.R.; BRAS, G., and CLEARKIN, K.P.: *W Indian Med J, 4:*91, 1955.
REYE, R.D.K., and MORGAN, G.: *Lancet, 2:*1061, 1963.
STEJSKAL, J., and KLUSKA, V.: *Lancet, 1:*615, 1964.

B. THE SECOND STAGE

i. Metals

(a) Thallium

In the forms of the soluble acetate and sulphate, thallium is a highly toxic rodenticide and is favoured by criminal poisoners.

Therapeutic accidents occur because the effective dose is too close to a toxic one. Dermatologists should be warned that 8.5 mg/kg is likely to cause death in children. The outstanding point of interest for the toxicologist is that symptoms are delayed for several days after ingestion and death for much longer.

The outstanding symptoms are burning sensations over the lower extremities, so that even the bedclothes become an intolerable burden, and the loss of hair about fourteen days after ingestion. A microscopical examination of the hair root is most useful because the medulla becomes grossly enlarged, virtually filling the bulb. It is said that repeated doses lead to similar enlargements along the length of the hair, but this requires further substantiation. There is, similarly, no published evidence to show whether thallium is incorporated, like arsenic, into the growing hair. The loss of hair, presumably because of the toxic action of the metal, is apparent from small doses and so chronic criminal administration from low doses over a long period is probably less likely than with arsenic.

There is a danger that thallium could be missed if analysis is confined to the alimentary tract and it is recommended that a portion of tissue be analysed routinely. Kidney is probably the best theoretical choice but the limited amount, which may be required for other purposes, leaves liver or muscle with the second highest expected concentration.

Full experimental details are given in Part II.

(b) Other Metals

The purpose of the analysis described below is to detect any imbalance in the metals normally present in liver tissue. Copper, zinc, iron, lead and aluminum are present in relatively large amounts in all tissue and it is likely that, with the exception of lead, the ingestion of large doses of their soluble salts in quantities sufficient to cause poisoning will not raise the concentrations in tissue above normal limits. However, there is nothing to be lost by an investigation into tissue metals and there is always the chance that a case of poisoning will be detected. The analysis also provides a means of searching for unusual metals.

Method. Liver, 100 g, is heated on a boiling water bath with 100 ml of concentrated nitric acid in a Kjeldahl flask. After the reaction has subsided, 10 ml of concentrated sulphuric acid are added and the mixture is gently boiled over a Bunsen flame. When the first signs of charring are seen, 5 ml of nitric acid are added and the heating repeated. This procedure is continued until all the organic matter is destroyed. If necessary, more sulphuric acid may be aded during the digestion. The digest is then diluted with 20 ml of water, cooled and neutralised to pH 5 with ammonia. Any precipitate is removed by centrifuging. Hydrogen sulphide is passed and, after allowing several hours for precipitation, any solid is removed. More hydrogen sulphide is passed after making the solution alkaline when a copious black precipitate is seen. This is also removed and washed. Ammonium phosphate is then added to the supernatant and, after warming, any Group V precipitate is centrifuged off.

Examination of the precipitates is preferably done by arc spectroscopy but paper chromatography is an acceptable and simpler method. Full details have been given on page 106. The paper chromatographic method enables any gross abnormality to be detected immediately by visual inspection.

It is rare for the toxicologist to perform routinely quantitative assays for the common metals but if any suspicion of abnormality is detected then, obviously, such analyses must be done. Lead will be discussed in Part II and it is probable that even in the absence of a clinical history that full analyses will be done if lead is detected in the screening test for metals done on this aliquot of liver.

Zinc salts occasionally give rise to poisoning and a method is described in Part II.

ii. Continuous Extraction With Alcohol

In order to ensure the detection of many highly toxic organic solvent soluble poisons that may have been injected, or whose concentration in the alimentary tract is likely to be very low, it is essential to analyse a major quantity of tissue using an extraction process of tried efficacy. Unfortunately, with the vast increase in the number of poisons available to the medical profession and to the general public in the last few years, no toxicologist has had the opportunity to test the efficiency of any one particular method in extracting from viscera all the known poisons in this group. On a theoretical basis ethanol is chosen and its use described here. Methods using other solvents, for example, 95% ethanol 1 volume, hexane 2 volumes, and acetone 2 volumes, such as that recommended by Parker, are possibly even more attractive, but all methods are to some extent a compromise; purification of poison involves the rejection of unwanted compounds and, because no process is ever perfectly efficient, experience in a theoretically sound method is the guiding principle.

At least 250 g of liver should be used; in the case of young children this quantity may not be available and the relatively large quantity of brain in such cases may make that the organ to be used.

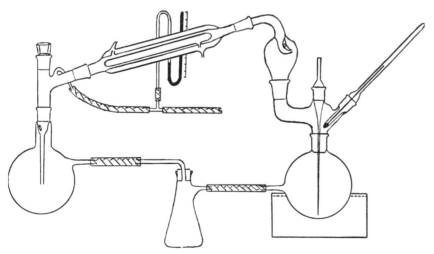

FIGURE 8. An apparatus for the continuous extraction under reduced pressure of tissue with ethanol.

Method (Curry, A.S., and Phang, S.E.: *J Pharm Pharmacol, 12:*437, 1960). Liver, 250 g, is macerated with 500 ml of 95% ethanol and 5 g of tartaric acid and placed in the left hand flask, which is of 1 litre capacity, in the apparatus shown in Figure 8. This is known as the extraction flask. Additional ethanol is added to bring the level just to the overflow into the conical flask which is filled with absolute ethanol. The 500 ml evaporation flask on the right of the figure is filled to approximately three-fourths full, also with absolute ethanol. This evaporation flask sits on a water bath held at 90°C and its upper surface is covered by cotton wool to reduce heat losses. When pressure is reduced in the apparatus by means of a water pump to 14 cm of mercury, the ethanol in the evaporation flask boils, aided by a fine air leak, is condensed by the triple surface condenser and is returned to the extraction flask under the settled tissue. A clear circulating flow, of liquid ethanol from left to right is thus established through the apparatus. The conical flask acts as an intermediate settling tank and the plastic or rubber connectors between the flasks allow for easy assembly. The small hole in the return from the condenser to the extraction flask equalises pressure and avoids disturbance of the tissue on slight unavoidable pressure changes.

There are many advantages to the use of this simple apparatus*; the extraction is at room temperature and, because of the reduced pressure, it is at no time higher than 30°C to 35°C. These conditions are so mild that glycosides and such labile alkaloids as atropine and cocaine are not destroyed. The volume of ethanol is kept to a minimum by the use of continuous extraction and, even if pressure is accidentally allowed to rise, all the extracts and tissue are safe and cannot be lost down the pump. The other outstanding advantage is the fact that this type of extraction which used to take days can now be completed in a matter of hours.

The only precautions that are necessary are to ensure that the pressure does not fall too low so that there is a gross loss of ethanol down the pump; the water flow through the condenser must be as cold and as fast as possible to ensure efficient cooling of the ethanol vapour, and sufficient heat must be applied to the evaporation flask to ensure a rapid boiling of the solvent.

When the extraction is finished, which can be seen by observing the clearance of colour above the tissues, the fluid in the evaporation flask is evaporated to dryness under reduced pressure. It is then re-extracted with hot absolute ethanol which is filtered

---

*Obtainable from Wood's Glass Works Ltd., Barnsley, Yorkshire, England.

and evaporated to dryness. The fatty solid is then shaken with 150 ml of cold 0.001N sulphuric acid, for at least thirty minutes in an effort to bring into solution, without loss, heat labile alkaloids and glycosides. After filtration the solid is again extracted with 150 ml of 0.001N sulphuric acid but this time by boiling. After filtering, the filtrates are combined when cold and extracted with ether, first from acid and then from ammoniacal solution. Morphine, caffeine antipyrine, and the glycosides can then be extracted from the neutralised combined aqueous solutions by chloroform + isopropanol (4 + 1). In general, the volume of the organic phase should at least equal that of the aqueous. Subsequent examination follows that detailed in Chapter 4.

If solanine poisoning is suspected, warm pentanol will extract it from alkaline solution. Detection is by dipping a citrated chromatogram run as for other alkaloids in 1% paraformaldehyde in concentrated phosphoric acid. A blue colour at Rf 0.23 indicates this poison.

The most common glycoside in medicinal use is probably digoxin; it is commonly eaten accidentally by young children. The obvious place to seek it is in the alimentary tract but liver should not be neglected. It can be extracted in the apparatus described above and recovered from the chloroform phase. Some measure of purification can be achieved by shaking a 70% ethanol in water solution of the glycosides with carbon tetrachloride; fat is removed and the poisons can be recovered after evaporation of the ethanol phase by distillation under reduced pressure. Paper chromatographic separation followed by colour tests on the paper or screening of eluates on the isolated frog heart are then indicated. In chloroform:methanol:water (10:2:5), organic layer, it has an Rf of 0.71. Detection is by a spray of 5% m-dinitrobenzene in benzene (beware fumes) followed by heating at 80°C for fifteen minutes and finally dipping in 20% sodium hydroxide when the blue colours are obtained.

For a separation using TLC plates the reader is referred to Part II, Digoxin.

A TLC separation of cardiac glycosides has also been reported by Johnston and Jacobs. Activated (120°C) plates of Silica-Gel G

are used with a solvent of benzene:ethanol (7:3 v/v). Detection
is achieved either by a spray of perchloric acid which produces
spots fluorescing under 365 mμ light, or by a spray of p-anisalde-
hyde which produces blue spots (oubain, yellow) after heating
at 100°C for a few minutes. Rf values are oubain, 0.09; deslano-
cide, 0.27; lanatoside C, 0.36; digoxin, 0.62; digitoxin, 0.72; and
acetyldigoxin, 0.82. Jelliffe and his co-workers have reported the
detection of urinary digitoxin and digoxin in man on twenty-four-
hour urine samples using a chloroform extraction and TLC (see
Part II).

Interpretation of Results. The main purpose of this extraction
process is to extract sufficient of the poison to enable identification
to be achieved. When this has been done it is probable that another quantitative analysis on a smaller quantity of tissue will be
done using a method of extraction and assay most suited to that
particular poison.

As was indicated in Chapter 4B, the main approach to the analyses consists of paper chromatographic examinations coupled
with colour tests, ultra-violet spectrophotometry and infra-red
spectroscopy. The importance of routine sublimation of an aliquot of the neutral ether and of the chloroform extraction fractions must be stressed because these usually consist of several
milligrams of fatty material from which crystalline poison can
often be obtained by this simple technique. The absence of crystals, however, should not indicate the absence of poison — in such
cases the challenge to the toxicologist is even greater.

Full consideration of the interpretation of results cannot be
given because each poison requires specific mention and the number to be discussed would amount to many thousand. It is important to remember that an assumption that a poison is evenly distributed in the body tissues must not be made without experimental verification. In some cases a much higher concentration of
poison can be found in the liver than in any other organ, for example in poisonings by orphenadrine, nupercaine and imipramine
but in others notably salicylate in aspirin poisoning the concentration is usually lower than in the blood. The ratios may also vary
greatly with the time between ingestion and death.

Some poisons do not appear in the liver unchanged but must be sought as metabolites; for example, 2,4-dichlorophenoxyacetic acid from its ethyl ester, and diethylacetyl urea in carbromal intoxication.

The difference in half-lives must also be considered — some are very short measured in minutes while those of drugs like quinine are so long that the drug can be detected for days after the ingestion of therapeutic quantities.

Generally, phenothiazines, orphenadrine, propoxyphene, amitriptyline, opipranol, pethidine, morphine, imipramine and desipramine have toxic blood levels well below 0.5 mg/100 ml but, for the majority of these drugs, the liver should contain concentrations of milligrams/100 g. Choroquine, hydroxychloroquine, methaqualone, nicotine and tolazoline, will probably appear in the blood with levels over 0.5 mg/100 ml but, even in these cases, liver tissue will give higher levels. There is, in my view, in fatal cases, the strongest support for analysing liver tissue both by a tungstic acid and a strong hydrochloric acid digestion if a general search for alkaloid type bases is required.

It should be noted that morphine is a most elusive poison to find and before a negative report is presented, liver, kidney, bile and urine should have been analysed. Methaqualone, whose highly toxic blood range is over 3 mg/100 ml is a very weak base and to extract from organic solvent at least 2N acid strength is required. It has a high ultra-violet absorption suitable for quantitative assay (see Table XIII and Part II).

REFERENCES

BROWN, B.T., SHEPHEARD, E.E., and WRIGHT, S.E.: The distribution of digitalis glycosides and their metabolites within the body of the rat. *J Pharmacol, 118:*39, 1956.

CLARKE, E.G.C.: The identification of solanine. *Nature, 181:*1152, 1958.

JELLIFFE, R.W.: *J Lab Clin Med, 67:*694, 1966.

JOHNSTON, E.J., and JACOBS, A.L.: *J Pharm Sci, 55:*531, 1966.

PARKER, B.P.: Group isolation of toxicological substances from heterogenous material. Thesis for degree of Master of Criminology, University of California, 1960.

Chapter 8

BRAIN AND KIDNEY

A. VOLATILE POISONS

INHALATION OF MANY volatile poisons can cause death and the tests on the gastrointestinal tract which were described above will not reveal their presence. It is essential, therefore, that they be sought in a blood containing organ.

In theory, tests on the lungs would be desirable and, indeed, many toxicologists do perform these. However, it is unusual for the lungs always to be submitted for analysis and, because it is said that the brain retains chloroform exceptionally well in putrefied bodies, it seems logical to analyse this organ on a routine basis. At the same time other volatile compounds can be sought, such as the anaesthetics fluothane and ether, the cleaning agents carbon tetrachloride, trichloroethylene and perchloroethylene as well as other toxic solvents such as benzene. All of these are highly volatile and special care must be taken to ensure an efficient cold trap. All the joints of the apparatus must be Teflon® sleeved because gross loss of poison will occur by its solution into any grease. The best method of identification and assay is undoubtedly gas chromatography.

Method. Brain, 100 g, is macerated and diluted to approximately 500 ml with water; 25 ml of dilute sulphuric acid are added and distillation is commenced. The precautions outlined above must be observed: 3 ml of distillate are collected. This is divided into 3 x 1 ml aliquots. One aliquot is mixed with 1 ml of pyridine and 2 ml of 20% sodium hydroxide in a test-tube. The time is taken T_0. The test-tube is then immersed in a boiling water bath for exactly one minute when it is removed and cooled in ice-water; 4 ml of water are added and exactly thirty minutes from T_0 the optical density is read at 520 mμ against a reagent blank. For 1 cm cells the calibration graph is made from 0-250μg of chloral hydrate per millilitre of solution. This gives optical density readings in the range 0-1.0.

For interpretation of results see Chapter 3,A (x).

The other two aliquots are examined by gas chromatography (see Chap. 3,A (ii). If gas chromatography is not available, apart from ultra-violet spectrophotometry, there is no alternative but to distil at least 500 g of brain tissue and attempt to isolate the few milligrams of volatile poison in a pure state. Fractional redistillation and the use of Dry Ice traps are essential and rewarding techniques. Identification can be by measurement of micro boiling points although infra-red examination is a more sensitive and more specific choice.

B. CHOLINESTERASE

In some cases the quantity of blood that the pathologist can obtain from a body is severely limited and there is insufficient for the toxicologist to perform all the tests that normally would be done. Tissue must then be used and, for the assay of cholinesterase activity, brain is recommended. Poisoning by organo-phosphorus compounds manifests itself in a gross reduction of this normal body enzyme and even when the blood level is depressed in cases of poisoning a reduction in brain activity should also be sought.

C. METALLIC POISONS

In a routine search the kidney should be analysed for mercury, manganese and cadmium. The details for these metals are given in Part II.

D. TOXIC ANIONS

Because death may not follow for several days after the ingestion of such toxic anions as chlorate or oxalate their concentration in the alimentary tract may be too low for certain detection and a search in the kidney may be considered desirable. This is often the case if methaemoglobinaemia has been noticed, and chlorate poisoning is suspected. The tissue should be well macerated before dialysis and the tests described in Chapter 6B (i) carried out. Negative results are usually obtained even in strongly suspicious circumstances but the efficiency of the extraction and tests can be easily demonstrated; even though much hope of successful detection cannot be held, the possibility cannot be ignored.

PART II

ALPHABETICAL LIST OF POISONS

ABORTION ENQUIRIES

If oral ingestion of an abortifacient is suspected the death usually occurs many days afterwards and unless quinine is involved, very little can usually be done analytically. Often herbal brews figure whose chemistry and pharmacology can only be a matter of conjecture. Even herbal pills and tablets are a great problem and without a control collection of local manufacturers' products, the analysis becomes more a matter for the pharmacognisist.

Pennyroyal can be readily detected by smell and GLC. Extraction from aqueous acidic solution with ether followed by a TLC separation of the concentrated extract enables aloes, rhubarb and cascara to be differentiated. Benzene:chloroform (30:70) is used as the developing solvent on Silica-Gel G plates and the spots are inspected in visible, 254 and 365 mμ light before and after exposure to ammonia vapour. Spot tests for ferrous and ferric ions should be also routine. The problems of the analyst can be exemplified by one of my cases in which the dose was a teaspoonful of a mixture of an ounce of pennyroyal plant, an ounce of Canadian ginger, an ounce of thyme, simmered for two hours and decanted into a bottle of stout. The mixture was not successful!

Where death follows suddenly after the introduction of disinfectant or soap solution by enema syringe into the vagina, then analysis can often help. Vaginal swabs should be examined first by GLC using the head space method (Chap. 3Aii). Isopropanol is a common constituent of disinfectants. The smell of the swab or drainings can often give a valuable lead. Its pH should be measured. Local irritation may be associated with alum, borax, or permanganate. To detect soap, a portion of the swab and separate 2 ml blood samples from the heart, peripheral veins and uterine contents are heated with 10 ml ethanol at 80°C for five minutes. The filtrates are evaporated, redissolved in hot ethanol, refiltered and evaporated. The resulting solids are dissolved in water, 5 ml, acidified with O.1N H_2SO_4 and extracted with ether, 20 ml. The separated ether fractions are evaporated to dryness, redissolved in 10μl of ethanol and examined by paper chromatography or GLC. For paper, a Whatman No. 1 paper is dipped in 10% liquid paraffin in benzene, drained and dried. After applying control spots of soap fatty acids in ethanol and the extracts, the paper is run in glacial acetic acid. The spots can be detected as follows: (a) Dip in 1% lead acetate solution; wash thoroughly in running distilled water and then immerse in water saturated with H_2S; or (b) Dip in 5% mercuric oxide in 20% sulphuric acid, wash thoroughly in running distilled water, drain, dip in 0.1% diphenylcarbazone in ethanol.

The fatty acids show up as a series of spots between Rf 0.5 and Rf 0.8.

REFERENCE

CURRY, A.S.: The isolation and detection of ergometrine in toxicological analysis. *J Pharm Pharmacol, 11*:411, 1959.

AMANITA PHALLOIDES

A general screening test for detecting toxins in the amanita mushrooms has been described and it may prove useful in confirming a fresh botanical specimen.

Method

(Block, S. S., Stephens, R. L., Barreto, A., and Murrill, W. A.: *Science, 121*:505, 1955.)

The plant tissue is extracted with ethanol and after evaporation is examined by paper chromatography. A solvent consisting of methyl-ethyl ketone:acetone:water:butanol (20:6:5:1) is used and development takes forty minutes. The spray is 1% cinnamaldehyde in methanol after which the paper is exposed to fumes of hydrochloric acid. Violet or blue colours indicate amanita toxin and the test is sensitive to 0.1 g of fresh tissue.

In the examination of intestinal contents for this toxin, which is a peptide, the alcohol extraction procedure is recommended. Obviously, some of it must be used to test for other poisons but the proportion used to test for phalloidin must be decided having regard to the circumstances of the case. Acetone is also a suitable solvent for this poison which can be purified on cellulose powder columns eluting with a methanol, acetone, water, mixture. Paper chromatography is, however, simple and because of the very high toxicity of phalloidin — 50μg will kill a mouse — is a convenient purification procedure for crude extracts.

The following solvents have been suggested:

1. Ethyl formate:acetone:water (100:145:40)
2. Methyl-ethyl ketone:acetone:water (20:2:5)

In each case the spray reagent is 1% cinnamaldehyde in methanol followed by exposure to hydrochloric acid fumes. Phalloidin gives blue colours. Extracts from similar positions on other chromatograms should be eluted and injected into mice after solution in saline. It is also desirable to show that extracts from other positions on the chromatogram are nontoxic and that other colour tests for peptides such as the chlorine — starch iodide reaction

(Table XVIII) are also positive. Phalloidin shows an absorption maximum about 290 mμ in water.

Many workers have suggested that the spores of *Amanita Phalloides* should be sought in the intestinal tract. These are said to be 8-11μ by 7-9μ white subgloboid bodies each with a central oil drop. Expert mycological advice informs me that this approach is unsatisfactory on specimens isolated from the large intestines, although several workers have found such bodies and in any such cases, the isolation of the peptide followed by its examination chemically and biologically is obviously desirable. If negative, an examination for spores is still necessary.

REFERENCE

WIELAND, T., and SCHMIDT, G.: *Annalen, 577*:215, 1952.

AMITRIPTYLINE

Method

(based on Sunshine, I., and Baumler, J.: *Nature, 199:*1103, 1965)

Stir 10 ml blood with 2 ml water and 8 ml concentrated hydrochloric acid and heat in a boiling water bath for five minutes. Remove and place in an ice bath. When cool, add 12 ml 60% w/v potassium hydroxide which has previously been washed with ether. Keep cool and check the pH for alkalinity. If acid, add more alkali. Shake with 150 ml ether breaking any emulsion by centrifuging. Separate and shake the aqueous phase with a further 50 ml portion of ether. Combine the ether fractions and wash in sequence with 10 ml 2.5% sodium hydroxide, 10 ml water and 5 ml water. Extract the ether with 5 ml 0.1N H_2SO_4 which is separated and read from 230-280 mμ. Amitriptyline peaks at 240 mμ with an $E_{1cm}^{1\%}$ value of 470. Nortriptyline has a very similar curve. The acid from the cuvette is made alkaline, extracted with 5 ml chloroform which is evaporated to near dryness and transferred to a Silica-Gel G thin layer plate. This is developed in methanol:acetone:triethanolamine (10:10:0.3) against control spots. Spray with Dragendorff's reagent.

Interpretation of Results

Blood levels in fatal overdose cases are very low; only 40μg/100 ml has been found in a twenty-five-year old male who took between 1.25-2.5 g and died within three hours. Liver levels are much higher and can be expected to be over 1 mg/100 g. Urinary excretion is normally small; Forbes *et al.* found only 50μg/100 ml in urine after consumption of 50 mg and 1 mg in a twenty-four-hour sample after 100 mg intake.

REFERENCES

FORBES, G.; WEIR, W.P.; SMITH, H., and BOGAN, J.: *J For Sci Soc, 5:*183, 1965.
SUNSHINE, P., and YAFFE, S.J.: *Amer J Dis Child, 106:*501, 1963.
STEEL, C.M., O'DUFFY, J., and BROWN, S.S.: Clinical effects and treatment of imipramine and amitriptyline poisoning in children. *Brit Med J, 2:*663, 1967.

AMPHETAMINE AND OTHER STIMULANTS
(Gas Chromatography)

Method

(Beckett, A. H., Tucker, G. T., and Moffett, A. C.: *J Pharm Pharmacol, 19*:273, 1967).

Extraction for Amphetamines and ephedrines. Urine (1-5 ml) is pipetted into a glass-stoppered centrifuge tube together with 0.5 ml 20% sodium hydroxide. The urine is then extracted with 2 x 2.5 ml freshly distilled ether using a mechanical test shaker, centrifuged, and the ether extracts transferred to a 15 ml Quickfit test tube with a finely tapered base. The extract is then concentrated to approximately 50μl on a water bath at 40°C.

Extraction for Phenolic Type Amphetamines. Urine (10 ml) is made alkaline to pH 9 to 10 with solid sodium carbonate and extracted and the extracts concentrated as described above except that 3 x 5 ml portions of ether are used.

One to 5μl portions of the ether extracts are examined. Beckett and his co-workers give four columns for general use. For screening the following is recommended. An acid-washed silanized support medium, i.e., Anakrom ABS or Chromosorb G(AW-DMCS) (80-100 mesh) is coated with 5% potassium hydroxide in ethanol which is evaporated off; it is then coated with 5% Apiezon L in ethylene dichloride and evaporated in a rotary evaporator below 40°C. A 6′ column is used at 160°C. Table XXII shows the retention times for a number of compounds.

Identification (Formation of Derivatives Detected by GLC). (a) 0.5 ml of acetone is added to 50μl of the concentrated ethereal extract; it is then evaporated to 50μl on a water bath at 60°C. The Schiff's base formed with primary amines has a different retention time to the unchanged drug: 90% conversion is usually achieved.

(b) 0.5 ml carbon disulphide is used instead of acetone in test (a). This converts primary and secondary amines to give dithiocarbamates but only primary amines are converted to the isothiocyanate which gives a peak on GLC.

(c) Acetyl derivatives can be formed from primary and secondary amines by adding 5μl acetic anhydride to the concentrated ethereal extract and injecting 5μl of the mixture on the GLC.

TABLE XXII
RETENTION TIMES FOR AMPHETAMINES

Base	Mean Retention Time in Minutes
Cyclopentamine	2.75
Amphetamine	3.5
Methylamphetamine	4.0
Pargyline	4.4
Nicotine	9.1
Phenylpropanolamine (dl-Norephedrine)	10.0
Ephedrine	11.9
Chlorphentermine	12.2
Methylephedrine	13.1
Phenmetrazine	15.0
*Diethylpropion	17.3
Nikethamide	22.7
Benzphetamine	100.0

*Diethylpropion; Major Peak at 17.3 min. Smaller peak at approximately 19 min.
Instrument: Perkin-Elmer F11, with F.I.D.
Column: 5% Apiezon L + 5% KOH on A. S. Anakrom:-
Oven Temp. 160°C; Carrier Gas; N₂ at 60 ml/min. Inj. Port. Temp '4' (approximately 200°C)

This method is very suitable for the detection and identification of amphetamine and methylamphetamine in very small volumes of urine. Naturally, control results must be obtained first, and the toxicologist will soon build up his own table of retention times for the common drugs found in this fraction.

Direct injection of urine (10μl) onto this column will also reveal amphetamine, providing the amplifier settings of the chromatograph can be set high enough. If control experiments show that less than a nanogram of amphetamine can be detected easily, then preliminary extraction is superfluous. This is the most rapid convenient method of screening for amphetamine. Confirmation by acetone derivatives is achieved by warming the urine with an equal volume of acetone and injecting 10μl again onto the column.

ANTABUSE
(Tetraethyldithiuram Disulphide)

This drug inhibits acetaldehyde oxidation and therefore gives rise to toxic and occasionally fatal results when ethanol is ingested even as long as a week after cessation of drug therapy. Because acetaldehyde disappears rapidly from the blood it may be worth attempting to show the presence of antabuse and alcohol and therefore by inference that acetaldehyde intoxication has taken place. However, antabuse itself is rapidly metabolised *in vitro,* the blood level is not proportional to the dose, it is not excreted in the urine and it is not extractable from tissues.

Heparin and sodium fluoride can cause interference and sodium oxalate is the recommended anticoagulant.

Methods

(Divatia, K. J., Hine, C. H., and Burbridge, T. N.: *J Lab Clin Med, 39*:974, 1952)

To 1 ml of whole blood or plasma add 1 ml of 0.002M copper sulphate solution. Add 1 ml of phosphate buffer at pH 7.4 and 10 ml of redistilled ethylene dichloride. Shake for thirty minutes and then centrifuge. Read the dichloride at 270 mμ and at 320 mμ. The optical density difference at these two wavelengths is proportional to the concentration of antabuse. Ethylene dichloride is used in the compensatory cell; standards are prepared in the range 5-200μg/ml of blood.

ARSENIC

Method 1

In a Kjeldahl flask, 2 g of liver (5 ml of blood or 10 ml of urine) are evaporated with 10 ml of concentrated nitric acid and 2 ml of concentrated sulphuric acid. As soon as charring is seen more nitric acid is added. Charring carries with it the possibility of reduction of arsenic to the trivalent ion and its loss by volatility. The heating and addition of nitric acid is continued until all organic material has been destroyed. This takes about a quarter of an hour; 20 ml of water are then added and the volume is reduced by boiling to about 4 ml; 10 ml of a saturated solution of ammonium oxalate are then added and the boiling is continued until white fumes appear. After cooling, the digest is transferred with washing from the Kjeldahl flask into a suitable Gutzeit apparatus.

This is so well known that a complete description will be omitted: 4 ml of concentrated hydrochloric acid, 5 ml of 15% sodium iodide and 0.4 ml of 40% stannous chloride in 50% hydrochloric acid with 10 g 16-22 mesh zinc are added and the liberated arsine and hydrogen passed through a plug of cotton wool soaked in lead acetate, then through a filter paper which has been previously soaked in a saturated solution of mercuric bromide in alcohol and dried. The filter paper is held in an accurately machined metal or glass holder with a centre hole of diameter 5 mm (see Fig. 3). After one hour or less if control experiments so indicate the filter paper, now stained yellow, or brown if large quantities are present, is removed and placed in a cardboard or metal frame for insertion in a spectrophotometer. This frame is fixed so that light from the spectrophotometer is made to pass through the area of filter paper showing the stain on to the photocell where optical density readings at 400 mμ and 500 mμ are taken.

Calibration graphs are prepared for stains from 0-1μg at 400 mμ and 0-10μg at 500 mμ. Any subsequent stain from 0-10μg can therefore be accurately measured. The great advantage in using this method of assay is that standard stains do not have to be prepared every day as they do if visual comparison is used: in addition, a black cardboard or metal holder for the Beckman or Unicam spectrophotometers can easily be made to give an accuracy of ±5 per cent even in the 0-1μg range. Black is used to prevent errors from reflectance of light from the front of the holder; the filter paper is held by tape on the face of the holder away from the light (see Figure 9) .

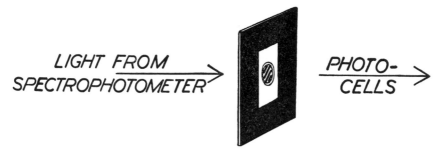

FIGURE 9. Method of measuring stains from a Gutzeit holder.

Method 2

(Fisher Scientific Company. Technical data: TD142. 633, Greenwich Street, New York 14) .

Concentrated hydrochloric acid (2 ml) , 2 ml of 15% potassium iodide solution and eight drops of a stannous chloride solution containing 40 g of stannous chloride in 100 ml concentrated hydrochloric acid are added to the solution containing the arsenic salt in 35 ml of water. Swirl the flasks and allow them to stand for fifteen minutes to ensure complete reduction to the trivalent stage; 3 g of granulated zinc are then added and the liberated arsine is passed through a scrubber of lead acetate on glass wool and then through 3 ml of a 0.5% solution of silver diethyldithiocarbamate in pyridine. The scrubber and the reagent with which arsine forms a red complex are part of special Gutzeit type of apparatus known as an arsine generator (Fisher Company No. FSCo 1-405) . The reaction is usually complete in thirty minutes after which the colour is read at 560 mμ. Standards are prepared in the range 0-15μg. Stibine gives a red colour as well and could therefore interfere but this has maximum absorbance at 510 mμ.

Interpretation of Results

In general, the figures of Hansen and Moller (1949) show accepted levels and their interpretation. These are shown in Table XXIII: all concentrations are in mg/100 g.

TABLE XXIII
ARSENIC CONCENTRATIONS IN TISSUE

	Liver	*Kidney*	*Blood*	*Brain*	*Kidney*
Normal healthy adults	0.001–0.01	0.001–0.01	0–0.002	—	—
Treated with inorganic arsenicals	—	—	0.01–0.025	—	—
Treated with organic arsenicals	ca 0.1	ca 0.02	ca 0.1	—	—
Acute arsenical poisoning	1 – 50	0.5–15	0.1 –1.5	0.05–2.0	0.5–15

The clinical chemist must remember that the blood concentrations are much lower than the liver or kidney figures. My own experience shows that if the patient survives for a period of about four days that the blood figure can be even lower than that suggested by Hansen and Moller: $20\mu g/100$ g was the figure in one fatal case following ingestion of arsenious oxide. In a case of death following the insertion of thirty pessaries of Stovarsol into the vagina over a period of three days the concentration of arsenic (as trioxide) in the liver was 1.6 mg/100 g (Bowen *et al.* 1961).

Smith, using neutron activation analysis on freeze dried tissue, found values of 0.5-$24.6\mu g/100$ g in "normal" liver, 0.2-36.3 in kidney and 0.1-92 in blood. This last figure seems extremely high and Smith (personal communication) reports later work in which his highest dried blood value is $20\mu g/100$ g; as the dry blood weighs about 15 per cent of whole blood, these figures do not agree with those of Hansen and Moller.

Smith has published most useful information on the distribution and measurement, using activation analysis, of arsenic in hair. There seems little doubt that exposure results in the deposition of arsenic in the root and as the hair grows repeated administration causes concentration peaks along the hair length. It is, therefore, possible by sectional analysis to deduce when arsenic was ingested and on how many occasions.

Clinicians very often underestimate the quantity of hair the analyst requires for these analyses. If the Gutzeit procedure is used then about 3,000 hairs (1 g) are necessary. This will enable analysis on about half-inch lengths to be done. If an atomic reactor is available, the quantity need only be about 100 hairs. The hair should be cut as close to the head as possible, tied immediately in locks, and which is the cut end clearly indicated.

It is most important that if the hair has been pulled from the scalp by the pathologist, which is the recommended procedure, that before analysis *each hair* be aligned by the roots. This is a tedious procedure taking several hours work but it is essential. The act of pulling the hairs from the scalp causes slipping of a few roots into the body of the lock; in a case of acute arsenical poisoning the concentration in the roots can be very high — several milligrams per 100 g, and it requires only a few hairs to slip to give a misleading impression that the concentration of arsenic along the length is uneven and above normal levels, i.e., a case of chronic poisoning being superimposed on an acute case. Alignment is therefore essential to overcome this artefact. Smith says categorically that the hair should *not* be washed before analysis.

In the United Kingdom in people not exposed to arsenic, the overall concentration median values of arsenic in hair are 0.62 and 0.67μg/g for males and females respectively. Smith says that values over 2μg/g merit further investigation *but* this advice must include the caveat that in acute poisoning the roots must be separately analysed. He quotes a case with a whole hair value of 0.86μg/g with 90μg/g in the first millimeter from the root.

The rate of hair growth varies over a fairly wide range. The average rate is said to be about 13 mm a month although Stolman and Stewart in a review of the literature give a range of 9.3-10.2 mm per thirty days.

Teichmann and his co-workers reported at the 1st International Meeting in Forensic Toxicology, London, 1963, the range of "normal values" for urinary arsenic excretion. It is clear from the literature quoted in this paper, involving over 500 persons and eight surveys, that the majority of workers found mean values of the order of 1μg/100 ml, although amounts varied considerably presumably due to diet and industrial exposure. Levels can rise up to 200µg/100 ml in arsenic workers. In acute arsenic poisoning values higher than this are normally found, but if several days have elapsed between ingestion and the taking of the sample the interpretation of levels in the range 1-200µg/100 ml may be necessary and will be difficult.

Kingsley and Schaffert showed that "therapeutic" arsenic solutions (Fowler's solution) gave urinary excretions up to 30µg/100 ml which dropped to 2µg/100 ml in ten days.

REFERENCES

BOWEN, D.A.L., LEWIS. T.L.T., and EDWARDS, W.R.: *Brit Med J, 1*:1282, 1961.

HANSEN, F., and MOLLER, K.O.: *Acta Pharmacol Toxicol, 5*:135, 1949.

KINGSLEY, G.R., and SCHAFFERT, R.R.: Microdetermination of arsenic and its application to biological material. *Anal Chem, 23*:914, 1951.

NATELSON, S.: *Microtechniques of Clinical Chemistry,* 2nd ed. Springfield, Thomas, 1961, p. 113.

SMITH, H.: The estimation of arsenic in biological material by activation analysis. *Anal Chem, 31*:1361, 1959.

SMITH, H.: The distribution of antimony, arsenic, copper and zinc in human tissue. *J For Sci Soc, 7*:97, 1967.

SMITH, H.: The interpretation of the arsenic content of human hair. *J For Sci Soc, 4*:192, 1967.

STEWART, C.P., and STOLMAN, A.: *Toxicology, Mechanisms and Analytical Methods.* New York, Academic, 1960, vol. 1, p. 203.

Taylors Principles and Practice of Medical Jurisprudence, 11th ed. London, J. & A. Churchill, 1956-57, vol. II, p. 359.

TEICHMANN, T.; DUBOIS, L., and MONKMAN, J.L.: Proceedings of the 1st International Meeting in Forensic Toxicology, London, 1963.

BARBITURATES, GLUTETHIMIDE AND MEPROBAMATE
(Gas Chromatography)

In cases of acute poisoning 1 ml of blood buffered to approximately pH 7 is extracted with 5 ml chloroform which is separated and evaporated to 50μl. A 1-10μl aliquot of this solution is injected directly onto the GC column. For meprobamate a 2.5% SE 30 column on 80/100 Chromosorb G (AW-DCMS) at 195°C is recommended. Similar columns have been recommended for barbiturates but better results have been obtained in my hands using the work of Leach and Toseland, and Blackmore and Jenkins.

Method 1

(Leach, H., and Toseland, P. A.: *Clin Chem Acta, 20:*195, 1968)

Twenty-five grams of 80-100 mesh Chromosorb W is washed with acid by suspending the material in several volumes of concentrated hydrochloric acid and stirring gently for two hours. The acid is decanted and the material washed by decantation using several lots of water until the reaction is neutral. The acid and water are poured off as soon as the bulk of the material is deposited so the fine particles are removed. Filter under suction and, after drying at 110°C suspend the material in 200 ml of 2% DMCS in toluene; apply vacuum to assist penetration and after standing several hours, with periodic gentle agitation, filter, wash with toluene then methanol and dry at 110°C. Treat 22.5 g of the treated support with 2.5 g of Apiezon L grease in hexane and evaporate off the hexane under vacuum at 60°C. Cool before letting in air. Treat all glass surfaces, liners, and glass wool with DMCS, pack the column and condition at 225°C for forty-eight hours with a very slow flow of carrier gas. Column temperature is between 200-225°C.

Method 2

(Blackmore, D.J., and Jenkins, R.: *J For Sci Soc, 8:*34, 1968)

A Perkin-Elmer commercially available packing is used; this is 5' of 3% neopentyl glycol adipate with 0.75% trimer acid on AW-

DMCS Chromosorb W 80-100 mesh. Column temperature is 220°C (Table XXIV gives typical retention times); 3% w/w cyclohexane dimethanol succinate with 1% trimer acid on Chromosorb W is also suitable. It should be noted that meprobamate does not emerge from either of these columns. Blackmore and Jenkins have injected 10μl of urine direct onto the NGA/trimer acid column from patients who were receiving barbiturate therapy with excellent results. They showed the presence of amylobarbitone and hydroxy amylobarbitone eighteen hours after ingestion of 400 mg of amylobarbitone by this direct injection technique.

TABLE XXIV
RETENTION TIMES OF BARBITURATES

Compound	Mean Retention Time Column (1)	Relative R.T. c.f. Butobarbitone Column (1)	Mean Retention Time Column (2)	Relative R.T. c.f. Butobarbitone Column (2)
Barbitone	4.05	0.67	7.5	0.60
Butobarbitone	6.30	1.00	12.55	1.00
Amylobarbitone	6.8	1.08	14.60	1.16
Hydroxyamylobarbitone	26.8	4.25	64.0	5.1
Hexobarbitone	6.70	1.06	13.85	1.10
Pentobarbitone	7.60	1.21	15.15	1.21
Cyclobarbitone	22.30	3.55	48.80	3.90
Methylphenylbarbitone	9.65	1.53	19.3	1.54
Quinalbarbitone	9.60	1.52	18.8	1.50
Phenobarbitone	33.50	5.33	75.2	6.05
Secbutobarbiturate	6.25	0.98	12.55	1.00
Glutethimide	6.40	1.02	12.60	1.01

Column (1)
Column Neopentyl Glycol adipate and trimer acid on A.W.– DMCS Chromosorb W. 80–100 mesh. 3: ¾: 96¼
Temperature: 220°C. Carrier gas: N_2 at 60 ml/min.
Inj. Temp. '5'
Gas Chromatograph: Perkin-Elmer F11. with F.I.D.
Column (2)
Temp. 200°C. Other conditions as above. All times in minutes.

REFERENCES

ANDERS, M.W.: Rapid micromethod for the gas chromatographic determination of blood barbiturates. *Anal Chem, 38*:1945, 1966.

BOGAN, J., and HAMILTON SMITH: Analytical investigations of barbiturate poisoning. *J For Sci Soc, 7*:37, 1967.

MADDOCK, R.K., and BLOOMER, H.A.: The gas chromatography of meprobamate. *Clin Chem, 13*:333, 1967.

SKINNER, R.F.: The determination of meprobamate in blood, urine and liver by gas chromatography. *J For Sci, 12:*230, 1967.

STEVENSON, G.W.: On column methylation of barbituric acids. *Anal Chem, 38:*1948, 1966.

WINSTEIN, S., and BRODY, D.: Rapid determination of glutethimide by gas liquid chromatography. *Clin Chem, 14:*589, 1967.

BENZENE

This is an extremely toxic solvent and a method for its colorimetric determination is described below. A gas chromatographic examination is also an obvious method of enquiry (see p. 35).

Method

(Gararde, H. W., and Skiba, P.: *Clin Chem, 6:*327, 1960.)

Added to 5 ml of blood are 35 ml 0.1N hydrochloric acid in a two-ounce wide-mouthed bottle and mixed by inversion; 5 ml of carbon tetrachloride are added and the whole is shaken for three to five minutes. The water layer is removed and the centrifuged, separated carbon tetrachloride layer transferred to a test tube; 5 ml of reagent (1 ml of 40% formaldehyde and 100 ml concentrated sulphuric acid) are added and, after stoppering, the mixture is shaken for two minutes. After centrifuging at 2,000 rpm for five minutes the colour is read at 490 mμ. Standards are prepared in the range 1-10 mg/100 ml of benzene in blood.

Interpretation of Results

In my opinion, because of the leukaemia inducing properties of benzene, any measurable blood level must be regarded extremely seriously. It is most important that rubber-capped vials should not be used for the submission of blood samples in cases of suspected benzene intoxication.

BERYLLIUM

Industrial poisoning as a result of inhalation of dust containing beryllium compounds occasionally occurs. In such cases the metal can be detected in the lungs and in mediastinal lymph for periods up to at least ten years after exposure.

Method

(Peterson, G. C., Welford, G. A., and Harley, J. H.: *Anal Chem, 22*:1197, 1950)

Lung tissue, 100 g, is wet ashed with nitric and sulphuric acid in a Kjeldahl flask keeping the volume of sulphuric acid as low as possible. The total volume used should not exceed 5 ml of concentrated acid. The final destruction of organic material is effected by the addition of 0.5 ml of 60% perchloric acid: heating being continued to the production of white fumes. Decant and wash into a centrifuge tube with water and ethanol and then evaporate on a water bath. Make up to about 20 ml with water and add ammonia dropwise to appearance of a precipitate. Cool, and add 2 ml glacial acetic acid and dilute hydrochloric acid dropwise until the precipitate just redissolves. Now add 5 ml of 12% oxine in glacial acetic acid and adjust the pH to 6 with ammonia. Centrifuge and decant through a loose filter paper into a 125 ml separating funnel. Wash the filter paper with water and combine the washings and the filtrate. Extract filtrate with 10 ml of chloroform to remove the excess oxine and repeat the washing if the aqueous phase is not colourless. The aqueous phase is then transferred to a 50 ml centrifuge tube and the pH adjusted to 7; 1 ml of aluminum salt solution containing 2.5 mg of aluminium per millilitre is then added. The precipitate is centrifuged and washed and the supernatant discarded; 40 mg of sodium chloride are added and after evaporating to dryness arc spectroscopy is performed. Lines at 2348.6, 2650.8, 3130 and 3131 Å are examined. Suitable standards are in the range 0.1-5μg.

Interpretation of Results

There is usually no difficulty in the interpretation of the results in a case of berylliosis but the toxicologist must be aware that the amounts for which he is searching are usually very much less than with normal "poisons." Lung tissue and lymph in such cases can contain less than $1\mu g$ of beryllium per 100 g of tissue. In a case in which I did the analyses the levels were $20\mu g$ per 100 g of formalin treated lung tissue and $10\mu g$ per 100 g of mediastinal lymph. Death occurred seven years after exposure to dust.

REFERENCES

McCALLUM, R.I., RANNIE, I., and VERITY, C.: Chronic pulmonary berylliosis in a female chemist. *Brit J Indust Med, 18:*133, 1961.

SMYTHE, L.E., and WHITTEM, R.N.: A Review of the analytical chemistry of beryllium with 159 references. *Analyst, 86:*83, 1961.

BORON

This is usually encountered as borax or boric acid especially in the accidental poisoning of young children by these medicaments. Because the borate ion will not dialyse, presumably because of the formation of sugar complexes in biological media, it is essential that a sample of blood or tissue be separately analysed for its total boron content.

Method

(Smith, W. C., Goudie, A. J., and Sivertson, J. N. M.: *Anal Chem*, 27:295, 1955)

One tenth of a gram (0.1 g) of lithium carbonate and 2 ml of blood or tissue slurry are evaporated to dryness on a steam bath in a platinum crucible. The crucible is then transferred to a muffle furnace when the temperature is slowly raised to 650°C where it is held for $1\frac{1}{2}$ hours or until the sample is free of carbon. After cooling, 2 ml of 6N hydrochloric acid are added and after mixing well are centrifuged: 1 ml of the supernatant is mixed in a boron free test tube with 5 ml of concentrated sulphuric acid containing 250 mg of carminic acid per litre. The violet colour from the reaction with boron develops at a rate dependent on the quality of carminic acid reagent. Some batches produce a stable colour within a few minutes but in others several hours are necessary. The zero blank reagent is put in the compensatory cell and when the reading at 575 mμ reaches a stable value the optical density is measured. A calibration graph for 0-25μg boron standards gives optical readings in the range 0-0.5 at this wavelength.

Interpretation of Results

McBay, in a paper to the Toxicology Section of the American Academy of Forensic Sciences in 1961, reviewed the literature on boron poisoning in young children and reached the conclusion that blood levels over 4 mg/100 ml total boron were suggestive of poisoning.

Cases of poisoning analysed before the era of accurate colorimetry gave tissue values of over 25 mg/100 ml and sometimes over

100 mg/100 ml but these are much higher than the average case nowadays. Blood boron levels in normal healthy infants are in the range 0-.08 mg/100 ml.

BROMIDE

This can be encountered either as a result of ingestion of inorganic bromide or as a metabolite of organo-bromo compounds
such as carbromal or bromvaletone.

Method 1

(Hall, T. C.: *Lancet, ii:*355, 1943)

Mixed in the ratio 1:1 are 20% trichloroacetic acid and
0.25% auric chloride solutions. One drop of serum is spread over
the area of a sixpence and one drop of reagent dropped into the
centre. The circular ring of precipitated proteins has a yellow
colour at bromide levels of about 25 mg/100 ml and red-brown at
levels in excess of 50 mg/100 ml.

Method 2

(Street, H. V.: *Clin Chim Acta, 5:*938, 1960)

Two millilitres of blood diluted 1:1 with water are deproteinised with 10 ml of 20% trichloracetic acid. 9 ml of filtrate are
extracted with 5 millilitres of ether. 7 ml of the aqueous phase are
then mixed with 2 ml of 6N sulphuric acid and a knife blade point
of potassium permanganate. It is then shaken with 3 ml of cyclohexane and the brown solution of bromine in the organic solvent
read against exact standards at 405 mμ.

Interpretation of Results

After ingestion of a single overdose of an organo-bromo compound, blood levels do not rise above what may be present in
normal blood, that is up to 5 mg/100 ml. In these cases the concentration of total bromide in the liver may be as high as 15-25
mg/100 g and therefore provides a lead to the probable ingested
poison. An alkaline fusion of the blood is necessary to destroy the
organic compound in these cases although continued therapy with
these drugs will lead to blood levels of over 100 mg/100 ml of inorganic bromide at which level psychiatric disturbances manifest
themselves.

Accumulation with inorganic bromide therapy also occurs and

mental disturbances and skin rashes at blood levels over 200 mg/ 100 ml are common. Its use as a sedative in the treatment of mentally ill patients should include routine blood determinations because of this probability.

BUTAZOLIDINE (PHENYLBUTAZONE)

Because this drug has been noted as causing agranulocytosis clinicians often ask for routine determinations of its concentration in blood. In my experience it does not appear in the usual deproteinised extracts and the following method can be used. It is emphasised that in this determination standards must be prepared by adding the drug to blood and performing the isolation procedure, hydrolysis and coupling in exactly the same way as for the sample under investigation.

Method

(Pemberton, M.: *Brit Med J, i*:490, 1954)

Add 1 ml of serum to 4 ml of acetone in a glass stoppered centrifuge tube. Shake well and stand for thirty minutes. Centrifuge, retaining the stopper in the tube. Take 1 ml of the supernatant in a graduated 15 ml centrifuge tube and cautiously evaporate off the acetone, agitating gently. Add 1 ml 1N sulphuric acid and heat in a boiling water bath for four hours keeping the volume at 1 ml by periodic additions of water. Chill in ice water and add 0.5 ml 0.05% sodium nitrite and 2 ml 1.8% N-sulphatoethyl-m-toluidine in water. After thirty minutes at room temperature when the purple colour is fully developed clear any slight opacity by shaking with 0.25 ml light petroleum (40-60°C). Take 3 ml of the aqueous phase and read at 525 mμ. Convenient standards are multiples of 30μg added to 1 ml blood samples.

The majority (about 90%) of phenylbutazone is bound to protein. Its main metabolite is p-hydroxyphenylbutazone which appears in both the strong and weak acid fractions in routine extractions. In sodium hydroxide solution the unchanged drug has an absorption maximum at 265 mμ $E_{1cm}^{1\%} = 820$, whereas the corresponding metabolite figures are 253 mμ $E_{1cm}^{1\%} = 630$. In a fatal case of accidental poisoning in a child in my experience the drug could not be detected after a tungstic acid isolation method.

Interpretation of Results

Normal blood levels for patients under routine therapy are about 10 mg/100 ml.

CADMIUM

Cadmium salts are highly toxic; most recorded cases of poisoning refer either to inhalation of fumes in industrial processes or to accidental ingestion from solutions of citrous fruits made in cadmium plated containers, but Sachs and Calker noted an unusual case from the plating in a coffee percolator in which the clinical diagnosis was extremely difficult. This type of metallic poisoning usually manifests itself in an outbreak involving several persons, with copper as the most usual impurity; Sachs and Calker's case, therefore, emphasises again the need for extensive toxicological investigations in unusual or unexpected deaths and cadmium must not be forgotten.

Method 1.

(Saltzman, B. E.: *Anal Chem*, 25:493, 1953)

Tissue, 5 g, is heated in a Kjeldahl flask with 1 ml of concentrated sulphuric acid and 2 ml of concentrated nitric acid. When digestion is complete the clear solution is neutralised to just yellow to thymol blue with 40% sodium hydroxide. The volume is adjusted to 25 ml and the following solutions are added in order; 1 ml of 25% sodium potassium tartrate, 5 ml of a solution containing 40 g of sodium hydroxide and 1 g potassium cyanide per 100 ml, 1 ml of 20% hydroxylamine hydrochloride and 15 ml of 0.008% dithizone in chloroform. After shaking, the chloroform layer is run into a second separating funnel containing 25 ml of 2% tartaric acid which should be ice-cold. Add 10 ml of chloroform to the first separator, shake and run it into the second separator. Shake the second funnel for two minutes and discard the chloroform. Add 5 ml chloroform, shake again and discard. Add 0.25 ml hydroxylamine hydrochloride solution (20%) and 15 ml of a 0.008% solution of dithizone in chloroform and 5 ml of a solution containing 40 g of sodium hydroxide and 0.05 g of potassium cyanide per 100 ml. Shake for one minute and run the chloroform through a cotton wool plug into the measuring cell. Read at 518 mμ. The calibration curve is prepared with standards in the range 0-10μg of cadmium.

Method 2.

(Berman, E.: *Perkin Elmer Atomic Absorption Newsletter, 6:* 58, 1967)

Oxalated blood, 5 ml, and 10 ml 5% trichloroacetic acid are mixed in a centrifuge tube. After one hour the contents are centrifuged and the supernatant decanted into a 60 ml cylindrical separating funnel. The precipitate is washed with another 10 ml of 5% TCA and centrifuged. The washings are added to the separating funnel. Adjust the pH to 6-7.5 by addition of 2N sodium hydroxide; add 1 ml 1% aqueous sodium diethyldithiocarbamate and 2.5 ml of water saturated methyl-isobutyl ketone. Shake for two minutes; separate the organic phase and feed into the Perkin-Elmer 303 Atomic Absorption Spectrophotometer (at 2288 Å). For urine make 10 ml to pH 6-7.5 and proceed with the complexing extraction as described above. Tissue (1 g) is destroyed by a concentrated nitric and sulphuric acid digestion, diluted to 25 ml, made to pH 6-7.5 and analysed as above.

Interpretation of Results

Cadmium is said to be a normal constituent of tissues and Stitch, using arc emission spectroscopy, said that *ashed* kidney can contain up to 10 mg/100 g. Because cadmium salts are toxic in doses of 50 mg it is clear that, as in the case of mercury, the analyses alone cannot in many cases provide unequivocal proof of poisoning, although its detection in kidney in amounts over 2 mg/100 g and the finding of a similar level in the liver would warrant a full investigation into the circumstances of the death. Normal urinary excretion is said to be 0-20μg/litre but in workers in the cadmium industry it can rise as high as 580μg/litre.

In nonfatal cases reported by Berman the blood level was only 5μg/100 ml with 710μg/litre in the urine. The sources were silver polish and shoe whitener.

REFERENCES

BERMAN, E.: *Perkin-Elmer Atomic Absorption Newsletter, 6*:58, 1967.
MANLEY, C.H., and DALLEY, R.A.: Analytical findings in a death following inhalation of cadmium fumes. *Analyst, 82*:287, 1957.

SACHS, H.W., and CALKER, J. VAN: *Deut Z fur Gericht Med, 49*:157, 1959.

STITCH, S.R.: *Biochem J, 67*:97, 1957.

SMITH, J.C.; KENCH, J.E., and LANE, R.E.: Observations on urinary excretion of cadmium. *Biochem J, 61*:698, 1955.

CANNABIS

About 0.1 g suspected material, plant, resin, cigarette stub or pipe residue is extracted with methanol which is evaporated to dryness. The residue is triturated with 2 ml warm benzene and poured down a Florisil column prepared in a Pasteur disposable pipette. The column is eluted with 5-10 ml benzene which is evaporated to 50μl. This solution is suitable for a paper or gas chromatographic separation.

Paper Chromatography

Whatman SG81 paper is used with a solvent of benzene:carbon tetrachloride (1:1). Detection is by a spray of Beams reagent (5 g potassium hydroxide in 100 ml ethanol). A blue colour, slowly developing, at Rf 0.7 is specific for cannabidiol. Follow with a spray of 1% aqueous solution of Brentamine Fast Blue B salt. Red spots of various hues are seen at Rfs 0.1, 0.6, 0.7 and 0.9. This last test is very sensitive but not specific for cannabinols.

Gas Chromatography

(Heaysman, L. T., Walker, E. A., and Lewis, D. T.: *Analyst,* *92:*450, 1967)

A 5' x 4mm column at 220-230°C of 1% carbowax 20M on AW-DMCS Chromosorb G with a flame ionisation detector is used. An internal reference of dibenzyl phthalate is added and retention times relative to it are cannabidiol 0.33, tetrahydrocannabinol 0.37, cannabinol 0.71.

CARBON MONOXIDE

Identification and Assay

The gas liberated from a blood or tissue sample by addition of a ferricyanide reagent (see below) can be identified in one of three ways. Firstly, it can be bubbled through a dilute freshly prepared solution of oxyhaemoglobin and the characteristic shift in the visible spectrum to carboxyhaemoglobin observed; secondly, it can be passed into an infra-red gas cell and the infra-red spectrum observed; or lastly, an identification can be achieved by the characteristic gas chromatographic retention time coupled, if the refinement is available, with mass spectrometry.

It is not safe to rely on an identification and assay based on direct visible spectroscopy for blood samples more than a day or two old, and especially if the blood has been warmed at any stage.

The assay of carbon monoxide in blood by three different methods is described below.

Method 1

The palladium chloride diffusion method: this can also be used as a quantitative procedure either by measuring the quantity of palladium chloride used up in the reaction or by titrating the liberated hydrochloric acid. Both techniques require skill and should not be undertaken without much practice. A simpler method which gives a result in about one minute is described below.

Method 2

The apparatus, devised by E. R. Rutter and shown in Figure 10, is set up. The principle of the method rests on the liberation of carbon monoxide from a measured volume of blood whose haemoglobin content has been found on a separate aliquot. The gas reacts in a commercially available carbon monoxide detector tube, T2,* to give a visible black stain whose length is proportional to the volume of gas. In this way, the volume of carbon monoxide per 14 g of haemoglobin can be calculated. In practice, 0.5 ml of blood

---

*Draeger Normalair Ltd., Blyth, Northumberland, England, or Siebe Gorman and Co., Ltd., Neptune Works, Tolworth, Surrey, England.

is put in Tube B, diluted with 3 ml of water and a mixture of lactic acid-potassium ferricyanide quickly added; air is sucked through the apparatus from left to right at a rate of approximately 60 ml/min. The tube, T1, acts as a purifier of the air and Tube A contains water to act as a flow meter; in the neck of Tube B is a pack of cotton wool impregnated with lead acetate to remove any sulphide impurities. The length of stain for blood 100 per cent saturated with carbon monoxide should also be obtained. The apparatus is equally suitable for measuring low concentrations — that is, of the order of 5 per cent saturation — by increasing the volume of blood used to 5 ml.

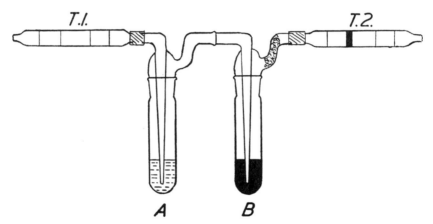

FIGURE 10. Apparatus for the determination of carbon monoxide in blood.

A haemoglobin determination should be done on an exactly similar aliquot of blood; the following method is simple and quick.

Haemoglobin (Khalifa, A.A., and Salah, M.K.: *Nature, 168:* 915, 1951). 0.02 ml blood is added to 10 ml of 0.1N hydrochloric acid. After at least ten minutes the optical density of the acid haematin is measured at 372.5 mμ using a 1 cm cell and 0.1N hydrochloric acid as compensator. The grams of haemoglobin in 100 ml of blood are given by multiplying the intensity reading by 15.5.

Alternative methods based on cyanmethaemoglobin are commercially available: one form is Aculute.[†] In cases involving carboxyhaemoglobin this reaction with Drabkin's reagent should be warmed to 56°C for three to five minutes before reading at 540 mμ.

REFERENCE

RICE, E.W.: Rapid determination of total haemoglobin in blood containing carboxyhaemoglobin. *Clin Chem, 13*:686, 1967.

Method 3

(van Kampen, E. J. and Klouwen, H. M.: *Rev Trav Chim Pays-bas, 73*:119, 1954)

This depends on reducing blood, diluted with 0.5N ammonia, with a small spatula end of solid sodium hydrosulphite to give a mixture of reduced haemoglobin (from the oxyhaemoglobin and any methaemoglobin in the sample) and carboxyhaemoglobin. The optical densities at the point of maximum difference of density, 540 mμ (D_m), and the point of equal optical density, 579 mμ (D_1) are measured. It can be shown that

if a = the fraction of total haemoglobin present as carboxyhaemoglobin, then

$$\frac{D_m}{D_1} = a \left(\frac{1}{x} - \frac{1}{y} \right) + \frac{1}{y}$$

where $x = \dfrac{D_1}{D_m}$ for 100% COHb and $y = \dfrac{D_1}{D_m}$ for 0% COHb.

A calibration curve is prepared by plotting $\dfrac{D_m}{D_1}$ i.e. $\dfrac{\text{(reading at 540 m}\mu\text{)}}{\text{(reading at 579 m}\mu\text{)}}$

for 0%, i.e., reduced haemoglobin, and for 100% COHb. The dilution is relatively unimportant — one or two drops of blood are added to 5 ml of 0.5N ammonia — the ratio being independent of concentration. The readings should however be arranged to be in the most sensitive part of the scale of the spectrophotometer which is usually about 0.3-0.4. The ratio for 0% should be 1.10 and for 100%, 1.50. As the equation shows, the calibration is linear for intermediate samples.

[†]Ortho Diagnostics, Saunderton, Bucks, England.

The method is an excellent one, very sensitive, works well with post-mortem blood and does not need a separate haemoglobin determination. It is not to be recommended to the beginner without full comparative controls. One precaution must be observed: the reading at 579 mμ is taken on a very steep slope and the wavelength is critical. The spectrophotometer must be not only routinely aligned for wavelength calibration but minor variations must be minimised by the following procedure: set the wavelength first at 540 mμ and take the reading of a control sample of 0% reduced blood against the compensatory ammonia; knowing the ratio for 0% blood (1.10) the reading at 579 mμ can then be calculated. The wavelength giving this reading (it may be 578 or 580 mμ on the dial) is used for subsequent determinations.

The reduction of oxyhaemoglobin with sodium hydrosulphite has been the subject of a study by Dalziel and O'Brien who have shown that it is a complex reaction fraught with the possibility of complications for spectrophotometry. Their paper indicates that 0.5N ammonia is too alkaline for rapid and full reduction but, in contrast to ones at a lower pH, this strength gives clear solutions and in practice does not lead to error. Theoretically more weakly alkaline buffer solutions are preferable, a pH of 8.5 and the taking of readings between ten and thirty minutes after adding the hydrosulphite are indicated.

Method 4

(D. J. Blackmore, personal communication)

Three millilitres of reagent (20g sodium hydrogen carbonate AR, 20 g sodium carbonate AR, 15 g potassium ferricyanide AR, 10 ml Triton-X 100 diluted to 600 ml with distilled water) is mixed with 1 ml of blood and 1 ml air for not less than ten minutes in one of two 5 ml plastic disposable syringes joined together with a short length of plastic tubing. After this time, the 1 ml of air is withdrawn into the second syringe and all of it is injected into a 5 ml gas loop on a gas chromatograph. It is essential that the whole of the syringe air space be injected if maximum sensitivity and linearity of recorder response to air/carbon monoxide volume are to be achieved. The column consists of a 6′ length of Linde molecular sieve 5A at 100°C with helium carrier gas flowing at 45 ml/min. A Katharometer detector is used at ambient temperature with a detector current of 225 milliamps (Pye 104 apparatus). Peak height measurements give excellent quantitation. Comparison to results from 100% saturated blood and to blood iron provide assay. To saturate old blood with carbon monoxide requires the addition of solid sodium hydrosulphite and bubbling with pure gas for at least half an hour.

For interpretation of results see p. 43.

REFERENCES (see p. 44)

CHLORDIAZEPOXIDE (Librium®), DIAZEPAM (Valium®), NITRAZEPAM (Mogadon®)

Although many cases of overdosage with these tranquillisers have been reported, the mortality is obviously extremely low.

Method

(Based on Smyth, D., and Pennington, G. W.: *Arch Int Pharmacodyn, 145*:154, 1963)

Blood, 5 ml, is made alkaline by the addition of 0.5 g potassium carbonate and extracted with 3 x 20 ml chloroform. The combined chloroform extracts are washed with water and extracted with 3 ml 2N hydrochloric acid. The separated acid is centrifuged and then read in an ultra-violet spectrophotometer in a 1 cm cell from 230 to 320 mμ.

Chlordiazepoxide shows a major peak at 245 mμ with a minor peak at 310 mμ. Diazepam peaks at 240 mμ with a minor peak at 285 mμ. Nitrazepam shows a peak at 278 mμ. Standards should be prepared from the pure drugs at concentrations in 2N HCl of approximately 0.5 mg/100 ml.

It is probable that for diazepam and nitrazepam the background absorption will be too high for the necessary sensitivity to be achieved. If this is so and it is desired to confirm suspected intake, the best, quick approach is to re-extract the tranquillisers from the hydrochloric acid solution into chloroform after making alkaline with ammonia; the evaporated chloroform extract should then be examined by TLC using methanol on Silica-Gel G plates and sprayed with iodoplatinate (see Chap. 4Bii) .

Interpretation of Results

Large toxic doses of chlordiazepoxide will give blood levels of the order of 1 mg/100 ml or higher; diazepam levels are lower — after a single intake of 100 mg the blood level will only be of the order of 25μg/100 ml although patients on long-term therapy with this drug can have levels of about 100μg/100 ml. Nitrazepam levels in toxic doses are also relatively low — and detection of levels below 100μg/100 ml should be ensured.

REFERENCE

GJERRIS, F.: Poisoning with chlordiazepoxide. *Danish Med Bull, 13:*170, 1966.

CHLORPROMAZINE (Largactil®)

Free Chlorpromazine in Urine

Method

(Bolt, A.G., Forrest, I.S., and Serra, M.T.: *J Pharm Sci, 55:* 1205, 1966)

Urine, 10 ml, is adjusted to pH 9-9.5 and extracted with 3 x 10 ml dichloromethane. The organic layer is separated and evaporated under a stream of nitrogen, dissolved in 5 ml 0.1N sulphuric acid and immersed in an ice bath; 5 ml concentrated sulphuric acid is added very slowly down the wall of the flask and the mixture heated at 65°C for fifteen minutes. It is cooled to room temperature, one drop of 0.1% H_2O_2 added, stood for fifteen minutes and adjusted to 10 ml with cold 50% sulphuric acid. The spectrum is measured from 400-700 mμ and the absorption maximum at 530 mμ measured; the difference in optical density between the maximum and the background is proportional to the concentration of free chlorpromazine sulphoxide.

Conjugated Chlorpromazine in Urine

Method

(Bolt, A.G., and Forrest, I.S.: *J Pharm Sci, 56:*1533, 1967)

IRC-50 Analytical Grade 20-50 mesh ion exchange resin in the sodium form is made into a chromatographic column; 1 g is used. Wash with a few millilitres of Sorensen's buffer at pH 6. Then pass 1 ml of urine down the column and then pH 6 buffer to a volume of 5 ml. To the effluent add 5 ml of 50% sulphuric acid containing 75μg FeCl$_3$. 5H$_2$O/ml. Cool in ice during the addition. Make up to 10 ml with 25% H_2SO_4 and read at 400-700 mμ: maximum absorption is at 550 mμ. Calibrate using 7 methoxychlorpromazine.

Chlorpromazine in Blood

Method

Blood, 10 ml, is stirred with 2 ml water and 8 ml concentrated hydrochloric acid and heated in a beaker in a boiling water bath for five minutes. Remove and place in an ice bath. When cool, add 12 ml 60% w/v potassium hydroxide which has been previously washed with ether. Keep cool and check the pH to ensure alkalinity. If acid, add more alkali. Shake with 150 ml ether breaking any emulsion by centrifuging. Separate and shake the aqueous phase with a further 50 ml portion of ether. Combine the ether fractions and wash in sequence with 10 ml 2.5% sodium hydroxide, 10 ml water and 5 ml water. Extract the ether with 5 ml 0.1N sulphuric acid which is separated and read from 230-280 mμ. Chlorpromazine peaks at 255 mμ and has $E^{1\%} = 960$.

Interpretation of Results

Excretion of total chlorpromazine in the urine in patients receiving long-term therapy of 100-140 mg per day, varies from 21 to 70 per cent of the ingested dose. The ratio of conjugated to unconjugated metabolites varies from 2.1-11 (Bolt, Forrest and Serra).

The level to be expected in the blood after an acute toxic overdose of about 1 g or over, is of the order of 100μg/100 ml. Liver levels are much higher (see Chap. 7Aii).

REFERENCES

DRISCOLL, J.L.; MARTIN, H.F., and GULZINOWICZ, B.J.: A gas chromatographic method for quantitative analyses of some urinary metabolites of chlorpromazine. *J Gas Chrom, 2:*109, 1964.

HUANG, C.L.: Isolation and identification of urinary chlorpromazine metabolites in man. *Int J Neuropharmacol, 6:*1, 1967.

CHOLINESTERASE

This is an essential routine investigation because of the ready availability of organo-phosphorus insecticides in all parts of the world. Accidental contamination of foodstuffs leading to poisoning as well as their intentional ingestion for suicidal and homicidal purposes make a search for these compounds, which depress the enzyme cholinesterase in the blood, necessary. Fluoride does not inhibit this enzyme so the preserved sample of blood can be used. Refrigerated samples are stable for at least several weeks.

Method

(Michel, H.O.: *J Lab Clin Med, 34:*1565, 1949) .

Buffer solution. 1.237 g of sodium barbitone, 0.136 g of potassium dihydrogen phosphate and 17.535 g of sodium chloride are dissolved in 900 ml of water, made up to nearly one litre with water and the pH adjusted to 8 with 0.1N hydrochloric acid. The volume is then accurately made up to 1 litre. A few drops of toluene are added as a preservative and the solution keeps indefinitely in a refrigerator.

Substrate. 0.2 g acetylcholine bromide in 10 ml of water made fresh.

Take two stoppered test tubes and add 2.5 ml buffer and 2.5 ml substrate to each and 0.05 ml serum or whole blood to one. Take the pH immediately and again after incubation at 25°C for one hour. The control should not have altered its pH by more than 0.05 units. The difference in pH between the control and the incubated blood x 100 gives the cholinesterase activity in pH units.

Interpretation of Results

Normal whole blood gives values of 80-160 pH units; the average values are about 120 and the lowest value for a normal fit human is probably 75 units. Normal plasma is in the range 50-100 units. Although depression of cholinesterase activity can rarely decrease to zero without the death of the patient, the ChE value gives a useful lead to the probability that the ingested poison is an inhibitor and therefore an organo-phosphorus compound. Accumulation of small quantities of poison can result in cumulative depression of ChE activity which returns to normal only slowly — as much as a month may be required, after cessation of exposure.

REFERENCE
LATNER, A.L., and SKILLEN, A.W.: *Isoenzymes in Biology and Medicine.* New York Academic, 1968, pp. 108-113.

CYANIDE

See Chapter 3, but the following is an alternative method.

Method

(Tompsett, S.L.: *Clin Chem,* 5:587, 1959—modified) .

The following reagents are placed in an Öbrink diffusion vessel:

1. Sealing ring — 6N sulphuric acid.
2. Outer ring — blood or tissue macerate — 1 or 2 g: also 0.5 ml 6N sulphuric acid.
3. Inner ring — 1.0 ml of IN sodium hydroxide.

After mixing the blood and acid in the outer ring, diffusion is allowed to proceed at room temperature for two hours. To the sodium hydroxide in the inner ring are added in order, 0.1 ml of glacial acetic acid, 0.1 ml of bromine water, 0.1 ml of sodium arsenite solution and when the bromine has been decolourised, 0.5 ml of pyridine/benzidine reagent. The volume is then made to 3 ml by adding 1.2 ml of water. The mixture is transferred to a test tube and allowed to stand for fifteen minutes at room temperature and then read against a reagent blank together with exact controls from 2.5 to 10μg cyanide at 520 mμ. The sodium arsenite solution is made by dissolving 1 g arsenious oxide in as little 2N sodium hydroxide as possible and making up to 50 ml with water. The pyridine/benzidine reagent is made as follows: (a) 0.36 g benzidine is dissolved in 10 ml 0.5N hydrochloric acid; and (b) 12 ml of pyridine is made up to 20 ml with water: 2 ml concentrated hydrochloric acid is added. The reagent is made by adding 5 ml of (a) to 20 ml of (b) . It does not keep.

For interpretation of results see p. 48.

DDT, DIELDRIN AND OTHER ORGANO-CHLORO COMPOUNDS

These compounds can be demonstrated in normal tissue provided sufficiently sensitive methods of detection are employed. Normal levels in tissues in mg/100 g are as follows:

	Fat	Urine	Blood	Liver	Kidney	Brain
DDT and DDE	0.3–1.3	.001–.004	.0012–.0046	.01–.1	.001–.003	.001–.02
HEOD	0.02 – 0.026	.00005– .00019	0.00014	—	—	—

Reported toxic levels are as follows:

	Blood		Urine	Liver	Kidney	Brain
Aldrin		4.0				
Dieldrin	over	.02 (0.5–0.7)				
Endrin		.0053	.0004			
Toxaphene				.78	.67	1.4

Method

(based on de Faubert Maunder, M.J.; Egan, H.; Godly, E.W.; Hammond, E.W.; Roburn, J., and Thomson, J.: *Analyst, 89:*168, 1964.)

Tissue, 10 g, is ground in a glass mortar with an approximately equal weight of sharp sand and sufficient anhydrous sodium sulphate to a uniform dry powder. Transfer the ground material to a 150 ml beaker and simmer for about two minutes with 50, 20, 20 and 20 ml successive portions of hexane, stirring carefully. Allow each solution to cool for a few minutes before decanting them separately into 100 ml calibrated flasks. Dilute the solutions to the mark and take a 25 ml portion of each. Shake with 10 ml of dimethylformamide saturated with hexane and run the clear DMF phase into a 100 ml separating funnel, centrifuging if necessary. Repeat with two further portions of 10 ml of DMF and combine the extracts. Wash them with 10 ml of hexane saturated with DMF. Separate the hexane, wash this with a further 10 ml of DMF which is added to the original 30 ml of DMF. The DMF extract is shaken briskly for two minutes with 200 ml of 2% aqueous sodium sulphate solution and after twenty minutes the hexane, previously held in solution, separates and is collected. The stem of the separating funnel is washed with hexane and the combined extracts are passed down the following previously prepared column: 10 g of activated alumina (heat aluminium oxide at 800°C for 4 hours, cool, add carefully 5% v/w water and mix thoroughly in a closed vessel; use within 10 days) in hexane is poured into a chromatographic column and kept covered in hexane; the alumina is covered with a 5 cm layer of anhydrous sodium sulphate and the hexane level allowed to fall to its upper level. Run the solution prepared above, concentrated to 2 ml onto the column, wash with three successive 2 ml portions of hexane, and elute with 90 ml of hexane. Collect a similar volume. Evaporate the eluate to 0.5 ml. This extract can be concentrated and half of it examined by a thin layer system using a Silica-Gel plate with hexane or carbon tetrachloride as the solvent. Rf values for hexane are as follows:

Aldrin	0.7	op' DDT	0.50	Heptachlor	0.58
α BHC	0.34	pp' DDT	0.42	Heptachlor epoxide	0.17
γ BHC	0.21	Dieldrin	0.12	pp' TDE	0.25
pp'DDE	0.65	Endrin	0.13		

The spots are made visible by spraying with a solution of 0.5% ethanolic silver nitrate solution containing 1% phenoxyethanol and exposing to 254 mμ ultra-violet light. Black spots appear in a short time. Alternatively, a GLC separation can be achieved on a 10μl extract. A 5' column of SE30 at 175°C using an electron capture detector will demonstrate normal levels if the above procedure is followed and hence detection of poisoning is ensured. It should be noted that TDE and little DDT will be found in livers analysed more than a few days after autopsy.

A 6' column of 2% OV-1 and 3% QF-1 on gas chrom. Q 80/100 at 180°C is said to give excellent resolution.

REFERENCES

ADAMOVIC, V.M.: Aromatic amines as spray reagents in the thin layer chromatography of chlorinated organic pesticides. *J Chrom, 23*:274, 1966.

BENYON, K.I., and ELGAR, K.E.: The analysis for residues of chlorinated insecticides and acaricides. A Review. *Analyst, 91*:143, 1966 (324 references).

BROWN, V.K.H.; HUNTER, C.G., and RICHARDSON, A.: A blood test diagnostic of exposure to Aldrin and Dieldrin. *Brit J Ind Med, 21*:283, 1964.

COBLE, Y.; HILDEBRANDT, P.; DAVIS, J.; RAASCH, F., and CURLEY, A.: Acute Endrin poisoning. *JAMA, 202*:489, 1967.

CUETO, C., and BIROS, F.J.: Chlorinated insecticides and related materials in human urine. *Toxic Appl Pharmacol, 10*:261, 1967.

HAUN, E.C.: Fatal Toxaphene poisoning in a 9 month infant. *Amer J Dis Child, 113*:616, 1967.

HODGE, H.C.; BOYCE, A.M.; DEICHMANN, W.B., and KRAYBILL, H.F.: Toxicology and no-effect levels of Aldrin and Dieldrin. *Toxic Appl Pharmacol, 10*:613, 1967.

HUNTER, C.G.; ROBINSON, J., and RICHARDSON, A.: Chlorinated insecticide content of human body fat in Southern England. *Brit Med J, i*:231, 1963.

KOVACS, M.F.: Rapid detection of chlorinated pesticide residues by an improved TLC technique: 3¼ x 4" micro slides. *JAOAC, 49*:365, 1966.

RICHARDSON, A.; ROBINSON, J.; BUSH, B., and DAVIES, J.M.: Determination of Dieldrin (HOED) in blood. *Arch Environ Health, 14*:703, 1967.

RICHARDSON, A.; HUNTER, C.G.; CRABTREE, A.N., and REES, H.J.: Organochloro insecticide content of human adipose tissue in South East England. *Brit J Industr Med, 22*:200, 1965.

ROBINSON, J., and HUNTER, C.G.: Organochlorine insecticides: concentrations in human blood and adipose tissue. *Arch Environ Health, 13*:558, 1966.

SCHAFER, M.L., and CAMPBELL, J.E.: The distribution of pesticide residues in human body tissues from Montgomery County, Ohio. In *Organic Pesticides in the Environment,* Advances in Chemistry Series 60, A.C.S. publication 1966, p. 89

DIGOXIN AND DIGITOXIN IN URINE

The accidental ingestion of these compounds by young children sometimes occurs and the toxicologist is asked to confirm by analysis the circumstantial suspicions of intake. The stomach contents, and any vomit, are probably the best sources, but two recent papers (Doherty *et al.,* and Jelliffe) have given certain basic information which is of assistance in this field. Doherty's work using tritium-labelled digoxin on human subjects indicates that the drug will be found in the highest concentrations in the heart muscle, liver and kidney. Recovery from tissue using continuous alcohol extraction has been discussed in Chapter 7B (ii).

Method

(Jelliffe, R.W.: *J Lab Clin Med, 67*:694, 1966)

As much urine as can be obtained is used. If possible, a twenty-four-hour sample. It is stored under 50 ml heptane in a refrigerator and analysis performed within three days. The urine is diluted to 2 litres with water and extracted at 25-29°C with 1,500 ml chloroform after making the solution to pH 4 with sulphuric acid. The separated chloroform is shaken three times with 50 ml portions of 1N NaOH. It is then washed with 50 ml water and, after separating again, evaporated to dryness at 30°C in a rotary flask evaporator. The residue is dissolved in six washes of 2.5 ml chloroform:methanol (1:1) and the solvent evaporated to dryness under a stream of nitrogen. The urine extract is spread on a band on a TLC plate with controls. The plates (20 x 20 cm) are prepared by shaking 30 g Silica-Gel G with 60 ml 0.05N NaOH for one minute and spreading to 250μ in the usual way. They are dried at 120°C for one hour and cooled in a desiccator.

The solvent used is methylene chloride:methanol:formamide (90:9:1) with a filter paper liner to facilitate equilibration. Plates are run to 10 cm at 25-29°C. They are then removed and allowed to dry for about five minutes. They are then slowly and gradually sprayed with water which reveals digoxin and digitoxin as frosty white spots just separated on the semitransparent background at Rfs of about 0.35. The positive reacting areas are scraped off into stoppered centrifuge tubes, 5 ml of xanthydrol reagent (30 mg in 100 ml redistilled glacial acetic acid plus 1 ml concentrated hydrochloric acid) is added, vigorously shaken for exactly two minutes and placed in a boiling water bath for three minutes. It is then cooled in ice water for five minutes and then centrifuged. The supernatant rose-wine colour is read within twenty minutes at 550 mμ and 580 mμ. The optical density difference at these two wavelengths is proportional to the digitoxose in the sample. Reference standards in the range 5-30μg of digitoxin and 30-50μg digoxin should be used. Traces of nonspecific material may be found to the equivalent of 12.5μg digoxin per day but, in acute poisoning, the expected urinary concentration at its maximum should be considerably above this background. On a maintenance dose of 1 mg per day, digoxin patients excrete about 200μg per day; on 300μg digitoxin a day excretion is about 45μg per day.

REFERENCES

DOHERTY, J.E.; PERKINS, W.H., and FLANIGAN, W.J.: The distribution and concentration of tritiated digoxin in human tissues. *Ann Int Med, 66:* 116, 1967.

JELLIFFE, R.W.: A chemical determination of urinary digitoxin and digoxin in man. *J Lab Clin Med, 67:*694, 1966.

GRADE, R.; FORTER, W., and SCHULZECK, S.: An improved method for the isolation of heart glycosides from tissues using Sephadex G200. *Biochem Pharmacol, 16:*1299, 1967.

LUKKARI, I., and ALHA, A.: Forensic chemical detection of digitalis glycosides in autopsy material. *Anal Abstr,* 1556, 1967.

WILSON, W.E.; JOHNSON, S.A.; PERKINS, W.H., and RIPLEY, J.E.: Gas chromatographic analysis of cardiac glycosides and related compounds. *Anal Chem, 39:*40, 1967.

DINITRO-O-CRESOL

The toxicologist is occasionally asked to determine the concentration of this agricultural compound in blood because from it can be determined the exposure severity and the time that the worker must remain away from further spraying.

Method

(Fenwick, M.L., and Parker, V.H.: *Analyst, 80:*774, 1955).

Blood, 1 ml, is shaken for thirty seconds with 5 ml of methylethyl ketone and 1 g of a 9:1 solid mixture of sodium chloride + sodium carbonate. The ketone layer is then filtered into the cell of a spectrophotometer and read at 430 mμ. One drop of concentrated hydrochloric acid is added, any cloudiness removed by centrifuging, and the optical density again read. The difference in readings is plotted against the amount of DNOC to prepare a standard curve; 0-40μg gives readings of 0-0.625 in a 1 cm cell in our hands.

Interpretation of Results

Toxic effects in man appear at levels of about 3-4 mg/100 ml. Levels of 6.5 mg/100 ml are extremely serious and above 7.5 mg/100 ml will probably be fatal. After cessation of exposure the blood level falls by about 0.1 mg/100 ml per day.

REFERENCE
EDSON, E.F.: Agricultural pesticides. *Brit Med J, i:*841, 1955.

ETHANOL

Gas Chromatography

Method

(Curry, A.S.; Walker, G.W., and Simpson, G.S.: *Analyst, 91:* 1088, 1966).

A Pye 104 gas chromatograph is used with 5' of 10% PEG400 on 100-120 Celite with a flame ionisation detector at 85°C. The temperature of the injection port is the same as that of the column. A Kent Chromalog integrator is fitted in parallel with the recorder. A Griffin and George "Type 221" Diluspence or similar automatic device is used to dilute 100μl blood with 10μl of an aqueous n-propanol solution (approximately 20 mg/100 ml). (The diluspence gives accurately measured dilutions; the absolute dilution ratio is not important provided it is constant for standards and samples: a better than 1 per cent accuracy is normally achieved over several months.) If a Diluspence or an equivalent device is not available, manual dilution (0.1 ml blood + 1 ml aqueous n-propanol) can be used but operator fatigue introduces significant errors (up to 5%) late in the day if large numbers are being analysed. Approximately 1μl of the diluted blood sample is injected into the machine by means of a Hamilton syringe. Ethanol has a retention time of about two minutes, propanol $3\frac{1}{4}$ minutes and the "water" appears in $4\frac{1}{2}$ minutes. There must be no overlap of the compounds. Analysis is achieved by comparison of the digital integrator outputs for the ethanol:propanol ratio with known standards. Peak height measurement can be used provided a single operator standardises himself; variations between operators are considerable unless the integrator is used. Because the detector behaves similarly to the ethanol and propanol the calibration curve is constant from month to month and alterations in the injected volumes, column packing, gas flow rates and temperature changes are of no consequence. Isopropanol and chloroform have similar retention times to ethanol, but a second column of 100/120 Porapak Q at 180°C satisfactorily resolves these compounds.

Very low concentrations of alcohol in blood can be measured

if the injected volume is increased and the propanol concentration reduced. Propanol solutions of 8 mg/100 ml "lose" propanol even in the dark in a refrigerator at about 1 per cent per day and it is, therefore, advisable to run standards more frequently than in the routine case.

Because of the high accuracy of the method, care must also be taken in the preparation of standards. It is advisable to make up direct standards in large quantities, i.e., to weigh 5 g of purified absolute ethanol and dilute to 5 litres with water, and not attempt to weigh 100 mg and dilute to 100 ml. A standard deviation of 1% can be achieved easily.

When a new column is used large "'water" peaks may be found, but these can be diminished by injecting repetitive 50μl quantities of water to flush out the column. This peak decreases as the column ages. It is most important to get a very stable baseline in this method and conditioning for forty-eight hours at 120°C with nitrogen passing through the column at 40 ml/min is recommended when a new column is installed. After this, if the apparatus is only used intermittently, purging for two hours at 120°C is usually sufficient.

When the column has been in use for some time, broadening of peaks will occur; instead of repacking the whole column it will be found necessary only to repack the top two to three inches; reconditioning however must be done.

An alternative procedure is Machata's head space method which, however, uses larger volumes of blood.

For interpretation of results see p. 38.

REFERENCE
MACHATA, G.: Uber die gaschromatographische Blutalkoholbestimmung. *Blutalkhol, 4*:252, 1967.

Dichromate Methods

Two methods are recommended, serving slightly different purposes. Both are exactly similar dichromate oxidation methods but, whereas the former gives a quantitative determination in about half an hour, the latter requires an overnight period for diffusion. The first method is the one used for rapid clinical estimations, the second is suitable if large numbers of determinations from drunken drivers are being routinely analysed.

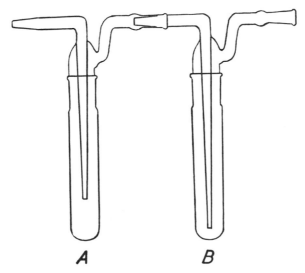

FIGURE 11. Apparatus for the determination of alcohol, cyanide and phosphorus.

Method 1

Ten millilitres of a potassium dichromate-sulphuric acid mixture (0.1N $K_2Cr_2O_7$ in 60% v/v H_2SO_4) are placed in tube B (Fig. 11). The tube A is then weighed empty and again after the addition of about 2 g blood; 2 ml of 10% sodium tungstate are then added to the blood followed by about four drops of bench dilute sulphuric acid. The thick protein precipitate can be easily coated over the inner surface of the tube by a flick of the wrist. If urine is used 2 ml is taken: no protein precipitation is necessary. Alcohol and the aqueous phase are then rapidly and completely volatilised when both tubes are placed in a water bath at 80°C and a stream of air is blown or sucked over the blood into the dichromate mixture in Tube B. Two precautions are necessary — the air must be cleaned by prior passage through a strong chromic acid mixture, and the bubbling orifice into the reaction mixture must be as small as possible to ensure complete oxidation of the alcohol. Physiological quantities of acetone do not interfere under these conditions. When the blood has completely dried, the dichromate is washed into a 1 litre conical flask with about 250 ml of distilled water; 5 ml of 10% potassium iodide are added and the liberated iodine is titrated with exactly 0.1N sodium thiosulphate using starch solution as the final indicator. A similar titration is then performed on 10 ml of the potassium dichromate-sulphuric acid mixture which has been used in a blank determination.

Let the blank determination be "y" millitres and the alcohol determination "z" millilitres.

Let the weight of blood be "w" grams.

Then $(y - z)$ millilitres of 0.1N sodium thiosulphate = alcohol from "w" grams of blood

But 1 ml of 0.1N sodium thiosulphate = 1.15 mg of alcohol

$$\frac{1.15 \times (y - z) \times 100}{w} = \text{milligrams of alcohol per 100 g of blood}$$

or

$$\frac{1.15 \times (y - z) \times 105}{w} = \text{milligrams of alcohol per 100 ml of blood.}$$

Method 2

(L. C. Nickolls: *Analyst, 85*:840, 1960.)

This is a macro diffusion method using cylindrical jars.* About 2 g of blood are accurately weighed into one half of a small Petri dish; 1 ml of saturated potassium carbonate solution is then added and the dish is placed supported on a small glass tripod in the jar; 10 ml of the potassium dichromate-sulphuric acid reagent are placed in the base of the jar. A glass plate with ground glass edges makes an airtight seal and is held in place by a metal screw cap. The jar is incubated at 37°C overnight. The titrations and calculations are exactly the same as in Method 1.

For interpretation of results see p. 38.

———

*Obtainable from Aimer Products, Ltd., Camden Road, London, England.

ETHCHLORVYNOL

Method

(Wallace, J.E., and Wilson, W.J.: *J For Sci, 9:*342, 1964.)

Blood (2 ml), homogenated tissue slurry or 10 ml urine are mixed with 20 ml of 5% v/v sulphuric acid in a 1 litre round-bottomed flask. The contents are steam distilled at a rate of 7-10 ml/min and 10-100 ml of the distillate are collected depending on the amount of ethchlorvynol suspected to be present. The volume collected is recorded: 2 ml of the distillate is reacted with 2 ml of semicarbazide reagent at pH 7 (0.1N in sodium phosphate buffer). After twenty minutes at 25°C the absorbance is read against a blank of 2 ml water with 2 ml semicarbazide reagent at 292 mμ. Standards are prepared in the range 0-10μg/ml. A check can be obtained by reading the optical density of the carbonyl compound obtained by the acid distillation as this has an absorption maximum at 265 mμ.

Interpretation of Results

Therapeutic blood levels, even on long-term dosing, rarely exceed 1-2 mg/100 ml in blood, although Millhouse *et al.* reported a chronic intoxication in a female aged twenty-nine, with a blood level of 3.7 mg/100 ml. Fatal levels are high in blood, liver and kidney — a level as high as 65 mg/100 g has been reported (Finkle, personal communication). Kimber (personal communication) reports a case where the blood level was only 1.7 mg/100 ml (liver 8.3 mg/100 g) but the patient had died ninety hours after ingestion.

REFERENCE
MILLHOUSE, J.; DAVIES, D.M., and WRAITH, S.K.: *Lancet, ii:*1252, 1966.

ETHYLENE GLYCOL

Method

(Harger, R.N., and Forney, R.B.: *J For Sci, 4:*136, 1959) .

Blood. Blood, 1 ml, is diluted with 7 ml water and 1 ml of 10% w/v sodium tungstate solution added. With vigorous shaking add dropwise 1 ml of 0.67N H_2SO_4. Shake well and then filter through a small dry filter paper. Place 1 ml filtrate in a small test tube, add 4 ml water and 0.25 ml of a solution of 2.13% w/v $NaIO_4$ in 0.67N H_2SO_4; stand for ten minutes. Quickly introduce 2 ml Schiff's reagent and mix. After twenty-five minutes read at 555 mμ. Compare with 10-70μg ethylene glycol determined in the same way. Schiff's reagent is made by adding 0.2 g basic fuchsine to 120 ml almost boiling water. Dissolve and cool in running water. Dissolve 2 g sodium metabisulphite in 20 ml water and add to the cooled fuchsine. Next add 2 ml conc HCl and 60 ml water. Keep in a refrigerator and use within two to three weeks.

Tissues. Macerate 50 g tissue with 200 ml water. Take 25 ml, add 15 ml water, 5 ml 10% w/v sodium tungstate and 5 ml 0.67N H_2SO_4. Shake and filter. Proceed as for protein free blood filtrate.

Interpretation of Results

Even in the refrigerator loss of ethylene glycol occurs on storage. Harger and Forney note that the blood level in one case dropped from 384 mg/100 ml to 80 mg/100 ml on twelve days' storage.

Fatal blood and tissue levels usually are high if death is rapid — often several hundred milligrams/100 ml. If death is delayed for several days, only traces may be found and it should be noted that "blank" values up to the equivalent of 35 mg/100 ml in blood have been noted.

Oxalic acid determinations (p. 237) are useful confirmatory tests.

FLUORIDE

Method 1

Quantitative Procedure (Teichmann, T.; Dubois, L., and Monkman, J.L.: The determination of fluoride by microdiffusion. *Proc First Intern Meeting on Forensic Toxicol,* 1963, London). In this procedure, disposable plastic Petri dishes* are used. To the inside of the Petri dish cover, 0.1 ml of 0.5N sodium hydroxide solution is distributed by successively touching the pipette tip to the plastic. The individual spots dry rapidly; 1 ml of urine or dilute tissue slurry is transferred to the lower section of the dish and 0.3 g solid silver sulphate added to it; 2 ml of 66% sulphuric acid is placed beside the urine, the vessel tilted to mix the urine and acid and immediately covered with the prepared lid taking care to maintain the assembly horizontal at all times. After a period of twenty hours at 50°C in an oven, the covers are carefully removed and the sodium hydroxide absorbent is transferred to a 10 ml volumetric flask with successive washings from a 5 ml pipette; 3 ml of Belcher's reagent are added and the volume made up to the mark with water. Readings are taken at 622 mμ. Standards of 0-4μg, including the diffusion stage, are similarly prepared.

Belcher's Reagent: 8.2 g sodium acetate in 6 ml glacial acetic acid and sufficient water to effect solution. Transfer quantitatively to a 200 ml volumetric flask. Dissolve 0.0479 g alizarin complexone in 1 ml 20% ammonium acetate with the assistance of 0.1 ml ammonium hydroxide and 5 ml water. Filter this solution through a Whatman No. 1 filter paper into the 200 ml flask. Wash the filter with a few drops of water. Add 100 ml of acetone to the flask, slowly with swirling. Dissolve separately 0.0612 g lanthanum chloride in 2.5 ml 2M hydrochloric acid warming gently and add this to the contents of the volumetric flask. Dilute to 200 ml with water. Mix well, cool to room temperature and adjust accurately to 200 ml.

Urines should be stored in polyethylene vessels, not glass. The range of the method as described is 0-4μg of fluoride, but in-

*Millipore No. PD 10.04700, available from British Drug Houses.

creased sensitivity may be obtained by using 281 mμ. Urine levels do not normally exceed 50μg/100 ml.

For interpretation of results see p. 54.

Method 2

(Hall, R.J.: *Analyst, 88:*76, 1963) .

One millilitre of blood, CSF or urine is mixed with 0.3 ml of N lithium hyroxide and 0.2 ml of 0.2M magnesium succinate in a platinum crucible and dried at 110°C. The crucible is covered with a lid and placed in a small metal cannister having a tightly fitting lid. This is placed in a cold muffle furnace and the temperature is slowly raised to 400°C which is maintained for fifteen hours. When cool the ash is transferred to a polythene diffusion bottle together with 0.4 ml of 0.5N perchloric acid and 2 x 0.3 ml portions of water as washings.

Rectangles of 3.0 x 1.2 cm, Whatman 541 filter paper, previously washed with hot distilled water and dried, are pushed into the lumen of an adaptor of 5 mm internal diameter polythene tubing inside the well of the bottle cap. The free 2 cm of paper is impregnated with 15μl of 0.2M magnesium succinate placed 0.5 cm from the free edge; 2 ml of silver sulphate in perchloric acid (4 g finely powdered silver sulphate with 2 ml water and 23 ml 72% perchloric acid and warmed to 80°C, add 75 ml of 72% perchloric acid and cool) are added immediately from a burette and the cap is screwed tightly into position. Seal the junction between cap and bottle with a mixture of equal parts of ceresine and carnuba waxes. Diffuse at 60°C for twenty-four hours. Remove the paper with forceps and place in stoppered 5 ml tubes. Add 2 ml lanthanum alizarin complexanate reagent and place in a water bath at 60°C for ten minutes. Cool and extract the blue complex with 1.5, 1.0 and 1.0 ml portions of butanol solvent. Adjust the volume to 4.3 ml with solvent, shake for thirty seconds with 1 ml of water and cool to 0°C. Separate the aqueous phase by centrifuging and adjust the volume to 4 ml. Read at 570 mμ. Prepare standards in the same way of 0.1-1.0μg F.

Lanthanum Reagent: Suspend 38.5 mg of reprecipitated alizarin complexone in 2 ml of water in a test tube; add 0.2 ml of M sodium acetate and warm to dissolve. Make up to 200 ml with water. Take 30 ml with constant mixing into 50 ml of succinate buffer (0.4724 g succinic acid in 96 ml water with warming; cool; add 3.2 ml of N sodium hydroxide and make up to 100 ml) and 20 ml of lanthanum nitrate (43.3 mg La(NO)$_3$ 6H$_2$O in 100 ml water). Add 25 ml of t-butanol. Prepare fresh each day.

Butanol Solvent: 3 ml of hydroxylamine hydrochloride solution (6.95 g recrystallised in 100 ml water) with 97 ml isobutanol, shake until homogeneous.

For interpretation of results see p. 54.

FLUOROACETATE

Sodium fluoracetate and fluoroacetamide are widely used as rodenticides and their detection used to be ensured by the determination of organic fluorine but, recently, a gas chromatographic method has been developed which provides a most useful alternative method.

Method

Tissue (Ramsey, L.L., and Clifford, P.A.: *JAOAC, 32:*788, 1949). Grind 10 g of tissue and put in a 100 ml beaker and boil gently with 300 ml water for about half an hour. Transfer and comminute rinsing with 2 x 25 ml water. Add 5 ml of 0.67 N sulphuric acid and 50-75 ml 20% w/v phosphotungstic acid to precipitate all the proteins. Add water to make the total weight 600 g. Shake and filter through a Buchner funnel. Add 12 ml 0.67 N sulphuric acid and extract continuously with ether for one hour. Proceed as for ether extract below.

Urine (Sawyer, R.; Cox, B.G.; Dixon, E.J., and Thompson, J.: *J Sci Fd Agri, 18:*287, 1967). To an ether extract of urine is added 1 ml of N-methyl-di-N-octylamine and evaporated to approximately 20 ml. The concentrate is poured onto a 2 cm plug of anhydrous sodium sulphate prepared into a 2 cm x 25 cm column with tapered tip. Collect the eluate in a Danish-Kuderna flask and evaporate to 1 ml over a boiling water bath. Wash down with 5-10 ml, repeat the evaporation and disconnect the 5 ml flask. Remove the remaining ether by blowing air on the surface. Wash down the sides with 0.1-0.2 ml ether and evaporate again. Add 10μl of freshly prepared diazomethane in ether, stopper and stand for one to two minutes. A microlitre aliquot is examined by GLC using a 5′ column of (a) PEG on AW-DCMS Chromosorb W 20/80, and (b) dinonylphthalate on silanised Chromosorb, with an injection block temperature at 100°C and a column temperature at 50°C. Methyl fluoroacetate has retention times of 22.0 minutes and 7.2 minutes on the two columns respectively.

FOOD AND DRINK

The toxicologist is often asked to examine these items in suspected criminal cases or in outbreaks of widespread illness thought to be associated with poisoning. Even sealed pharmaceutical ampoules may come under suspicion. Perhaps the best advice that can be offered is never to taste the offending article. A sample of whisky that turned out to be adulterated with urine is perhaps the example most likely to deter enthusiasts.

The elementary tests of a close visual inspection coupled with smell, and a pH measurement are the first preliminary tests and the analysis should then follow the procedure outlined for analysis of the alimentary tract (Chap. 6). The variety of potential adulterants is endless and circumstances should not be allowed to stop or distract systematic analysis. Vomiting, diarrhoea and convulsions occur from so many adulterants that, as has been said above, guesses only waste valuable material. Biological tests must be considered — especially if sealed ampoules are involved. The substitution of insulin for morphine is a bizarre example in which chemical analysis might only reveal the phenolic preservative but injection into mice would readily show the presence of the poison.

The toxicologist must be prepared to analyse many of these samples with the assurance of the police that the complaint is from a person of devious psychological personality and that there is no doubt nothing to be found. The number of times these complaints turn out to be justified must keep the analyst constantly on his guard.

IMIPRAMINE (Tofranil®) and DESMETHYLIMIPRAMINE (Pertofran®)

Method

(Rutter, E.R., based on Forrest, I.S.; Forrest, F.M., and Mason, A.S.: *Amer J Psy, 116:*1021, 1960) .

Blood, 10 ml, is stirred with 2 ml water and 8 ml concentrated hydrochloric acid and heated in a beaker in a boiling water bath for five minutes. Remove and place in an ice bath. When cool, add 12 ml 60% w/v potassium hydroxide which has been previously washed with ether. Keep cool and check the pH to ensure alkalinity. If acid, add more alkali. Shake with 150 ml ether, breaking any emulsion by centrifuging. Separate and shake the aqueous phase with a further 50 ml portion of ether. Combine the ether fractions and wash in sequence with 10 ml 2.5% sodium hydroxide, 10 ml water and 5 ml water. Extract the ether with 5 ml 0.1N sulphuric acid. To 1.5 ml of this sulphuric acid add 1.5 ml of reagent and transfer immediately to a 1 cm glass cell and into a spectrophotometer already balanced at 580 mμ against water. Read continuously until a maximum reading is obtained (about 30 seconds) . A calibration graph is obtained with standards in the range 0-50μg giving optical density readings in the range 0-1.0.

Reagent: This is prepared as follows: mix 25 parts 0.2% potassium dichromate, 25 parts 30% sulphuric acid, 25 parts 20% perchloric acid and 25 parts 50% nitric acid.

Interpretation of Results

Imipramine is metabolised to desmethylimipramine and in patients on long-term therapy of 50-300 mg per day blood levels of total drug and metabolite are in the range of 5-60μg/100 ml. Levels in cases of acute poisoning exceed the upper range figure. There are many metabolites of imipramine and desmethylimipramine and these can be separated on TLC. To the toxicologist requiring to show an overdose had been ingested, the colorimetric method described above will give the answer quickly and simply without recourse to the study of the metabolites. It should be noted that renal failure occurs in imipramine overdose and extremely low, virtually nil, levels can be obtained on urinanalysis. Liver levels are much higher (see Chap. 7Aii).

REFERENCES

BICKEL, M.N.; BROCHON, R.; FRIOLET, B.; HERRMANN, B., and STOFER, A.R.: Clinical and biochemical results of a fatal case of desipramine intoxication. *Psychopharmacologia (Berlin)*, *10*:431, 1967.

CURRY, A.S.: Seven fatal cases involving imipramine in man. *J Pharm Pharmacol, 16*:265, 1964.

MOODY, J.P.; TAIT, A.C., and TODRICK, A.: Plasma levels of imipramine and desmethylimipramine during therapy. *Brit J Psy, 113*:183, 1967.

INSULIN

Proof of insulin poisoning with its clinical picture of hypo-glycemic coma, convulsions, sweating and altered size of eye pupils can be obtained either by demonstrating reversal of the condition by oral and intravenous glucose during life and by ante-mortem blood sugar determinations, or by the demonstration of insulin at the site of the injection in fatal cases.

It is rare that there is any useful purpose served by the meas-urement of post-mortem blood sugar concentrations because gly-cogenolysis in the liver with consequent diffusion of glucose into the heart raises such levels by many hundreds of milligrams per 100 ml within a few hours of death and glycolysis lowers the peripheral blood sugar levels at a slower but still significantly rapid rate. The terminal agonal release of adrenaline and hence a rise in blood glucose at about the moment of death must also be remembered. However, if analyses are done within an hour or two of death on blood from two or more sites from the body, and all show a normal value of glucose, the absence of ante-mortem sugar abnormalities can probably be excluded.

Tissue taken from injection sites should be kept in the refrig-erator up to analysis; once deep frozen it must not be allowed to thaw. Insulin is destroyed in the pancreas very rapidly after death and there is no fear of artefacts in peripheral injection sites. In-sulin is relatively stable in muscle and a delay of several weeks before analysis is of little consequence. Recovery can be expected to be about 50 per cent even after three weeks at 0°C.

The method of processing the tissue for the isolation of the protein is not difficult but requires experience. Anyone wishing to perform the extraction is advised to contact the nearest drug firm processing pancreas for insulin and obtain their guidance. It is most important to test the extraction process by adding insulin to muscle before attempting to isolate any from the case sample. This procedure also provides control extracts for the assay stage. The stability of insulin in muscle but its instability during extraction processes are very pertinent reasons for this advice.

Two methods are available for testing the crude protein extract which usually weighs about 1 g from each 50 g aliquot of tissue; these are to demonstrate its activity on the glucose uptake of the isolated rat diaphragm and to show, its hypoglycaemic activity when injected into animals, usually mice. The former is a research technique and, although very sensitive, its use cannot be recommended for routine use in toxicological analysis. The injection of aliquots of the extract in very weakly acidic saline into mice is a reliable and fairly sensitive procedure: 20 milliunits are usually sufficient to produce convulsions, reversed by an injection of 50 mg of glucose in mice which have not been recently fed. Five mice batches are suitable for rough screening although several hundred are needed for accurate quantitation. Because 20 mg of extract is a convenient weight for injection these figures mean that if about 1 unit of any type of insulin is present in the tissue its detection should be straightforward.

A a result of the extensive work done in an investigation in a murder case (Birkinshaw *et al.*, 1958) no compound other than insulin was suggested as being capable of reacting in the mouse test exactly in the same way. If, however, further confirmation is required the following tests were found to be suitable:

1. Abolition of the biological activity in the rat diaphragm test under anaerobic conditions.
2. Loss of activity on treatment with cysteine.
3. Loss of acivity on treatment with proteolytic enzymes such as pepsin and, in particular, insulinase.
4. Comparison of the rate of hypoglycaemic effect in guinea pigs compared with insulin.
5. Loss of activity when insulin antisera is added to the extract.
6. Chromatographic separation of the insulin from other proteins using paper or columns and demonstration that the activity parallels that of insulin.

It is obvious that these techniques require experience not usually within that of the average toxicologist. He should however, be aware of their use and be able of carrying out the isolation and the mouse assay.

An immunological method of assaying insulin in plasma using iodine 125 is now available, together with the necessary reagents.* A liquid or crystal scintillation counter or windowless gas-flow counter is necessary.

In Los Angeles in 1968 William Dale Archerd was convicted on three counts of first degree murder involving insulin and Professor E.R. Arquilla at UCLA Medical Centre gave evidence that the insulin level in the formalin-treated brain which had been preserved for more than a year was higher than in control brain. Biological (alloxan diabetic mice) and radioimmunological assay methods were used.

REFERENCES

BIRKINSHAW, V.J.; GURD, M.R.; RANDALL, S.S.; CURRY, A.S.; PRICE, D.E., and WRIGHT, P.H.: *Brit Med J, ii:*463, 1958.

JANITZKI, VON U.; PROCH, W.; SCHLEYER, F.; DITSCHUNEIT, H., and PFEIFFER, E.: *Medicina Experimentalis, 3:*17, 1960.

---

*From the Radiochemical Centre, Amersham, Bucks, England. (Data sheet 5581.)

IODIDE

Method

Blood, 10 ml, is mixed with 12 ml of saturated potassium hydroxide in a 300 ml nickel crucible and evaporated on a steam bath. The crucible is then placed in a muffle at 250°C for thirty minutes and the temperature raised to 360°C where it is kept for ten minutes. On removing and cooling, the potassium iodide is removed from the mass of carbonate and hydroxide by dissolving it firstly with 25 ml 95% ethanol followed by four further portions of 10 ml ethanol, 0.5 ml saturated potassium hydroxide is added to the combined alcoholic extracts which are evaporated on a steam bath and then in a muffle at 385°C for fifteen minutes. The dried extracts are transferred to a distillation flask and 2 ml 50% sulphuric acid, one drop 10% $Fe_2(SO_4)_3$, and 2 ml 3% hydrogen peroxide are added quickly. A bead is inserted and the liberated iodine is distilled into water containing 0.2 ml 3% sulphuric acid and 0.2 ml 10% sodium bisulphite. Distillation is carried out almost to dryness with additions of 2 ml 3% hydrogen peroxide at intervals. The distillate is boiled for two minutes and then evaporated to 5-6 ml after it has been made alkaline to litmus with 10% potassium hydroxide. Add one drop methanol and enough 3% sulphuric acid to make the solution neutral: then add two drops of 3% sulphuric acid, and five drops of bromine water. Boil down cautiously to 2 ml which converts the hydriodic acid to iodic acid and removes excess bromine. The solution is cooled, a little boiled starch added together with excess potassium iodide, and the liberated iodine titrated with 0.005N thiosulphate — 1 ml of 0.005N thiosulphate is equivalent to 106μg of iodine.

Interpretation of Results

Little is known of the toxic concentration of iodide in the blood. Absorption via the bladder when sodium iodide is used as a contrast medium is extremely rapid. It can be detected in the blood within thirty seconds of irrigation. In one fatal case investigated by the author in which the sodium iodide was accidentally left in the bladder for two hours, when a further pint of 10% solution was introduced, the blood level was 100 mg/100 ml.

IRON

Occasionally, when ingestion of ferrous or ferric salts is suspected, a method for iron assay on the acid dialysate from the gastro-intestinal tract is of value.

Method

(Kennedy, R.P.: *J Biol Chem, 74*:385, 1927 [modified]) .

An aliquot of the dialysate is digested with 5 ml of concentrated sulphuric acid and 2 ml of perchloric acid in a Kjeldahl flask over a flame until white fumes appear.

After cooling, one drop of nitric acid is added and the volume made up to 100 ml. To a 10 ml aliquot is added 0.1 ml of 30% w/v aqueous ammonium persulphate solution and 7 ml of 20% w/v aqueous ammonium thiocyanate solution. The optical density of the solution is measured after two, and before thirty, minutes at 470 mμ.

A 50 mg/100 ml standard gives an optical density of approximately 0.6.

Interpretation of Results

Whole blood contains about 50 mg/100 ml of iron. Most of this is in the red cells. Because of this very high normal concentration no useful conclusions can be drawn from blood or tissue iron levels after the ingestion of toxic doses of soluble iron salts; but see below for iron in serum.

IRON IN PLASMA OR SERUM

Method

(Ramsey, W.N.M., *Clin Chem Acta*, 2:214, 1957).

Mix 2 ml of serum or plasma with 2 ml fresh 0.1M sodium sulphite and 2 ml 0.1% 2:2'-dipyridyl in 3% v/v acetic acid in a tube with a ground glass neck. Heat in a boiling water bath for five minutes and cool. Add 1 ml of chloroform, stopper and shake violently for thirty seconds. Remove the stopper and centrifuge. If not clear, repeat the shaking and centrifuging. Remove the supernatant and read at 520 mμ. Standards are prepared from ferric ammonium sulphate in 0.005N hydrocloric acid.

An alternative method is given by D.S. Fischer in *Clinical Chemistry* (13:7,1967) and he suggests that a serum iron level of 600μg/100 ml is in the low part of the toxic range.

ISONICOTINYL HYDRAZIDE

Method

(Bjornesjo, K.B., and Jarnulf, B.: *Scand J Clin Lab Invest, 20:* 39, 1967).

Mix carefully 2 ml of serum, 4 ml of distilled water and 2 ml of 20% w/v metaphosphoric acid and allow the mixture to stand for ten minutes. The protein precipitate is centrifuged off and 4 ml of supernatant are transferred to another tube and mixed with 2 ml 2N acetic acid and 2 ml of a freshly prepared solution made by mixing aliquots of 2% w/v sodium nitroprusside and 4N sodium hydroxide. The absorbance is measured after exactly two minutes at 440 mμ in a 3 cm cell against a reagent blank prepared by mixing 3 ml distilled water, 1 ml 20% metaphosphoric acid, 2 ml 2N acetic acid and 2 ml of the nitritopentacyanoferroate reagent. Standards of 20, 30 and 40μg isoniazid per millilitre are run in parallel. The drug may be also extracted from tissues by a mixture of n-butanol and ether and assayed by comparative ultra-violet spectrophotometry.

Interpretation of Results

Pragowski reported seven cases of lethal suicidal intoxication and noted the clinical signs of convulsions, cyanosis and unconsciousness with autopsy findings of generalised congestion with haemorrhages within the CNS. He noted large quantities of unchanged drug in the alimentary tract and concentrations from 9 mg/100 g in the kidney in one case (with blood and liver levels of 41.0 and 78.5 mg/100 g respectively) to 35.18 and 61.64 mg/100 g in liver and kidney in two other cases. Death usually occurred in one to four hours, although one survived two days.

REFERENCE

PRAGOWSKI, T.: *Proc. 3rd Int. Meeting in Forensic Medicine, Pathology and Toxicology, London, 1963.*

LSD AND OTHER HALLUCINOGENS

I know of no suitable method for screening urine routinely for LSD, but sugar-cubes, blotting paper and other media which might be impregnated with LSD often come to the toxicologist's laboratory. LSD is light- and heat-sensitive and precautions to minimise its decomposition must be taken. It is not very soluble in organic solvents and extraction is achieved at pH 8.5-9 from the minimum saturated aqueous sodium chloride solution with at least a three volume excess of organic solvent which may be chloroform of 2% isoamyl alcohol in n-heptane. LSD can be purified by extraction into 0.01M hydrochloric acid and then re-extracted from alkaline solution into organic solvent. Evaporation should be in the dark under nitrogen and reduced pressure at ambient temperature.

Identification and Assay

The blue fluorescence of LSD in ultra-violet light, which can be seen on sugar-cubes, paper, etc., is a most useful screening test; it can be quantitated using a spectrofluorometer using an excitation wavelength of 335 mμ and a fluorescence wavelength of 435 mμ. Sensitivities of 10 nanograms/ml can be obtained. A sensitive rapid colour test is to evaporate an aliquot on a piece of filter paper and test with 1% p-dimethylaminobenzaldehyde in ethanol containing 10% concentrated hydrochloric acid. On warming, a blue colour is obtained. To differentiate LSD from ergot alkaloids and other hallucinogens, paper and thin layer chromatography are used.

Method

(Clarke, E.G.C.:see Table XXV).

Paper Chromatography: System Butanol/citric acid on citrated paper — see Chapter 4.

TLC: Silica-Gel G; methanol: 880 NH$_3$ (100: 1.5).

TABLE XXV
CHROMATOGRAPHY OF HALLUCINOGENS

Rf on Paper	Compound	Fluorescence 254 mµ	pDMB Reaction Colour	Rf TLC System
0.05	Psilocybin	dark blue	grey	0.34
0.11	Lysergamide	blue	blue	0.18
0.12	Serotonin	pale yellow	purple	0.25
0.13	6-hydroxy DMT	blue	blue	0.32
0.16	Bufotenin	pale blue	purple	0.32
0.18	7-hydroxy DMT	absorbs	green	0.33
0.18	Lysergic acid	blue	blue	0.33
0.25	Ergometrine	blue	blue	0.23
0.25	5-methoxytryptamine	white	purple	0.25
0.25	Mescalin	nil	faint yellow	0.23
0.26	5-methoxy DMT	white	purple	0.32
0.31	Psilocin	absorbs	grey	0.34
0.35	Tryptamine	blue	purple	0.27
0.38	Dimethytryptamine	blue	purple	0.34
0.40	Methylergometrine	blue	blue	0.30
0.40	N-methyltryptamine	blue	purple	0.16
0.45	Methylsergide	blue	blue	0.49
0.47	LSD	blue	blue	0.63
0.63	Dihydroergotamine	green	blue	0.56
0.65	Ergotamine	blue	blue	0.58
0.65	Ergosine	blue	blue	0.58
0.80	Dihydroergotoxin	green	blue	0.68
0.82	Ergotoxin	blue	blue	0.78

REFERENCES

AXELROD, J.; BRADY, R.O.; WITKOP, and EVARTS, E.V.: The metabolism of LSD. *Nature, 178:*143, 1956; *ibid,* The distribution and metabolism of LSD. *Ann NY Acad Sci, 66:*435, 1957.

AGHAJANIAN, G.K., and BING, O.H.L.: Persistence of LSD in the plasma of human subjects. *Clin Pharm Ther, 5:*611, 1964.

CLARKE, E.G.C.: The identification of some proscribed psychedelic drugs. *J For Sci Soc, 7:*46, 1967.

DAL CORTIVO, L.A.; BROICH, J.R..; DIHRBERG, A., and NEWMAN, B.: Identification and estimation of LSD by TLC and fluorimetry. *Anal Chem, 38:*1959, 1966.

WAGNER, J.G.; AGHAJANIAN, G.K., and BING, O.H.L.: Correlation of performance test scores with "tissue concentration" of LSD in human subjects. *Clin Pharm Ther, 9:*1985, 1968.

LEAD

Ingestion of paint by young children often leads to lead poisoning. This clinical entity can undoubtedly be unrecognised and in any seriously ill child it must be considered. Poisoning of adults is not as common but I have experience of two cases in which it was used with criminal intent. The adulteration of health salts with powdered metallic lead was one instance and illustrated that the toxicologist must be on his guard for such bizarre occurrences.

Analyses for metals using dithizone are never simple procedures and lead is probably the most tedious one. It is advisable to keep a set of lead-free glassware especially for the determination. Every piece of glass should be well washed with hot dilute hydrochloric acid and then stood in concentrated dithizone in chloroform. The glass cells used in the spectrophotometer must not be forgotten. At any filtering stage the filter paper must be pre-cleaned by running hot dilute hydrochloric acid through it followed by copious amounts of distilled water. It is emphasised that all these procedures are essential.

The dithizone used in the determination should be purified before use by shaking a strong solution in carbon tetrachloride with ammonia. The separated alkaline layer is then shaken with fresh carbon tetrachloride after adding dilute hydrochloric acid to acidity. The purified dithizone is then in the organic solvent. The solution should be shielded from the light and prepared fresh daily.

If reagents are also kept separately, after purification by continued washing with dithizone in chloroform, then this too can shorten each subsequent analysis. Potassium cyanide cannot be purified in this way and special lead-free reagent must be used: this can be purchased. The sulphuric acid used must also be lead free; this can only be determined by experiment. Hydrochloric acid often contains traces of lead and must be redistilled before use. Care must be taken to use pipettes whose calibrations are not marked in lead paint. This stresses that *every* piece of glassware must be examined and cleaned before use.

Method 1

(Tompsett, S.L.: *Analyst, 81:333,* 1956).

If urine is being analysed a volume of 250 ml is taken and is evaporated directly. It is then treated exactly the same as the phosphate-treated blood. Bone is boiled with N hydrochloric acid until it is dissolved. After dilution it is extracted with three portions of 25 ml ether after addition of 10 ml aqueous 2% sodium diethyldithiocarbamate. The ether is evaporated and the analysis continued as for blood. Tissue is homogenised with equal volumes of water and 10% sodium dihydrogen phosphate and the analysis continued as for blood.

If blood is being analysed 20 ml of blood and 100 ml 10% $Na_2HPO_4.12H_2O$ are evaporated on a boiling water bath in a silica dish and are then strongly heated over a bunsen flame to destroy the organic material. A little nitric acid is added and the digest is again heated. The residue is dissolved in 75 ml of water containing 5 ml concentrated hydrochloric acid and filtered into a 250 ml flask. The crucible and filter funnel are washed with 25 ml of water. Add 50 ml 20% sodium citrate and adjust the pH to 7.5-8.0 by addition of ammonia. Cool, add 5 ml 10% potassium cyanide and extract with 3 x 50 ml portions of ether adding 5 ml of 2% sodium diethyldithiocarbamate after the first ether portion. Shake each extraction for at least two minutes. Wash the combined ether extracts with water and, after separating, evaporate the ether. If 20 g of blood are being analysed the residue should be digested by boiling with 0.4 ml of concentrated sulphuric acid and 1 ml of 100 volume hydrogen peroxide. The cooled digest should be dissolved in 0.4 ml glacial acetic acid, 2 ml of 880 ammonia and water to 10 ml. If urine, tissue or bone are being analysed the expected amount of lead will be higher and the digestion is made with 1 ml of concentrated sulphuric acid and 1 ml of hydrogen peroxide. Dilution to 25 ml is made with 1 ml glacial acetic acid and 5 ml of ammonia and water. To a 10 ml aliquot are added six drops 5% w/v sulphurous acid, 5 ml 1% potassium cyanide and 10 ml carbon tetrachloride. A solution of dithizone in ammonia is then added with vigorous shaking dropwise until the brownish colour of the dithizone is seen in the aqueous phase. This dithizone reagent is made by shaking 5 ml of 1% dithizone in carbon tetrachloride with 10 ml of 0.1N ammonia solution: the mixture is then centrifuged and the supernatant fluid used. It must be freshly prepared. The optical density readings of the separated carbon tetrachloride layer are then read at 525 mμ and at 620 mμ. The carbon tetrachloride is then shaken with 5 ml of 0.1N sulphuric acid to decompose the lead dithizonate: the carbon tetrachloride is separated and the readings are taken again at the same wavelengths.

Calculations: The first set of readings give a measure of the lead-dithizone complex at 525 mμ and of unreacted dithizone at 620 mμ. The second set of readings give the zero reading at 525 mμ for lead dithizonate and also measures the increase in dithizone at 620 mμ caused by the decomposition of the lead dithizonate by the sulphuric acid. The optical density difference at 620 mμ is therefore directly proportional to the molecular amount of dithizone liberated by the lead in solution and is independent of the actual amount of dithizone used or of the impurities it contains. The calibration graph using this wavelength (620 mμ) difference is therefore a constant which, if the instrumentation is the same, should be reproducible in every laboratory. The difference in readings at 525 mμ is a useful cross check on the analysis being a normal colorimetric measure of lead dithizonate. In our hands the O.D. difference for 10μg lead in 10 ml carbon tetrachloride gives an O.D. difference at 620 mμ of 0.29.

Method 2

Atomic Absorption (A.R. Knott, personal communication). A Perkin-Elmer 303 Atomic Absorption Spectrophotometer with a Boling three slot burner is used in the method described below. Scale expansion (x 10) is used: 1 g of a 1:1 macerate of liver is evaporated to dryness in a silica dish on a water bath. The residue is then dampened with 50% w/v magnesium nitrate solution, which has been freed of lead by adjusting to pH 9 with ammonia and thymol blue indicator and extracted repeatedly with a solution of 2 mg/100 ml of dithizone in carbon tetrachloride until successive extracts remain green and then washed with carbon tetrachloride three times. The dampened residue is again dried and placed in a muffle at 500°C for one hour. The crucible is removed, cooled and the ash dampened with the minimum volume of concentrated nitric acid, dried carefully under an infra-red heater, and replaced in the muffle for a further one hour. After cooling, 1 ml lead-free 5N hydrochloric acid is added with agitation and the solution gently evaporated to dryness with a watch glass three-quarters covering the crucible. The residue is dissolved in 1 ml 0.1N hydrochloric acid and washed with water into a 20 ml vial fitted with a snap-on polythene cap. The pH is adjusted to 2-3 using thymol blue and an indicator paper; 0.5 ml of 1% w/v aqueous ammonium pyrrolidine dithiocarbamate is added and the lead chelate extracted in 2.5 ml of water-saturated methyl isobutyl ketone by hand shaking for two minutes; stand for five minutes and centrifuge for ten minutes. The top organic layer is aspirated into the atomic absorption flame and readings taken at 2833 Å and 2203 Å. The difference reading gives a quantitation. Standards are in the range of 0.2-2μg per 2.5 ml organic solvent.

For urine (5-10 ml) the pH is adjusted to pH 2-3 with 5% trichloroacetic acid; any precipitate is centrifuged off and the extraction with ammonium pyrrolidine dithiocarbamate and methyl isobutyl ketone is performed direct, as described above. Blood is ashed in the same way as diluted macerated tissue. This method is suitable for nontoxic levels; in cases of suspected poisoning an aliquot of the hydrochloric acid extract is taken.

Interpretation of Results

Levels over 70μg per 100 ml of lead in the blood of adults are indicative of abnormal exposure.

Koumides (*Proc. 1st Int. Meeting in Forensic Toxicology London, 1963*) reported that he had not seen a case of lead intoxication in a child at, or within a few days of, the time of onset of the illness in whose blood the concentration of lead was lower than 45μg/100 g. However, it is clear from this report that levels only slightly above this will be found in mentally intoxicated children suffering from lead poisoning. Normal blood levels in children not exposed to lead are in the range 0-30μg/100 g.

Urine is extensively used for testing for lead and it is generally agreed that levels over 8μg/100 ml are indicative of exposure. Usually a diagnosis is made on a consideration of lead analyses on blood and urine, coupled with a consideration of the clinical symptoms and examination of a blood film for punctate basophilia. In addition, there may be a coproporphyrinuria and an elevated δ-amino laevulinic acid excretion. In fatal cases, which are often unrecognised until they come to the attention of the toxicologist, analyses on the other organs are performed; Tompsett gives the following figures for normal healthy adults. Obviously these should be exceeded for a positive diagnosis. X-ray examination of bone also enables the lead lines to be seen and if the ingested poison is a lead paint it too can be seen in the gastrointestinal tract on x-ray.

Normal levels:

Liver: 0.09-0.46 mg/100 g
Kidney: 0.07-0.37 mg/100 g
Brain: 0.02-0.07 mg/100 g
Bone: Rib: 0.05-1.29 mg/100 g
Vertebrae: 0.26-1.47 mg/100 g
Femur: 1.82-10.8 mg/100 g
Tibia: 1.53-9.65 mg/100 g

MAGNESIUM

This metal is of importance in general medicine but the toxicologist must also bear it in mind in relation to attempts to procure an abortion and deaths of very young children.

Method

(Orange, M., and Rhein, H. C.: *J Biol Chem, 189*:379, 1951)

Take 0.5 ml of blood and deproteinise with 5.5 ml of 10% trichloroacetic acid. Centrifuge, and to 5 ml of supernatant add 5 ml of 0.1% gum ghatti solution and 5 ml titan yellow solution (7.5 mg/100 ml). Make up to 25 ml with 7.5% sodium hydroxide.

After a few moments read at 540 mμ in the 10 cm path length cells. Calibration standards for solutions in the range 0-5 mg/100 ml blood give optical densities in the range 0-0.53.

Interpretation of Results

Post-mortem peripheral blood usually contains about 5 mg/100 ml of magnesium. Mr. P. O. Rees tells me that in a fatal case of magnesium sulphate poisoning in a young woman he obtained levels of 14 mg/100 ml.

MANGANESE

This metal as one of its salts is frequently a component with iron salts in "anaemia tablets."

Methods

(Copeman, P. R. v. d. R.: *J Forensic Med, 1*:56, 1955)

In a Kjeldahl flask, 10-20 g of tissue are boiled with nitric acid and sulphuric acid to completion of destruction of the organic matter. The volume of sulphuric acid should be 10-15 ml, nitric acid is added when charring seen. Cool when complete and make up to 50 ml with water. Take 20 ml and evaporate in a silica basin on a sand bath until no more white fumes are seen and finally over a flame until all traces of sulphuric acid are removed and the residue is clear. Cool, and treat with 10 ml of water containing 1 ml of a mixture of equal amounts of sulphuric acid and 80% phosphoric acid. Transfer to a 6 x 1¾ Pyrex test-tube and wash with 2 x 5 ml similar portions. Add 0.2-0.3 g potassium periodate and bring to the boil over a flame. Place in a boiling water bath until the permanganate colour is fully developed. There should be no covering to the test-tube: match the colour against 0.001N potassium permanganate standards: 1 ml is equivalent to 0.011 mg manganese.

Interpretation of Results

Copeman gives the following figures for normal levels in nontoxic tissue.

	mg/100g	Maximum Observed
Liver	0.13	0.16
Kidney	0.076	0.10
Intestines	0.064	0.083

MEPROBAMATE

For the quantitative determination of meprobamate in blood and tissues several methods have been published. Bedson's method (see below) is not highly reproducible nor specific, but alternatives are time-consuming. Reagents are unstable, but this is so far unavoidable. Undoubtedly, gas chromatography is the method of choice, followed by weighing the neutral extract of an ether extraction provided levels are high and the product crystalline, but the following colorimetric procedure may be used.

Method 1

(Madsen, O. D.: *Clin Chim Acta,* 7:481, 1962. Merli, S., and de Zorzi, C., *Zacchia, 24:*274, 1961)

To 1 ml serum add two drops 25% ammonium hydroxide, 1 ml saturated aqueous potassium chloride and 25 ml of a mixture of equal volumes of carbon tetrachloride and chloroform. Shake and centrifuge and separate the organic layer. Filter it through glass wool. Wash the glass wool with 10 ml of solvent mixture and evaporate the combined organic fractions. To the extract add 0.2 ml AAA reagent, and 0.2 ml DMB and mix. Add 1 ml ATA and mix. Stopper loosely and heat at 50°C in a water bath for exactly ten minutes. Cool quickly. Add 1 ml benzene and filter through 6 cm-diameter Whatman No. 41H (541) paper into small glass tubes. Read at 550 mμ within fifteen minutes.

AAA — Reagent: Three volumes acetone and one volume glacial acetic acid prepared fresh.

ATA — Reagent: A saturated solution of 25% w/v antimony trichloride in chloroform prepared by heating the mixture on a hot plate until complete dissolution. Filter through Whatman No. 41 (H541) paper. Store the bottle in a plastic bag to avoid water absorption.

DMB Reagent: 1% w/v of p-dimethylaminobenzaldehyde in benzene.

Method 2

(Bedson, H. S.: Coma due to meprobamate intoxication, report of a case confirmed by chemical analysis. *Lancet, i:*288, 1959)

Meprobamate can be detected and estimated by heating an aliquot of the evaporated neutral ether extract (see p. 57) with 1 ml of concentrated sulphuric acid at 100°C for thirty minutes. After addition of 2 ml of water and cooling, the spectrum is measured fifteen minutes later. The optical density difference between 440 mμ and 500 mμ is suitable for quantitation, but the major peak at 245 mμ is better. A calibration for 0-100μg gives optical densities in the region 0-0.4 at the latter wavelength.

For interpretation of results see p. 69.

REFERENCES

KANTER, S.L.: Acetone as a source of error in the colorimetric determination of meprobamate. *Clin Chim Acta, 17*:147, 1967.

PROKES, L.H.J.: The oscillopolarographic determination of meprobamate in biological material. *Chemicke Zvesti, 18*:425, 1964.

HOFFMAN, A.J., and LUDWIG, B.J.: An improved colorimetric method for the determination of meprobamate in biological fluids. *J Amer Pharm Ass, 48*:740, 1959.

MERCURY

This is an extremely toxic metal when ingested in the form of its soluble salts. The variety of methods whereby absorption of these salts arises is very wide indeed, ranging from homicidal poisoning, the ingestion of calomel by infants, the absorption of mercury vapour from fingerprint powder by police officers, laboratory and industrial workers, skin absorption of mercurial ointments and vaginal pastes to the accidental ingestion by infants of grass treated with mercurial (lawn) sand.

Whenever a method for the estimation of mercury using dithizone is to be used the reader is recommended to read first the paper by Irving, Andrew and Risdon (1949).

Measurement of urinary excretion is a common method of screening for mercury poisoning but, in sudden deaths from an unknown cause, the kidney should be analysed. If a high concentration is found in the kidney the liver should then be examined.

Most mercuric salts are extremely volatile and students should beware of adding, say 5μg of mercuric chloride in 1 ml of water to a blood sample in beginning a positive control test for mercury and then evaporating the sample on a steam bath: all the mercury will be lost. Even the experienced worker may be misled into underestimating the volatility of mercuric salts and all stages of the analysis must be included when standard graphs are being prepared.

The use of "reversion technique" of spectrophotometry for mercury, as for lead, means that the calibration is independent of dithizone concentration or impurities.

Method 1

Kidney, 2 g, is refluxed with 2 ml of a 50:50 mixture of concentrated nitric and sulphuric acids for thirty minutes to destroy all organic matter. The conditions of refluxing are critical and must be checked by adequate control experiments. The reflux condenser must be especially efficient being preferably a coil type; the more usual double surface type is not sufficiently effective to prevent loss of mercury. The temperature of refluxing must be kept low. A micro burner is a convenient flame. When heating is finished, cool in ice, and pour 40 ml of water down the condenser into the flask. Cool again and add 2 ml of 50% aqueous solution of hydroxylamine hydrochloride and reflux again for one minute. Cool in ice, filter through a previously acid washed filter paper into a 50 ml flask and make up to the mark. Transfer to a separating funnel and shake with 2-3 ml of chloroform which is discarded. Shake next with 10 ml of an ice-cold solution of dithizone in chloroform which has an optical density at 600 mμ of approximately 0.6-0.7. Run off 3.5 ml of the chloroform layer into a 1 cm cuvette and read at 600 mμ. Next run off approximately 5 ml of the same solution into a 25 ml separating funnel and shake with 5 ml of a solution of 10.2 g potassium hydrogen phthalate and 30 g potassium iodide made up to 500 ml with water. Read the chloroform layer also at 600 mμ. Exact standards are done by adding known quantities of mercuric chloride to tissue that has been shown to be free of the metal. The calibration curve is prepared by plotting the difference in optical density readings at 600 mμ between the dithizone solutions before and after shaking with the reversion solution against the known amounts of mercury. In our hands 20μg of mercury gives a difference reading of 0.695.

Diagnosis of pink disease in children is often confirmed by urinalysis and tests on laboratory and industrial workers handling mercury are routine. Because of the difficulty in interpreting tissue levels of mercury the analysis of urine, which does not result in similar difficulties, is attractive.

Method (Gray, D.J.S.: *Analyst, 77:*436, 1952) : 25 ml of urine are refluxed with 50 ml of water, 10 ml of sulphuric acid (1 + 1) and 1 g potassium permanganate for thirty minutes. If the urine was highly coloured add a further 0.5 g of potassium permanganate and reflux again. Cool. Add 1 ml of 50% hydroxylamine hydrochloride and reflux for one minute. Cool and dilute to 100 ml with water and sufficient dilute sulphuric acid to bring the concentration to 0.25N. From this stage the dithizone assay is exactly as for digested kidney tissue as described above. Great care must be taken by the performance of control experiments to show that loss of mercury does not occur during the refluxing.

Method 2

Atomic Absorption (Based on Willis, J.B.: *Anal Chem, 34:* 614, 1962). *Urine:* 50 ml are made to pH 2.5-4 with trichloroacetic acid and 1 ml of 1% ammonium pyrrolidine dithiocarbamate added. The mercury complex is extracted by shaking with 2 ml methyl n-amyl ketone for two minutes. The organic phase is separated and centrifuged. This solution is aspirated into a Perkin-Elmer 303 Atomic Absorption Spectrophotometer fitted with a Boling three slot burner. Standards are made with 1, 2, 5 and 10μg of mercury in aqueous solution treated in the same way. The 2536 Å line is used.

Tissue: 2 g are refluxed with a 1:1 mixture of concentrated nitric and sulphuric acids as described in the dithizone method above. When digestion is complete the solution is cooled, diluted to about 20 ml with water and adjusted to pH 2-3 using ammonia and indicator paper. The extraction then proceeds as for urine above.

Interpretation of Results

Mercury is a constituent of some livers and kidneys, arising presumably from mercurial amalgams used in dentistry or from the use of ointments. Although normal levels can be as high as 1.72 mg/100 g in liver and 12.7 mg/100 g in kidneys, levels over 1 mg/ 100 g should be fully investigated. In persons receiving mercurial diuretics, levels of up to 2.5 mg/100 g have been found in liver and 27.5 mg/100 g in kidney. However normal nontoxic livers should average at less than 0.5 mg/100 g while in cases of poisoning from mercuric chloride it is likely that the level will be over 2 mg/100 g and, probably will be about 5 mg/100 g.

In two papers, Smith, with Howie and Rodger, has studied "normal" *dry* tissue mercury levels and concentrations in hair. Their values are as follows:

	mg/100g	
Hair	.003–2.44	median 0.420
Kidney	.008–7.93	
Liver	.015–2.0	
Blood	.006–.012	
Brain	0.12–1.52	

These values are difficult to compare accurately with wet tissue levels but appear to agree with normally accepted values.

Because normal healthy individuals can have such high tissue mercury levels the diagnosis of poisoning can rarely be made solely on the analytical results. Mercury excretion in the urine has been shown to vary considerably from minute to minute and, in the living patient, eight-hour samples are recommended for analysis. Rodger and Smith found in forty-six people not knowingly exposed to mercury, a median excretion of $1.3\mu g/100$ ml with a maximum of $13\mu g/100$ ml. Berman is in general agreement; her maximum noted was $3\mu g/100$ ml. Rodger and Smith have found symptoms with levels in the region $30\text{-}100\mu g$ per day, but in serious poisoning cases, one can expect much higher concentrations — up to many milligrams per day. In one case in my experience a transient rise in urinary mercury was observed and the only significant exposure that could be traced was that the patient had swallowed a mercury amalgam tooth filling that had broken off.

Berman reports excretions of $450\mu g/$litre in a patient addicted to a calomel-containing preparation and 2 and 5 mg/litre in two cases of pink disease.

REFERENCES

BERMAN, E.: *Perkin-Elmer Atomic Absorption Newsletter, 6:*58, 1967.

FORNEY, R.R., and HARGER, R.N.: *Federation Proc, 8:*292, 1949.

HOWIE, R.A., and SMITH, H.: Mercury in human tissue. *J For Sci Soc, 7:* 90, 1967.

IRVING, H., RISDON, E.J., and ANDREW, G.: *J Chem Soc, 537* and 541, 1949.

RODGER, W.J., and SMITH, H.: Mercury absorption by fingerprint officers using grey powder. *J For Sci Soc, 7:*86, 1967.

METHANOL

See Chapter 3: An alternative method is as follows.

Method

(L.A. Williams *et al.*: *J Forensic Sci, 6:*119, 1961)

Deproteinise 0.2 ml of serum with 1.8 ml of a solution made by mixing 10 g of trichloroacetic acid with 10 ml of 10% sulphuric acid. To 1 ml of the filtrate or centrifuged supernatant is added 0.1 ml of 5% potassium permanganate. After five minutes a little powdered sodium bisulphite is added until the solution is colourless. 0.2 ml of an 0.5% solution of freshly prepared chromotropic acid is then added with 6 ml of concentrated sulphuric acid. After mixing the solution is heated at 100°C in a boiling bath for five minutes. After cooling the optical density is read at 570 mμ. A calibration curve is prepared from exact standards prepared in the same way.

METHAQUALONE

This hypnotic is a very weak base with an excellent ultra-violet curve and, as such, its isolation and estimation is straightforward provided certain precautions are taken. In a routine screen it will be found in the neutral extract in a tungstic acid extraction procedure if the pH of the aqueous phase after precipitation is about 3; if acidification has resulted in a solution below pH 1, methaqualone will act as a base. Similarly, on shaking ether solutions with 0.1N strength acids will not extract it, but $2NH_2SO_4$ or HCl will remove it from ether. Direct extraction from blood with chloroform, extraction as a base after 40% hydrochloric acid digestion, or a tungstic acid precipitation all give good recoveries.

Method

Blood 5 ml is made alkaline by addition of 1 ml 2% sodium hydroxide and extracted with ether (50 ml). Shake slowly or preferably use a roller extraction technique. Separate the layers and wash the ether with 5 ml water. Separate and shake the ether with 5 ml, 2N H_2SO_4. Read the aqueous layer from 220-290 mμ. Methaqualone has a characteristic curve with λ max = 234 mμ and $E_{1cm}^{1\%}$ = approximately 1090.

Interpretation of Results

Therapeutic blood levels are below 0.5 mg/100 ml. In fatal cases noted by Maehly and Bonnichsen, blood levels were in the range 0.5-3.2mg/100ml with tissue concentrations somewhat higher (3.8-5.8mg/100g in liver and 2.2-9.2mg/100g in kidney). In the living patient recovery has been noted, after haemodialysis, with a blood level of 10.5mg/100ml.

REFERENCES

MAEHLY, A.C., and BONNICHSEN, R.: *Deutsch Z Gers Med,* 57:446, 1966.
YOUNG, J.P.W.: *Brit Med J, 1*:301, 1967.

METHYLPENTYNOL

Method

(Perlman, P. L., and Johnson, C., *J Amer Pharm Ass, 41*:13, 1952)

Alkaline Silver Reagent: To a 250 ml volumetric flask add 125 ml of 0.1N silver nitrate and 15 ml 6N sodium hydroxide solution. Dissolve the precipitate in concentrated ammonia and add 10 ml of ammonia in excess; make up to the mark with water. Prepare fresh.

Silver Standard: 177.45 mg of silver nitrate in 500 ml distilled water contains 0.2 mg/ml of silver. For a working standard dilute x 10.

Rhodanine Solution: A saturated solution of p-dimethylamino-benzal rhodanine in acetone is filtered and diluted x 5 with acetone.

Ammonium Acetate — Gelatin Solution: To 100 ml of a 1.0% filtered aqueous gelatine solution add 25 g of ammonium acetate. Stir until dissolved.

Procedure. A calibration curve is prepared as follows. To 0-80μg silver from the silver standard solution in 5 ml of solution, 1 ml of gelatin ammonium acetate solution is added followed by 2 ml of diluted rhodanine solution and mixed gently. The optical density is read within five minutes at 550 mμ against a blank containing all the reagents with 5 ml of water instead of the silver standard.

Urine: Extract an aliquot of urine with ether after adjusting the pH to 8. Shake the separated ether with 4 ml of alkaline silver reagent for thirty minutes. This volume is sufficient for 8.7 mg of drug. The precipitate is centrifuged and well washed with three portions of distilled water; 2 ml of concentrated nitric acid are added and the precipitate decomposed by immersion of the tube in a steam bath for one hour. The residue is dissolved in water and after adjusting the pH to 7 is made up to exactly 250 ml. A quantitative silver estimation gives a measure of the amount of the silver acetylide precipitate and hence the drug.

Blood: 5-10 ml oxalated blood samples after dilution with 30 ml of water and adjustment of the pH to 8 are extracted with 3 x 50 ml portions of ether. The method then is the same as for urine. In my hands it has been found necessary to wash the ether extracts with water before shaking with alkaline silver reagent. This prevents a slight cloudiness and any possible interference with silver chloride. The method is not specific for methylpentynol but can be used to assay any neutral ether soluble acetylenic compound. One such common drug is ethchlorvynol or 5 choloro-3-ethylpent 1-en-4yn-3ol. If a positive result is obtained in this test a differentiation must be made. The most probable line of successful attack is undoubtedly gas chromatography although in fatal cases it is likely that a few milligrams can be isolated and, in this event, infra-red examination of the liquid should be attempted.

MONOAMINE OXIDASE INHIBITORS

These drugs are widely used in psychiatric practice and the most common are phenelzine and tranylcypromine. The former is chemically unstable and so far no results are available on its efficient extraction from blood or tissue and specific assay. However, the substituted derivatives of hydrazine to which class nearly all these drugs belong, can be salted from stomach contents into ether from ammoniacal saturated ammonium sulphate solution and detected as blue colours on a butanol-citric acid chromatogram after spraying with a saturated aqueous solution of phosphomolybdic acid and exposing to ammonia fumes. Assay by comparison with standards and avoid loss of volatile drugs by not allowing the ether extract to evaporate to dryness.

Tranylcypromine is chemically related to amphetamine and its extraction and assay follows the procedure for this compound. (For assay by comparative TLC see p. 83; for a GLC separation see p. 156.)

Interpretation of Results

Monoamine oxidase inhibitors in therapeutic dosage, or even for several days after cessation of therapeutic dosage, can alter the body's biochemistry in such a manner that subsequent therapeutic doses of other drugs, particularly adrenaline type compounds, amphetamine and pethidine, cause serious clinical symptoms and even death. Serious interaction with the amino acid tyramine in such foods as cheese has also been described. The toxicologist is in a difficult position in these cases, as his analyses will only reveal traces of drug and the interpretation as to whether a therapeutic dose or an overdose has been taken will probably depend on the quantity of unchanged drug in the stomach and intestines. Demonstration of about a therapeutic dose several hours after ingestion infers the ingestion of a much larger quantity.

OXALATE

Method

(Zarembski, P.M., and Hodgkinson, A.: *Biochem J, 96:*717, 1965)

Whole blood or serum (2 ml) is mixed with 0.5 ml sodium formate (10% w/v), 0.2 ml of 0.1N acetic acid and 4.9 ml water in a 10 ml glass stoppered tube. The tube is heated in a boiling water bath for five minutes, then 0.4 ml calcium formate (10% w/v) added with mixing and heating continued for a further five minutes. After cooling, the tube is centrifuged and 6 ml of the supernatant is put into a tube and mixed with 98% formic acid (0.8 ml for serum, 0.1 ml for urine) and 10N HCl added to make the final pH 1 (0.7 ml for serum; 0.22 ml for urine). Tri-n-butyl phosphate, 12 ml, is added and the tube rocked gently for five minutes, centrifuged for five minutes and the ester phase transferred to another 25 ml tube with a Pasteur pipette. The extracted oxalic acid is transferred to an aqueous phase by shaking the tri-n-butyl phosphate with 1.9 ml 2N sodium hydroxide for two minutes. After centrifuging, the ester phase is discarded. Any residual ester phase is removed by 3 x 5 ml washes of 40/60 light petroleum, warming gently after the last removal.

One drop bromothymol blue solution is added and the pH adjusted to 7 ± 0.2 with dilute acetic acid and sodium hydroxide (match against standards) ; 2 ml of a saturated solution of calcium sulphate is added followed by 13.5 ml ethanol, mix gently, and stand overnight at room temperature. Centrifuge for ten minutes, remove the supernatant and dry the precipitate at 105-110°C for thirty minutes. Dissolve in 2 ml 1.25N hydrochloric acid, cool in ice, and shake gently for several minutes in a mechanical shaker. A freshly prepared zinc spiral (see below) is introduced and shaking continued at eight to ten strokes per second for a further twenty minutes. The spiral is then raised above the solution by bending the top end of the zinc wire over the lip of the tube, and is washed with 1 ml of 0.5% resorcinol solution and the tube centrifuged for three minutes. The dry spiral is now removed, 1.5 ml hydrochloric acid added, and the tube heated in a boiling water bath for five minutes. After cooling, 9.6 ml of 1.8M potassium carbonate is added followed by 1 ml of 10% (w/v) freshly prepared ascorbic acid and 1 ml of EDTA reagent (25 g dipotassium EDTA in 100 ml 1.8M potassium carbonate, prepared fresh). After twenty minutes at room temperature, the solution is diluted to 25 ml with carbonate-bicarbonate buffer (200 ml 0.1 M K_2CO_3 and 800 ml 0.1M $KHCO_3$). After a further ten minutes read the fluorescent intensity at 530 mμ with an excitation wavelength of 490 mμ (Aminco Bowman) or read the extinction at 490 mμ. Calibrate using 0-10μg oxalic acid. (1 ml urine and 1 ml water may be used instead of 2 ml serum.)

Zinc Spirals. One-eighth-inch diameter electrolytic zinc wire* is flattened with steel rollers to a thickness of about 2 mm. The flattened wire is cleaned with scouring powder, cut into 22 cm lengths and one end of each piece wound into a spiral approximately 1 cm long x 1 cm diameter. Immediately before use, it is placed in silicone MS 550, washed under a running tap and dipped in 10N nitric acid until brown fumes appear. Wash thoroughly in distilled water and place for about five seconds in a test-tube containing 2 ml of 1.25N HCl and one drop 0.5% methylene blue solution. Wash briefly in distilled water and place for five seconds in 1.25N HCl. Repeat before each use; each spiral lasts for about ten analyses.

Interpretation of Results

Whole blood contains 200-320μg/100 ml of oxalic acid; serum 135-280μg/100 ml. Daily urinary excretion is from 9-28.5 mg per twenty-four hours.

In fatal poisoning, blood levels over 1 mg/100 ml can be expected; recovery has been noted after a blood level of 370μg/100 ml. Concentrations in liver tissue can be expected to be higher than in blood. In a fatal ethylene glycol poisoning the concentration of oxalate in the liver was 24.5 mg/100 g.

REFERENCES

ZAREMBSKI, P.M., and HODGKINSON, A.: Plasma oxalic acid and calcium levels in oxalate poisoning. *J Clin Path,* 20:283, 1967.

*London Zinc Mills, Enfield, Middlesex, England.

ZAREMBSKI, P.M., and HODGKINSON, A.: The oxalic acid content of English diets. *Brit J Nutr, 16:*627, 1962.

ZAREMBSKI, P.M., and HODGKINSON, A.: The renal clearance of oxalic acid in normal subjects and in patients with primary hyperoxaluria. *Invest Urol, 1:*87, 1963.

PARACETAMOL

Method

(Gwilt, J.R.; Robertson, A., and McChesney, E.W.: *J Pharm Pharmacol, 15*:440, 1963. See also Turner, L.K.: In Curry, A.S. (Ed.) : *Methods of Forensic Science,* vol. 4. New York, Interscience, 1965)

Blood, 2 ml, is mixed thoroughly with anhydous sodium sulphate to form a dry friable mass. This is extracted in a Soxhlet thimble with 150 ml ether and 2.2 ml isopentanol for one hour. The solvent is concentrated to 70 ml and extracted with portions of 0.1 N sodium hydroxide (5 ml, 2 ml). The combined aqueous extracts are treated in a covered tube with 1.5 ml concentrated hydrochloric acid for forty-five minutes at 100°C. The solution is cooled to room temperature, five drops of α-napthol reagent and 2.5 ml 40% sodium hydroxide added, and stood for three minutes. The blue-violet colour is then extracted after addition of solid potassium chloride to saturate with 5 ml n-butanol. Read at 635 mμ.

α-*Napthol Reagent:* 1 ml 5% ethanolic α-napthol solution is mixed with 10 mg potassium dichromate and 1 ml of 2N hydrochloric acid. After five minutes add 19 ml of 5% α-napthol in ethanol.

Interpretation of Results

Forty-five minutes after ingestion of 1 g, blood levels are in the range 0.45-2.5 mg/100 ml. No significant difference exists between whole blood and plasma levels. In cases involving large overdoses the rapid excretion of paracetamol results in blood levels in the above range when the blood is not taken for several hours after ingestion. In acute poisoning, however, the blood level would be expected to be several milligrams per 100 ml.

REFERENCES

DAVIDSON, D.G.D., and EASTHAM, W.N.: Acute liver necrosis following overdose of paracetamol. *Brit Med J, ii*:497, 1966.

GWILT, J.R.; ROBERTSON, A.; GOLDMAN, L., and BLANCHARD, A.W.: The absorption characteristics of paracetamol tablets in man. *J Pharm Pharmacol, 15*:445, 1963.

HEIRWEGH, K.P.M., and FEVERY, J.: Determination of unconjugated and total NAPA in urine and serum. *Clin Chem, 13*:215, 1967.

KRICKLER, D.M.: Paracetamol and the kidney. *Brit Med J, ii*:615, 1967.

PARALDEHYDE

Method 1

(Figot, P.P.; Hine, C.H., and Way, E.L.: *Acta Pharmacol Toxicol, 3:*290, 1952)

Acetaldehyde is distilled from 0.5 g of blood after adding 10-15 ml of distilled water and 3-4 ml of concentrated sulphuric acid. The distillate is collected in 30 ml of buffered semicarbazide. (0.0067N semicarbazide hydrochloride buffered at pH 7.0:8.28 g $NaH_2PO_4 . H_2O$ + 19.88 g Na_2HPO_4 anhydrous per litre)

A special apparatus is used to assist the distillation by means of an air stream: seven minutes are required. The distillate is diluted to 100 ml and read against controls and standards at 224 mμ.

Method 2

Blood (10 ml), or tissue slurry, with 15 ml water and 25 ml dilute (6N) sulphuric acid are distilled; 22.5 ml are collected, the collection tube being cooled in ice. 2.5 ml of Schiff's reagent are added and after exactly twenty-five minutes the violet colour is read against exact blood controls containing paraldehyde in the range 0-50 mg per 100 ml at 560 mμ or with a Spekker No. 3 orange filter.

Schiff's Reagent: This is prepared by dissolving 0.2 g basic fuchsin in 120 ml of water, adding 2 g sodium metabisulphite in 20 ml of water, 2 ml concentrated hydrochloric acid and diluting to 200 ml. If necessary the reagent is decolourised with charcoal.

For interpretation of results see p. 41.

PARAQUAT

Paraquat (1,1′-dimethyl-4,4′-bipyridilium) dichloride or dimethyl sulphate is a herbicide which has caused death after ingestion of large overdoses. Tadjer reported the detection of this compound after direct extraction of 100-200 g of tissue with carbon tetrachloride using TLC (six different solvents) and sprays of iodine in chloroform, Dragendorff's reagent and iodoplatinate. The best TLC solvent was methanol:chloroform (19:1). The Rf value is about 0.37. Diquat was found to run best in methanol: chloroform (13:2) with an Rf of 0.84.

Method

(Daniel, J.W., and Gage, J.C.: *Brit J Ind Med, 23*:133, 1965)

A 10 mm internal diameter column is prepared from about 1 ml of DOW AG-50W-X8 cation exchange resin. The column is washed with water. To 50 ml of urine is added 12.5 ml 25% trichloracetic acid and centrifuged. The precipitate is washed with 6 ml 5% trichloracetic acid, centrifuged and the supernatants combined. The supernatant solution is passed at a rate of 3-4 ml a minute down the column which is then washed with 25 ml portions of water.

Paraquat is eluted from the column with 25 ml 5M ammonium chloride at a rate not exceeding 0.5 ml/min. To 5 ml of eluate are added 1 ml 0.2% sodium dithionite in N sodium hydroxide and readings are taken at 379 mμ in a 1 cm cell. Standards are prepared in the region 10-100μg.

Diquat can also be estimated with the following modifications: The column is prepared and washed with 25 ml water, 25 ml 6M sodium chloride and 25 ml water. After passing the TCA-treated urine down the column it is washed with 25 ml water, 25 ml 0.6M sodium chloride and 25 ml water. Diquat is eluted with 25 ml 5M ammonium chloride and estimated at 379 mμ by adding 1 ml of 0.2% w/v sodium dithionite in 5% aqueous sodium tetraborate to 5 ml of eluate.

A rapid test for paraquat is to add 0.1 g sodium bicarbonate and 0.1 g sodium dithionite to 5 ml of clear natural gastric contents or urine. A blue colour develops almost immediately and 20μg/ml gives an absorbance of 0.72 at 625 mμ in a Unicam SP600 (Matthew *et al.*).

REFERENCES

BULLIVANT, C.M.: Accidental Poisoning by Paraquat: Report of two cases in man. *Brit Med J, i:*1273, 1966.
MATTHEW, A.; LOGAN, A., WOODRUFF, and HEARD, H.: Paraquat poisoning —lung transplantation. *Brit Med J, ii:*759, 1968.
TEDJER, G.S.: The identification of Paraquat in biological material using TLC. *J For Sci, 12:*549, 1967.

PARATHION AND OTHER ORGANO-PHOSPHORUS COMPOUNDS

Method

(Turner, L.K.: In Curry, A.S. [Ed.]: *Methods of Forensic Science,* vol. 4. New York, Interscience, 1965)

The viscera are made acid to litmus and steam distilled. The distillate (5-10 ml) is made acid to litmus with dilute hydrochloric acid and extracted several times with ether. The combined ether extracts are dried over anhydrous sodium sulphate, filtered and evaporated. The extract is examined by paper chromatography using 10% aqueous acetonitrile as the stationary phase and light petroleum ether saturated with acetonitrile as the mobile phase. Control spots of parathion, paraoxon, methylparathion and p-nitrophenol are also run. TLC (Machata, *ibid* p. 243) may also be used; a Silica-Gel G plate is run in hexane acetone (4:1 and 9:1).

Detection

(Thomas, J., and Abbot, D.C.: *Pesticide Residues,* Lecture series 1966, No. 3, Royal Institute of Chemistry)

The most sensitive is by a spray of brilliant green (Colour index No. 42040) followed by exposing the plate to an atmosphere of ammonia. A spray of 0.5% palladium chloride in 1% hydrochloric acid, can also be used. Alternatively, one can demonstate cholinesterase inhibition by spraying with a solution at 37°C of 10 ml horse or human serum, 30 ml distilled water, 1 ml 0.1N sodium hydroxide and 4 ml 1.2% bromothymol blue in 0.1N sodium hydroxide. The plate is then allowed to incubate for twenty minutes at room temperature without being moved. The plate is then sprayed with 2% acetylcholine bromide in distilled water. Areas of cholinesterase inhibition are seen within two minutes and appear as bright blue spots on a yellow background in twenty to thirty minutes. Parathion and other phosphorothionate or phosphorodithioate compounds can be converted on the TLC to corresponding oxons which are highly active inhibitors by spraying with a fresh solution of n-bromosuccinimide in acetone and heating at 60°C for fifteen minutes in a forced air oven. Alternatively, exposure to bromine vapour may be used. The cholinesterase spray reagent is then used on top.

Hladka and Hladky separated the p-nitrophenol and p-nitrometacresol in urine in persons exposed to parathion by hydrolysing the urine with HCl (5:1) for one hour on a boiling water bath. Extraction is with four parts petrol ether and one part ether. The concentrated extract is run in 20% acetone and 80% hexane on TLC plates of Silica-Gel containing 15% plaster; it is then inspected under ultra-violet light to give black spots at Rf 0.33. Yellow colours are seen after exposure to ammonia vapour.

Heyndrickx, Maes and de Leenheer present the alternative method to steam distillation for the isolation of the OP compounds; they extract blood four times with petroleum:ether (40: 70) and examine the evaporated extracts by TLC (hexane:acetone, 4:2.5) followed by the bromine vapour/plasma-acetylcholine bromide technique described above. They were able to detect and estimate parathion in approximately 3 ml samples of blood and milk from a poisoned cow.

Parathion is relatively stable in buried bodies and exhumation is well worth trying if parathion poisoning is suspected. Van Hecke, Derveaux and Hans-Berteau give an account of criminal poisoning by parathion that illustrates the high degree of awareness that forensic pathologists and toxicologists must possess if homicide is to be detected. These workers also showed the Stas-Otto process followed by benzene and ether extraction stages also isolated parathion.

Vercruysse and Deslypere in a comprehensive paper suggest, after elution in hexane:acetone (4:2), an alternative spraying procedure that will detect 0.1μg of parathion. After exposure to bromine vapour for five minutes and aeration, the plate is sprayed with fresh horse serum. After thirty minutes the thin layer plate is further treated with an alcohol solution of phenyl acetate (0.25%), and then with 25 mg of Fast Blue RR salt in 10 ml water and 10 ml pH 7 buffer (0.2M $Na_2 HPO_4$ 35 ml + 0.1M citric acid 7.5 ml). White spots are seen on a red background.

REFERENCES

HLADKA, A., and HLADKY, Z.: Separation of p-nitro phenol and p-nitro-m-cresol from urine pigments by TLC. *J Chromat, 22:*457, 1966.

EL-REJAL, A., and HOPKINS, T.L.: Thin layer chromatography and cholinesterase detection of several phosphorothiono insecticides and their oxygen analogues. *J Agri Food and Chem, 13:*477, 1965.

HEYNDRICKX, A.; MAES, R., and DE LEENHEER, A.: Intoxication of a child due to parathion by drinking poisoned milk. *J Pharm Belge, 3-4:*161, 1964.

HEYNDRICKX, A.; VERCRUYSSE, A., and NOE, M.: A review of forty-one cases of parathion poisoning in man. *J Pharm Belge, 3-4:*127, 1967.

VAN HECKE, W.; DERVEAUX, A., and HANS-BERTEAU, M.J.: A case of criminal poisoning by parathion. *J For Med, 5:*68, 1958.

VERCRUYSSE, A., and DESLYPERE, P.: Acute parathion poisoning. *J For Med, 11:*107, 1964.

THALLIUM

Method 1

Liver, 50 g, is boiled with 200 ml of dilute hydrochloric acid and 100 volumes hydrogen peroxide is added periodically in 5 ml aliquots until there is complete solution of the tissue. The cooled, aqueous solution is then extracted with 3 x an equal volume of ether which is separated and evaporated. This procedure extracts thallic chloride, which is soluble in ether, and also any remaining fatty material. After evaporation, the organic matter is then destroyed by boiling with drops of mixed nitric and sulphuric acid. After dilution, reduction with sulphur dioxide and adjustment of the pH to approximately 5, thallous iodide is precipitated by the addition of potassium iodide solution. It is important to keep the volume as small as possible. The precipitate can be assayed gravimetrically after collection and washing on a weighed Gooch crucible. Confirmation of identity is obtained by arc emission spectroscopy, the indicating line being at 3262.3 Å. An accurate micro balance is essential if the gravimetric method is used.

In my experience, atomic absorption analysis is the best method for quickly and accurately analysing thallium in biological samples.

Method 2

(A.R. Knott, personal communication)

Blood or tissue (1-2 g) is heated in a Kjeldahl flask with 1 ml concentrated nitric acid and 1 ml concentrated sulphuric acid. More nitric acid is added as required until no further charring occurs on evolution of white fumes; cool; transfer with water washings to a boiling tube to a total volume of 10-15 ml. Add a few drops of thymol blue and adjust the pH with drops of concentrated ammonia with cooling until the solution turns yellow; 0.5 ml of 48% hydrobromic acid and one drop of liquid bromine are added and the solution is boiled until it is colourless, or a constant pale yellow colour. Transfer to a 50 ml separating funnel and shake with 5 ml of water-saturated methyl-isobutyl ketone for one minute. Separate and shake the organic phase with 5 ml 1N hydrobromic acid. Separate and centrifuge the organic phase for five minutes in a capped vial and aspirate into the flame of a Perkin-Elmer 303 Atomic Absorption Spectrophotometer set at 2768 Å with a Boling three slot burner (scale expansion x 3, noise x 2). Recovery is beter than 98%. Standards of added thallium to tissue in the range 0.5-2.0μg are suitable.

Urine: Direct aspiration into the flame is suitable; aqueous standards are used. 1% absorption is found for 80μg/100 ml. An alternative method is given by Berman.

Interpretation of Results

The minimum lethal dose for an adult is said to be about 0.8 g or 12 mg/kg. In fatal acute poisonings tissue levels can be expected in the range of 0.5-10 mg/100 g of tissue. The method described above, whereby thallous iodide is precipitated, is sufficiently sensitive provided 50 g of tissue at least is used.

Urinary excretion is said to vary considerably over even a twenty-four hour period and, therefore, estimates of dose from a single urine concentration are very difficult. In nonfatal poisonings, excretion has been shown to extend over a period of months. Concentrations vary from several milligrams per twenty-four hours to as low as 30μg/litre. The analyst must, therefore, be able to demonstrate certain detection at the lower end of this range. Blood levels in nonfatal cases have also been reported as low as 10μg/ 100 ml.

REFERENCES

BERMAN, E.: *Perkin-Elmer Atomic Absorption Newsletter, 6:*58, 1967.

DOMNITZ, J.: Thallium poisoning — a report of six cases. *Southern Med J, 53:*590, 1960.

HAUSMAN, R., and WILSON, W.J.: Thallotoxicosis, A social menace. *J For Sci Soc, 9:*72, 1964.

HUBLER, W.R.: Hair loss as a symptom of chronic thallotoxicosis. *Southern Med J, 59:*436, 1966.

LOOS, H., and TIMPERMAN, J.: A case of subacute thallium poisoning. *J For Med, 6:*166, 1959.

MATTHYS, R., and THOMAS, F.: Criminal thallium poisoning. *J For Med, 5:* 111, 1958.

PRICK, J.G.; SILLEVIO SMITH, W.G., and MULLER, L.: *Thallium Poisoning. New York,* Elsevier, 1955.

SUNDERMAN, F.W.: Diethyldithiocarbamate therapy of thallotoxicosis. *Amer J Med Sci,* 107/209, February, 1967.

WEINIG, E., and ZINK, P.: Quantitative mass spectrometry of the thallium content of the human body. *Arch Toxicol,* 22:255, 1967.

THIORIDAZINE (Mellaril®)

Method

(Zehnder, K., and Tanner, P., quoted by Neve, H.K.: *Acta Pharmacol and Toxicol, 17*:404, 1961)

Blood, 10 ml, is stirred with 2 ml water and 8 ml concentrated hydrochloric acid and heated in a beaker in a boiling water bath for five minutes. Remove and place in an ice bath. When cool, add 12 ml 60% w/v potassium hydroxide which has been previously washed with ether. Keep cool and check the pH to ensure alkalinity. If acid, add more alkali. Shake with 150 ml ether, breaking any emulsion by centrifuging. Separate and shake the aqueous phase with a further 50 ml portion of ether. Combine the ether fractions and wash in sequence with 10 ml 2.5% sodium hydroxide, 10 ml water and 5 ml water. Shake with 4 ml 0.1N sulphuric acid which is separated; to it add 2 ml of 50% sulphuric acid and 0.1 ml of 0.375% ferric nitrate hydrate. Read immediately at 635 mμ. Standards should be made in the range of 0-100μg giving optical density readings in the range 0-0.3 with a 1 cm cell.

Interpretation of Results

In general, blood levels over 0.1 mg/100 ml will be found in cases of sudden death following an acute overdose (see also Chap. 7Aii).

d-TUBOCURARINE, GALLAMINE, DECAMETHONIUM AND SUCCINYLCHOLINE

Method

(Fioro, A., and Marigo, M.: *J Chromat, 31:*171, 1967)

Urine: Filter and use direct.

Blood: Add 1 ml 20% w/v trichloroacetic acid to 50 ml blood; filter.

Tissues: 50-100 g of liver, brain, kidney, etc., homogenate is deproteinised with 20% w/v trichloroacetic acid and filtered.

The deproteinised filtrates obtained as above are adjusted to pH 6; one third the volume of Amberlite IRC50 (H) resin analytical grade, is added, and the suspension stirred four to five hours in a beaker. The supernatant is discarded and the resin carefully washed three or four times with distilled water, thirty minutes each time. Gallamine, succinylcholine and decamethonium are eluted from the resin by stirring with two volumes of 2N hydrochloric acid for one hour. Repeat three times, combine the washings and filter. Tubocurarine is eluted next by stirring three times, each for one hour, with successive fractions 50% alcoholic 2N ammonia. Combine the washings and filter.

Precipitate the reineckate salts from the aqueous washings by adding 1 ml 20% sulphuric acid and 3 ml 2% ammonium reineckate to 10 ml aliquots. Stand in ice-box for one hour, centrifuge off the precipitates, wash twice with water: dry. Add acetone to dissolve the salt (quantitation can be achieved by reading at 525 mμ) and then a slight excess of saturated aqueous silver sulphate solution. Remove precipitated silver reineckate by centrifuging, and excess sulphate and silver ions by dropwise addition of 4% w/v barium chloride while the solution is heated on a water bath (avoid excess barium chloride). Centrifuge off the precipitate and concentrate the supernatant to 10μl.

Identification

Paper Chromatography. Butanol: acetic acid: water (4:1:5) gives the following Rfs on spraying with iodoplatinate reagent:

	Rf
Partially hydrolysed salt of gallamine	0.45
acetylcholine	0.45
decamethonium	0.42
choline	0.37
gallamine	0.30
d-tubocurarine	0.22
succinylcholine	0.12
hydrolysed gallamine	0.02 and 0.12

Biological Test: Untreated spots are eluted from the paper with water, evaporated and redissolved in saline. Inject into the tail vein of a mouse. Compare with controls.

Thin Layer Chromatography. The authors recommend three solvents on alumina plates. These are chloroform:methanol (80:20) on a (Woelm) acid plate; methanol:chloroform (80:20) on a (Woelm) basic plate, and Alumina G (Merck) using methanol:acetic acid:water (9:3:5).

Ultra-violet spectrophotometry can also be used to assay d-tubocurarine.

WARFARIN

This rodenticide interferes with the clotting mechanism of the blood and extensive internal haemorrhages are found at autopsy. Pribilla (*Proc 1st Int. Meeting in Forensic Toxicology, London 1963*) reported a case of murder involving this poison and extremely low levels in the tissues were found (liver, 180μg; kidneys, 30μg; total musculature, 1200μg; stomach contents, 3.9μg). These levels show the care that must be exercised in a search for this poison, Fishwick and Taylor extract exhaustively dilute acidified macerated tissue with ether and purify by passage down a Silica-Gel column.* After re-extraction into chloroform and evaporation, TLC separation is done using Kieselguhr GF254 plates using ether:hexane:acetic acid (7:25:1) as a solvent. Inspection under 254 mμ light reveals the spot at Rf 0.46 which can be eluted with ethyl acetate. Ultra-violet spectrophotometry in 5 ml isopropyl alcohol with 1% acetic acid shows the characteristic curve with max = 305 mμ and $E_{1cm}^{1\%}$ of 361.

REFERENCES
FISHWICK, F.B., and TAYLOR, A.: The determination of warfarin in animal relicta. *Analyst, 92*:192, 1967.
CORN, M., and BERBERICH, R.: Rapid fluorometric assay for plasma warfarin. *Clin Chem, 13*:126, 1967.

*Hopkins and Williams MFC grade.

ZINC

The following method has been recommended for its analysis in tissue. Mr. Rutter, in my laboratory, has examined it and although finding it acceptable, feels that this is one of the less satisfying calibration graphs using dithizone. The curve is not linear except in the range 0-2μg and marked loss of sensitivity occurs above this amount. Scrupulous care must be taken in the cleaning of apparatus.

Method

(Malmstrom, Bo. G.: *Methods of Biochemical Analysis,* vol. 3. New York, Interscience, 1956, p. 346).

Reagents:

1. Deionised water.
2. 6N hydrochloric acid. This is made from pure concentrated acid and deionised water.
3. 20% and 10% trichloroacetic acid: the acid must be purified before use by vacuum distillation.
4. Concentrated ammonia.
5. Acetate buffer pH 5.5: 136 g $CH_3COONa.3H_2O$, 80 g $Na_2S_2O_35H_2O$ and 4.0 g KCN are dissolved in about 500 ml of water and brought to pH 5.5 with 15N acetic acid. The volume is then made to 1 litre with water. This buffer is made zinc free by repeated shaking with a strong solution of dithizone in chloroform.
6. Indicator: 0.04% bromocresol green in 96% ethanol.
7. 0.7 mg dithizone per 100 ml carbon tetrachloride.

The sample of tissue containing 0.2-2.0μg of zinc is placed in a centrifuge tube with 4 ml of 6N hydrochloric acid and stood at 37°C for one hour with occasional shaking: 4 ml of 20% trichloroacetic acid are added and the centrifuged supernatant is poured into a 150 ml separating funnel. The solid in the centrifuge tube is washed twice with 4 ml of 10% trichloroacetic acid and the washings are combined with the supernatant. One drop of indicator is added and then ammonia solution until the colour just changes to blue: this is followed by 50 ml of buffer solution and 10 ml of dithizone solution. After shaking for ten minutes the carbon tetrachloride layer is separated and read at 530 mμ. Suitable standards enable an assay to be obtained.

Interpretation of Results

Ingestion of about 3.5 g of zinc chloride has caused death in an adult but zinc sulphate does not appear to be as irritant to the gastrointestinal tract: doses of as high as four ounces having been survived. Normal liver is said to contain 5-14 mg of zinc per 100 g but blood levels are much lower, of the order of 0.6-0.7 mg/100 ml. This high content of normal tissue means that if a zinc insulin has been injected the amount left at the injection site will be too small to raise significantly the level.

NAME INDEX

257

McCallum, R.I., 169
McChesney, E.W., 240
McClymont, G.L., 51
McDonnell, H., 111
McGeer, E.G., 21
McGeer, P.L., 21
Machata, G., 35, 198
Maddock, R.J., 69, 71
Maddock, R.K., 165
Madsen, O.D., 226
Maehly, A.C., 35, 44, 49, 52, 128, 233
Maes, R., 246, 247
Malstrom, B.G., 255
Mant, A.K., 44
Manley, C.H., 176
Mannering, G.J., 87, 135
Marek, Z., 69
Markiewicz, J., 21
Marigo, M., 252
Martin, H.F., 187
Mason, A.S., 74, 208
Matthew, H., 244
Matthys, R., 249
Merli, S., 226
Michel, H.O., 188
Millhouse, J., 201
Mitchell, L.C., 120
Modglin, F.R., 44
Moeller, M., 35
Moffett, A.C., 156
Moghrabi, H., 127
Moller, K.O., 49, 161, 163
Monkman, J.L., 54, 163, 203
Moody, J.P., 209
Morgan, G., 136, 138
Moss, M.S., 53, 70, 120
Muelberger, C.W., 40
Muller, L., 249
Murrill, W.A., 153
Murrill, *W*.A., 153

N

Natarajan, A.R., 114
Natelson, S., 163
Newman, B., 218
Nickolls, L.C., 111, 200
Noe, M., 246, 247
Norden, A., 70
Nutter, J., 89

O

O'Brien, J.R.P., 44
O'Duffy, J., 155
Oliver, W.T., 100
Olsen, O.V., 71
Orange, M., 224
Otter, I.K.H., 120

P

Parker, B.P., 145
Parker, K.P., 40
Parker, V.H., 196
Pascal, S., 135
Patterson, W.I., 120
Patty, F.A., 49
Pemberton, M., 174
Pennington, G.W., 184
Perkins, W.H., 195
Perlman, P.L., 47, 234
Peterson, G.C., 168
Pfeiffer, E., 212
Phang, S.E., 141
Pilsbury, V.B., 71
Plaa, G.L., 66, 71
Plueckhahn, V.D., 40
Polson, C.J., 37, 111
Posnick, D., 137
Powell, H., 35, 81
Pragowski, T., 216
Price, D.E., 49, 136, 138, 212
Prick, J.G., 249
Proch, W., 212
Prokes, L.H.J., 227

R

Raasch, F., 193
Ramsey, L.L., 206
Ramsey, W.N.M., 215
Randall, S.S., 212
Rannie, I., 169
Read, J.F., 130
Rees, H.J., 193
Rees, P.O., 224
Rehling, C.J., 42, 49, 53, 71, 128
Rentoul, E., 70
Reye, R.D.K., 136, 138
Rhein, H.C., 224

SUBJECT INDEX

55857